MECHANICS

Part II · DYNAMICS

By **J. L. Meriam**

MECHANICS

Part I · Statics
Part II · Dynamics

MECHANICS

Part II · DYNAMICS

J. L. MERIAM

PROFESSOR OF ENGINEERING MECHANICS

UNIVERSITY OF CALIFORNIA

JOHN WILEY & SONS, INC., NEW YORK

CHAPMAN & HALL, LIMITED, LONDON

Printed in the United States of America

PREFACE

To the Student

Engineering analysis hinges directly on the basic principles of mechanics. The study of mechanics welds the tools of physics, mathematics, and graphics into an effective weapon of attack on engineering problems. The emphasis in this book is on engineering or applied mechanics, and it has been designed as a text for the basic mechanics courses in the normal engineering curriculum.

The representation of real situations by mathematical and graphical symbols constitutes an ideal descriptive model which approximates but never quite equals the actual situation. A useful understanding of mechanics requires a dual process of repeated transition of thought between the physical situation and its symbolic representation. The development of ability to make this transition of thought freely is one of the major aims of this book.

Mechanics is based on a surprisingly few fundamental principles. The more important equations are set in boldface type, and much secondary detail has been reduced or eliminated. Care has been taken not to sacrifice the rigor of the development, and attempt has been made to present the principles in clear and concise terms. The student will find that firm progress can be made only by an understanding of the physical and mathematical principles jointly and not by mere memorization of formulas with mechanical substitution of values therein.

Success in analysis depends to a surprisingly large degree on a well-disciplined method of attack from hypothesis to conclusion where a straight path of rigorous application of principles has been followed. The student is urged to develop ability to represent his work in a clear, logical, and neat manner. Very often the mere adherence to good form and procedure will in itself prove to be the needed guide toward a successful solution. The basic training in mechanics is a most excellent place for early development of this disciplined approach which is so necessary in most of the engineering work which follows.

As in all subjects the student learns more when his interest is stimulated. The author hopes that the reader will find interest and stimulation in many of the real and practical situations included in the problems. Arrangement of problems is generally in the order of increasing difficulty, and the most difficult ones are starred.

J. L. MERIAM

PREFACE

To the Instructor

The natural learning process begins with simple situations. Thus in mechanics the average student is best initiated by exposure to simplified, symbolic problems where irrelevant factors have been omitted and where attention is focused on the conditions which are pertinent. Problems presented in this way are already partially analyzed. A full and useful appreciation of mechanics does not come, however, until the analysis of real situations and actual working conditions is made. Here the student must be taught to define the problem by first isolating the pertinent factors and discarding the irrelevant ones. Principles are then applied and conclusions drawn. It is only when the principles of mechanics are applied to *practical* problems involving real situations that the full significance of mechanics can be seen. There has been a trend in the treatment of mechanics to avoid real problems of a practical and interesting nature in favor of the ideal symbolic problems which are stripped of reality, practical value, and interest. Such presentation places in jeopardy one of the most fundamental objectives of instruction in mechanics, namely, to develop ability in problem formulation where the connection between actuality and symbolic representation is required. It is true that many practical problems involve too many complicating factors for early exposure to the student. However, there is a wealth of problems which describe real, practical, and interesting situations that are not overly complex and which can enrich the experience and develop the ability of the student of mechanics far more than is possible with the overly idealized problems.

It is the purpose of this book to present a large selection of problems which illustrate wide application to the various fields of engineering and which will lead the student from the idealized and symbolic representation to the more practical, real, and interesting engineering situation. The author feels strongly that reality brought into the illustrations is of great help to the student in making the transfer of thought from the physical to the mathematical description. Consequently the book has been profusely illustrated, and effort has been made to produce reality and clarity. The problems in each set represent a considerable range of difficulty and are presented generally in order of increasing difficulty. Those problems which are considered the most difficult are starred. All problems have been worked and checked and are believed to be free of error. Computations have been made with the slide rule so that some disagreement in the third figures may be expected. Answers to approximately two thirds of the problems are given.

CONTENTS

Contents

CHAPTER I

(Part I)

Principles of Mechanics

1. Mechanics. Mechanics is that physical science which deals with the state of rest or motion of bodies under the action of forces. There is no one subject which plays a greater rôle in engineering analysis than does mechanics. The early history of this subject is synonymous with the very beginnings of engineering. Modern research and development in the fields of vibrations, stability, strength of structures and machines, engine performance, fluid flow, electrical machines and apparatus, and molecular, atomic, and subatomic behavior are highly dependent upon the basic principles of mechanics. A thorough understanding of this subject is an absolute prerequisite for work in these and many other fields.

Mechanics is undoubtedly the oldest of the physical sciences. The earliest recorded writings in this field are those of Archimedes (287–212 B.C.) which concern the principle of the lever and the principle of buoyancy. Substantial progress awaited the formulation of the laws of vector combination of forces by Stevinus (1548–1620), who also formulated most of the principles of statics. The first investigation of a dynamic problem is credited to Galileo (1564–1642) in connection with his experiments with falling stones. The accurate formulation of the laws of motion including the law of gravitation was made by Newton (1642–1727), who also conceived the idea of the infinitesimal in mathematical analysis. Substantial contributions to the development of the theory of mechanics were made subsequently by Varignon, D'Alembert, Lagrange, Laplace, and others.

Before 1905 the laws of Newtonian mechanics had been verified by innumerable physical experiments and were considered the final description of the motion of bodies. The concept of *time*, considered an absolute quantity in the Newtonian theory, received a basically different interpretation in the theory of relativity announced by Einstein in 1905. The new concept called for a complete reformulation of the accepted laws of mechanics. The theory of relativity was subject to early ridicule but has had experimental check and is now universally accepted by physicists the world over. Although the difference between the mechanics of Newton

341

A *rigid body* is one wherein exists no relative deformation between its parts. This is an ideal hypothesis since all real bodies will change shape to a certain extent when subjected to forces. When such changes are small, the body may be termed rigid without appreciable error. With the exception of deformable springs this book is a treatment of the mechanics of rigid bodies only. A body is considered *deformable* when the relations between the applied forces and the resulting deformations are investigated. This problem is taken up in the studies of strength of materials and the theories of elasticity and plasticity.

4. Scalars and Vectors. The quantities dealt with in mechanics are of two kinds. *Scalar* quantities are those with which a magnitude only is associated. Examples of scalars are time, volume, density, speed, energy, and mass. Quantities with which direction as well as magnitude is associated are called *vectors*. Examples of vectors are displacement, velocity, acceleration, force, moment, and momentum. Scalars may be combined according to the ordinary laws of algebra, whereas combination of vectors requires a particular form of algebra to account for both magnitude and direction.

A vector quantity V is represented by a straight line, Fig. 1, having the direction of the vector and having an arrowhead to indicate the

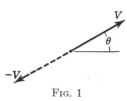

FIG. 1

sense. The length of the directed line segment represents to some convenient scale the magnitude of V, and the direction of the vector is specified by the angle θ measured from some convenient reference line. The negative of V is a vector $-V$ directed in the opposite sense to V as shown. There are three kinds of vectors, *free, sliding,* and *fixed.*

A free vector is one which may be represented by a vector arrow anywhere in space as long as the magnitude and direction remain fixed. If a body moves in a straight line without rotation, then the movement of any point in the body may be taken as a vector, and this vector will describe equally well the motion of every point in the body. Thus the displacement of such a body may be represented by a free vector. Velocity and acceleration are examples also of free vectors.

A sliding vector is one for which a unique line in space must be maintained along which the quantity acts. When dealing with the action of a force on a rigid body, the force may be applied at any point along its line of action without changing its effect on the body as a whole * and thus may be considered a sliding vector.

A fixed vector is one for which a unique point of application is speci-

---

* This is the so-called principle of transmissibility which is discussed in Art. 11, Chapter II.

fied, and therefore the vector occupies a fixed position in space. The action of a force on a nonrigid body must be specified by a fixed vector at the point of application of the force. In this problem the forces and movements internal to the body will be a function of the point of application of the force as well as its line of action.

Vectors may be added and subtracted according to the triangle and parallelogram laws. The two free vectors V_1 and V_2 in Fig. 2a may be

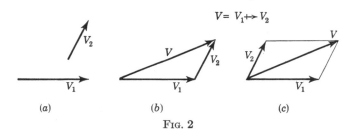

FIG. 2

added tip-to-tail to obtain their sum as shown in the b-part of the figure for the triangle law. The order of their combination does not affect their sum. The identical result in magnitude and direction is obtained by completing the parallelogram as shown in the c-part of the figure. In each case this vector addition is expressed symbolically by the equation

$$V = V_1 \leftrightarrow V_2,$$

where the symbol $\leftrightarrow$ is used to denote *vector addition* in contrast to the $+$ sign used for scalar addition.

The difference V' between the vectors V_1 and V_2 may be obtained by either the triangle or the parallelogram procedure as shown in Fig. 3. It is necessary only to add the negative of V_2 to V_1 in

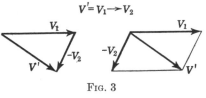

FIG. 3

order to obtain the vector difference. This difference is indicated symbolically by the equation

$$V' = V_1 \rightarrow V_2,$$

where the symbol $\rightarrow$ is used to denote *vector subtraction* as distinguished from the $-$ sign used for scalar subtraction.

Any two or more vectors whose sum equals a certain vector V are said to be the *components* of that vector. Thus the vectors V_1 and V_2 in Fig. 4a are the components of V in the directions 1 and 2, respectively. It is usually more convenient to deal with vector components which are mutually perpendicular, and these are called *rectangular components*. The gravitational attraction of the earth is the only gravitational force of any magnitude which need be considered for experiments conducted on the earth's surface.

The weight of a body is the force of attraction of the body to the earth and depends on the position of the body relative to the earth. An object weighing 10 lb. at the earth's surface will weigh 9.99500 lb. at an altitude of 1 mi., 9.803 lb. at an altitude of 40 mi., and 2.50 lb. at an altitude of 4000 mi. or a height approximately equal to the radius of the earth. It is at once apparent that the variation in the weight of high-altitude rockets must be accounted for.

Every object which is allowed to fall in a vacuum at the earth's surface will have the same acceleration g as can be seen by combining Eqs. (1) and (2) and cancelling the term representing the mass of the falling object. This combination gives

$$g = \frac{\gamma m_0}{r^2},$$

where m_0 is the mass of the earth and r is the radius of the earth.* The mass m_0 and mean radius r of the earth have been found by experiment to be 5.98×10^{27} gm. and 6.38×10^8 cm., respectively. These values together with the value for γ already cited when substituted into the expression for g give

$$g = 980 \text{ cm./sec.}^2 \qquad \text{or} \qquad g = 32.2 \text{ ft./sec.}^2$$

A more accurate determination must account for the fact that the earth is actually an oblate spheroid with flattening at the poles. The value of g has been found equal to 32.09 ft./sec.^{2} at the equator, 32.17 ft./sec.^{2} at a latitude of 45 deg., and 32.26 ft./sec.^{2} at the poles. The proximity of large land masses will also influence the local value of g to a small but detectable amount. It is sufficiently accurate in almost all engineering calculations to use the value of 32.2 ft./sec.^{2} for g.

The mass m of a body may be calculated from the results of the simple gravitational experiment. If the gravitational force or *weight* is W, then, since the body falls with an acceleration g, Eq. (1) gives

$$W = mg \qquad \text{or} \qquad m = \frac{W}{g}. \tag{3}$$

---

* It can be proved that the earth may be considered a particle with its entire mass concentrated at its center.

6. Units. There are a number of systems of units used in relating force, mass, and acceleration. Four of these systems are defined in the following table.

SYSTEMS OF UNITS

Type of System (fundamental quantities)	Gravitational (length, force, time)		Absolute (length, mass, time)	
Name of System	British or FPS	MKS	British or FPS	CGS
length L	foot (ft.)	meter (m.)	foot (ft.)	centimeter (cm.)
force F	pound (lb.)	kilogram (kg.)	poundal (pdl.)	dyne
time T	second (sec.)	second (sec.)	second (sec.)	second (sec.)
mass M	lb. ft.$^{-1}$ sec.^{2}	kg. m.$^{-1}$ sec.^{2}	pound (lb.)	gram (gr.)
System in use by	Engineers in English-speaking countries	Engineers in non-English-speaking countries	Physicists (occasionally)	Physicists everywhere

Engineers use a gravitational system in which length, force, and time are considered fundamental quantities and the units of mass are derived. Physicists use an absolute system in which length, mass, and time are considered fundamental and the units of force are derived. Either system, of course, may be used with the same results. The engineer prefers to use force as a fundamental quantity because most of his experiments involve direct measurement of force. The British or FPS gravitational system is the one used in this book. The engineer has not adopted a unit for mass which is universally used although *slug* and less often *g-pound* are seen occasionally in the literature. One slug (or *g*-pound) is the mass of a body which weighs 32.2 lb. at the earth's surface.

It is frequently necessary to convert a quantity from one set of units to another. During the process of conversion it is essential that the dimensions of the quantity remain unchanged. In order to convert a velocity of 30 mi./hr., for example, to the equivalent number of centimeters per second it is first necessary to know that

5280 ft.   are contained in 1 mi.,

30.48 cm. "   "   " 1 ft.,

3600 sec. "   "   " 1 hr.

may be used to describe the period for *any* similar pendulum of a different size as long as a consistent set of units is used. In the case of the simple pendulum direct solution will disclose the fact that $k = 2\pi$ for small amplitudes.

8. Accuracy. The number of significant figures shown in an answer should be no greater than that which corresponds to the least number of significant figures in the given data. Thus the cross-sectional area of a shaft whose diameter, 0.25 in., say, was measured to the nearest hundredth of an inch should be written as 0.049 in.^{2} and not 0.0491 in.^{2} as would be indicated when the numbers were multiplied out.

When calculations involve small differences in large quantities, greater accuracy must be achieved. Thus it is necessary to know the numbers 4.2503 and 4.2391 to an accuracy of five significant figures in order that their difference 0.0112 be expressed to three-figure accuracy. It is often difficult in somewhat lengthy computations to know at the outset the number of significant figures needed in the original data to insure a certain accuracy in the answer.

Sliderule accuracy, usually three significant figures, is considered satisfactory for the majority of engineering calculations. The decimal point should be located by a rough longhand approximation which also serves as a check against large sliderule error.

9. Mathematical Limits and Approximations. The essential purpose of applied mechanics is the mathematical description of engineering situations, and as such it is extremely necessary to understand and be able to apply certain limiting and approximating mathematical relations.

The *order* of differential quantities is the subject of frequent misunderstanding by students who are making application of the calculus for the first time. Higher-order differentials may always be neglected compared with lower-order differentials. As an example the element of volume dV of a right circular cone of altitude h and base radius r may be taken to be a circular slice a distance x from the vertex and of thickness dx. It can be verified that the exact expression for the volume of the element may be written as

$$dV = \frac{\pi r^2}{h^2}\left[x^2\, dx + x\,(dx)^2 + \frac{1}{3}\,(dx)^3 \right].$$

It should be recognized that, when passing to the limit in going from ΔV to dV, the terms in $(dx)^2$ and $(dx)^3$ drop out, leaving merely

$$dV = \frac{\pi r^2}{h^2}\, x^2\, dx,$$

which is an exact expression.

In using trigonometric functions of differential quantities it is well to call attention to the following relations which are true in the mathematical limit:

$$\sin d\theta = \tan d\theta = d\theta,$$

$$\cos d\theta = 1.$$

The angle $d\theta$ is, of course, expressed in radian measure. When dealing with small but finite angles it is often convenient to replace the sine by the tangent or either function by the angle itself. Likewise the cosine of a small angle may often be approximated satisfactorily by unity. As an example, for an angle of 1 deg.,

$$\sin 1° = 0.0174524 \quad \text{and} \quad 1° \text{ is } 0.0174533 \text{ radian.}$$

The error in replacing the sine by the angle for 1 deg. is only 0.005 per cent. For 5 deg. the error is 0.13 per cent, and for 10 deg. the error is still only 0.51 per cent.

A few of the mathematical relations which are useful in mechanics are listed in Table B3, Appendix B.

10. Method of Problem Solution. An understanding of the method of attack on engineering problems is an essential aspect of their solution. This method involves a logical sequence of steps from hypothesis to conclusion and should include the following:

(*a*) given data,
(*b*) statement of results desired,
(*c*) necessary diagrams,
(*d*) statement of principles and basic equations which apply,
(*e*) application of principles and equations,
(*f*) answers or conclusions.

Presentation of information in this order represents a logical sequence, and all problem work should follow this general pattern. It is also important that the arrangement of work be neat and orderly. Careless solutions which cannot be easily read by others are of little or no value. It will be found that the discipline involved in adherence to good form will in itself be an invaluable aid to the development of the powers of analysis. Many problems which at first may seem difficult and complicated become clear and simple once they are begun with a logical and disciplined method of attack.

The science of mechanics is based on a surprisingly few fundamental concepts and involves mainly the application of these basic relations to a variety of situations. In this application the *method* of analysis is all-important. In solving a problem it is essential that the laws which apply be carefully fixed in mind and that these principles be applied literally and exactly.   In applying the principles which define the requirements for forces acting on a body it is essential that the body in question be *isolated* from all other bodies so that complete and accurate account of all forces which act on this body may be taken.   This *isolation* should exist mentally as well as be represented on paper.   The drawing of such an isolated body with the representation of *all* external forces acting on it is called a *free-body diagram*.   It has long been established that the *free-body diagram* method is the key to the understanding of mechanics. This is so because the *isolation* of a body is the tool by which *cause* and *effect* are clearly separated and by which attention on the literal application of a principle is accurately focused.   The technique of drawing free-body diagrams is covered in Chapter III where they are first used.

In applying physical laws to the solution of a problem numerical values of the quantities may be used directly in proceeding toward the solution.   On the other hand algebraic symbols may be used to represent the quantities involved, and the answer left as a formula.   In the first scheme the magnitude of all quantities expressed in their particular units is evident at each stage of the calculation.   This is often an advantage when the practical significance of the magnitude of the terms is appraised. The second method, or symbolic solution, has several advantages over the numerical solution.   In the first place the abbreviation achieved by the use of symbols aids in focusing attention on the interconnection between the physical situation and its related mathematical description. Secondly, a symbolic solution permits a dimensional check to be made at every step, whereas dimensional homogeneity may not be checked when numerical values are used.   Furthermore a symbolic solution may be used repeatedly for obtaining answers to the same problem when different sets and sizes of units may be involved.   Facility with both methods of solution is essential, and ample practice with each should be sought in the problem work.

CHAPTER IX

Kinematics

68. Introduction. Dynamics is that branch of mechanics which deals with bodies in motion. There are two aspects to dynamics, first, *kinematics*, which is a study of motion itself without reference to the forces which cause the motion, and, second, *kinetics*, which relates the action of forces on bodies to their resulting motions.

Compared with statics, dynamics is a relatively new subject. Galileo (1564–1642) is credited with the first substantial contribution to dynamics. He refused to accept the long-established philosophies of Aristotle which held, for instance, that heavy bodies fall more rapidly than light bodies. Galileo was handicapped by the lack of accurate means for measuring time, and the further development of dynamics awaited the invention of the pendulum clock by Huygens in 1657. Newton (1642–1727), guided by Galileo's work, was able to make an accurate formulation of the laws of motion and hence to put dynamics on a sound basis. In terms of engineering application dynamics is an even more recent science. Only since machines have operated with high speeds and appreciable accelerations has it been necessary to make calculations based on dynamic principles rather than on static principles.

The principles of dynamics are basic to the analysis of moving structures and practically all types of machinery such as engines, ships, wheeled vehicles, aircraft, etc. The student of engineering whose interests lead him into one or more of these and many other fields will find that he can have no stronger basic tool in his technical work than a firm foundation in dynamics.

The vast majority of dynamics problems in engineering may be solved by treating the moving bodies in question as perfectly rigid. This book is a study of rigid body dynamics. The dynamics of nonrigid bodies is a much more difficult subject and one about which a great deal has yet to be learned. The response of structures and machines to shock and impact loads is an important problem in nonrigid body dynamics.

The subject of kinematics deals with displacement, velocity, acceleration, and time, and is often referred to as the "geometry of motion."

The designs of cams, gears, and linkages to control or produce certain desired motions are examples of kinematical problems. Kinematics is a necessary introduction to kinetics since ability to describe motion is pre-requisite to an understanding of the relations between force and motion.

69. Types of Motion. Most motions encountered in engineering work can be represented as occurring in a single plane, and such motion

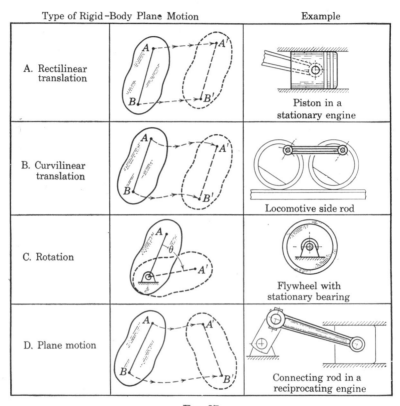

Type of Rigid-Body Plane Motion		Example
A. Rectilinear translation		Piston in a stationary engine
B. Curvilinear translation		Locomotive side rod
C. Rotation		Flywheel with stationary bearing
D. Plane motion		Connecting rod in a reciprocating engine

FIG. 87

is termed *plane motion*. The connecting rod of a stationary reciprocating engine, for example, may be represented as moving in a plane normal to the axis of the crankshaft. Three-dimensional motion is not commonly encountered although there are some important exceptions. The motions of a spinning projectile, a precessing gyroscope, and the coupling in a universal joint are examples of three-dimensional motion. Many of the principles developed for motion in two dimensions may be extended by inference to the three-dimensional case. The discussion which follows will be confined to rigid body motion in two dimensions.

The plane motion of a rigid body is logically divided into the four categories represented in Fig. 87. *Translation* is defined as any motion in which every line in the body remains parallel to its original position at all times. *Rectilinear translation*, part *A*, is translation in which all points move in straight lines. *Curvilinear translation*, part *B*, is translation in which all points move on congruent curves. It should be noted that in either case the motion of the body is completely defined by the motion of *any* point in the body, since all points have the same motion.

Rotation about a fixed axis, part *C*, is the angular motion about the axis. It follows that all particles move in circular paths about the axis of rotation, and *all* lines in the body (including those that do not pass through the axis) rotate through the same angle in the same time.

Plane motion of a rigid body, part *D*, is a combination of translation and rotation. The plane motion of points which are not joined by a connecting rigid body is also a problem often encountered.

The remainder of the chapter will be devoted to a description of the foregoing motions in the order mentioned.

PART *A*.   RECTILINEAR TRANSLATION

70. Definitions. As already noted the rectilinear translation of a body may be described by the translation of any point or particle in the body. Consider the motion of such a point *P*, Fig. 88, along the s-direction. The *linear displacement* of *P* relative to a convenient fixed origin *O* is the distance *s* from *O* to *P*. Displacement can be positive or negative, depending on the choice of the positive sense for measurement. If *P* moves a distance Δs to *P'* during the time interval Δt, the *average velocity* of the point during this interval is $v_{\text{av.}} = \Delta s/\Delta t$. The instantaneous velocity *v* of the point at any position on its path is the instantaneous time rate of change of displacement or

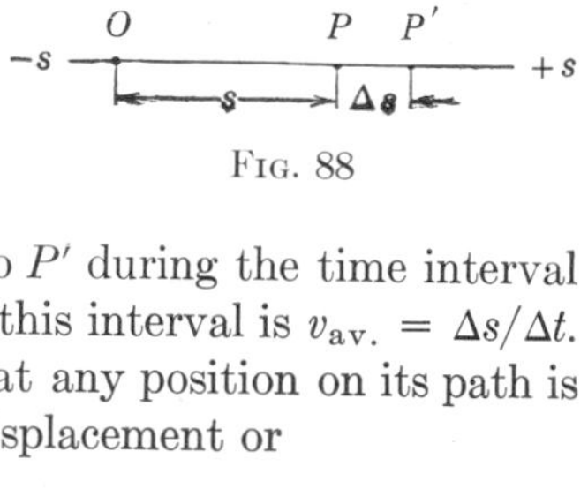

Fig. 88

$$v = \frac{ds}{dt}. \tag{48}$$

If the difference between the instantaneous velocities of the point at *P* and *P'* is Δv, the *average acceleration* during the corresponding time interval Δt is $a_{\text{av.}} = \Delta v/\Delta t$ and will be plus or minus, depending on whether the velocity is increasing or decreasing. The instantaneous

as can be seen from the fact that the two triangles shown are similar and that $a/v = dv/ds$ from Eq. (50). It is necessary that the velocity and displacement axes have the same numerical scale so that the acceleration read on the displacement scale in feet, say, will represent the actual acceleration in the units, ft./sec.^{2}

Many of the problems commonly encountered involve motion with *constant* acceleration. Under this condition the three differential relations can be integrated directly. If it is agreed that $s = 0$ when $t = 0$ and that the velocity at $t = 0$ is v_0, the first of Eqs. (49) may be integrated to obtain

$$\int_{v_0}^{v} dv = a \int_{0}^{t} dt \qquad \text{or} \qquad v = v_0 + at. \qquad (51)$$

Hence the velocity v at any time t equals the initial velocity v_0 plus the increment in velocity at due to the acceleration. Substituting this value of velocity as a function of the time into Eq. (48) and integrating yields

$$\int_{0}^{s} ds = \int_{0}^{t} (v_0 + at)\, dt \qquad \text{or} \qquad s = v_0 t + \tfrac{1}{2}at^2. \qquad (52)$$

A third relation is obtained from Eq. (50), which may be integrated as it stands since the acceleration is constant. Thus

$$\int_{v_0}^{v} v\, dv = a \int_{0}^{s} ds \qquad \text{or} \qquad v^2 = v_0{}^2 + 2as. \qquad (53)$$

Equations (51), (52), and (53) may, of course, be used *only* where the acceleration is constant. A very common error is the attempt to apply them to problems where the acceleration is not constant.

It should be noted that for constant acceleration the plot of s as a function of t, corresponding to Fig. 89a, gives a parabola as seen from Eq. 52. The plot of v versus t, corresponding to Fig. 89b, gives a straight line whose slope is the constant acceleration a. Third, the a–t curve is a horizontal line of constant acceleration.

In the case of bodies falling near the surface of the earth under the influence of gravity the acceleration is constant if air resistance is neglected and may be taken to be $g = 32.2$ ft./sec.^{2} directed down. If the positive direction for all measurements is taken to be upward, the acceleration is $-g$, and Eqs. (51), (52), and (53) become

$$v = v_0 - gt,$$

$$h = v_0 t - \tfrac{1}{2}gt^2,$$

$$v^2 = v_0{}^2 - 2gh,$$

where h is the vertical displacement above the datum plane at which $t = 0$.

The sign conventions in Eqs. (51), (52), and (53) must be understood. If the sign of s, v, or a turns out negative upon computation, this means that the quantity is directed in the sense opposite to that taken for positive s. If Eq. (52) is solved for t, there will be two solutions. Only one of the solutions may have practical meaning, and this one will be obvious in most instances from the requirements of the problem. It should be noted that s represents the net displacement. Thus, if a particle moves a positive distance d_1 along a straight line, reverses its direction, and returns a distance d_2, the calculated displacement will be $s = d_1 - d_2$.

SAMPLE PROBLEMS

611. The displacement of a particle which moves along a straight line is given by $s = 4t^3 + 3t^2 - 6$, where s is in feet and t is in seconds. Determine (a) the time it takes the particle to acquire a velocity of 6 ft./sec. from rest, (b) the acceleration of the particle when the velocity is 6 ft./sec., and (c) the displacement of the particle during the fifth second.

Solution: The velocity and acceleration are obtained by successive differentiation with respect to the time. Thus

$$\left[v = \frac{ds}{dt} \right] \qquad\qquad v = 12t^2 + 6t,$$

$$\left[a = \frac{dv}{dt} \right] \qquad\qquad a = 24t + 6.$$

Substituting $v = 6$ ft./sec. into the expression for velocity gives $6 = 12t^2 + 6t$, from which $t = \frac{1}{2}$ sec. or $t = -1$ sec. The negative answer describes a solution before the measurement of time had begun and so is of no interest. Therefore the positive root is the desired answer, and

$$t = \tfrac{1}{2} \text{ sec.} \qquad\qquad Ans.$$

The acceleration at $t = \frac{1}{2}$ sec. is

$$a = 24 \times \tfrac{1}{2} + 6 = 18 \text{ ft./sec.}^2 \qquad\qquad Ans.$$

The displacement when $t = 5$ sec. is $s_5 = 4 \times 5^3 + 3 \times 5^2 - 6 = 569$ ft., while that when $t = 4$ sec. is $s_4 = 4 \times 4^3 + 3 \times 4^2 - 6 = 298$ ft. Thus the net displacement during the fifth second of motion is

$$s = 569 - 298 = 271 \text{ ft.} \qquad\qquad Ans.$$

This result is identical with that obtained by evaluating the area under the v–t curve for the interval 4 to 5 sec. This area is

$$\Delta s = \int_4^5 v \, dt = \int_4^5 (12t^2 + 6t) \, dt = 271 \text{ ft.}$$

612. A point starts from the origin with an initial velocity in the x-direction and moves for 6 sec. with a constant acceleration of $a_z = -15$ ft./sec.^{2} If at this time the velocity is 30 ft./sec. in the negative x-direction, determine (a) the initial velocity v_0 at the origin, (b) the net displacement of the particle, and (c) the total distance covered by the particle.

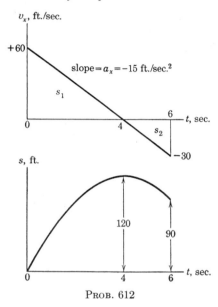

PROB. 612

Solution: The final velocity, the time, and the acceleration are known so that the initial velocity can be computed from Eq. (51), which applies to this case of constant acceleration. Thus

$$[v = v_0 + at] \qquad\qquad -30 = v_0 - 15 \times 6, \qquad v_0 = 60 \text{ ft./sec.} \qquad\qquad Ans.$$

The net displacement for constant acceleration is given by Eq. (52). Hence

$$[s = v_0t + \tfrac{1}{2}at^2] \qquad\qquad s = 60 \times 6 - \tfrac{1}{2} \times 15 \times 6^2 = 90 \text{ ft.} \qquad\qquad Ans.$$

Since the point reverses its direction on the x-axis, the total distance traveled will be that on the way out plus that on the way back. (The difference in these two distances is the net displacement of 90 ft. just found.) The point has a zero velocity for

$$[v = v_0 + at] \qquad\qquad 0 = 60 - 15t, \qquad t = 4 \text{ sec.}$$

Thus the two distances are

$$[s = v_0t + \tfrac{1}{2}at^2] \qquad s_1 = 60 \times 4 - \tfrac{1}{2} \times 15 \times 4^2, \qquad s_1 = 120 \text{ ft.,}$$
$$s_2 = 0 \times 2 + \tfrac{1}{2} \times 15 \times 2^2, \qquad s_2 = 30 \text{ ft.,}$$

and the total distance traveled is

$$D = s_1 + s_2 = 150 \text{ ft.} \qquad\qquad Ans.$$

The distances s_1 and s_2 may also be obtained without reference to the two time intervals by using Eq. (53).

The graphical representation of velocity against time is an aid to solution of the problem. It should be clear from the graph shown that the initial velocity of 60 ft./sec. will be determined by establishing the negative slope of 15 ft./sec.[2] through the point representing the given velocity of -30 ft./sec. for $t = 6$ sec. Also the triangular area above the axis is the positive displacement s_1 while the negative area is the negative displacement s_2 of the point. The corresponding plot of displacement versus time is also shown in the figure, and the ordinate s at any time t represents the integral of or area under the v–t curve up to that value of t.

613. The acceleration a of a slider block is controlled by its displacement s so that $a = k\sqrt{s}$, where k is a constant. The velocity v is in the direction of s, and both the displacement and velocity are zero when the time t is zero. Find s, v, and a as functions of the time t.

Solution: The given relation for a may be substituted directly into the differential expression $v \, dv = a \, ds$ which must be used here since a is not constant. Thus

$$v \, dv = k\sqrt{s} \, ds.$$

Using the indefinite integral gives

$$\int v \, dv = k \int s^{1/2} \, ds + C_1, \text{ a constant,}$$

or

$$\frac{v^2}{2} = \frac{2k}{3} s^{3/2} + C_1.$$

When $v = 0$, $s = 0$; thus $C_1 = 0$. The velocity becomes

$$v = \sqrt{\frac{4k}{3}} s^{3/4},$$

where the plus value of the radical is taken since it was stated that v is positive in the s-direction. Since $v = ds/dt$, this last expression may likewise be integrated. The integral is

$$\int \frac{ds}{s^{3/4}} = \sqrt{\frac{4k}{3}} \int dt + C_2, \text{ a constant}$$

or

$$4s^{1/4} = \sqrt{\frac{4k}{3}} t + C_2.$$

When $t = 0$, $s = 0$, so that $C_2 = 0$, and

$$s = \frac{k^2}{144} t^4. \qquad\qquad \textit{Ans.}$$

Two successive differentiations give v and a.   Thus

$$v = \frac{ds}{dt} = \frac{k^2}{36} t^3 \qquad\qquad Ans.$$

and

$$a = \frac{dv}{dt} = \frac{k^2}{12} t^2. \qquad\qquad Ans.$$

The student should recognize that the definite integral with the given limits is equivalent to the indefinite integral with added constant as used in this solution.

PROBLEMS

614. Determine the time t required for the space ship of the future to accelerate from rest to half the speed of light at the rate of $4g$.   The speed of light is 186,000 mi./sec.

615. Find the time t for an object to fall a distance h from rest in a vacuum.

$Ans.$ $t = \sqrt{2h/g}$

616. The shell in one type of bazooka rocket weapon has a muzzle velocity of 275 ft./sec. after a travel of 59 in. in the firing tube.   Find the average acceleration during this period.

617. The muzzle velocity of a 30 caliber rifle bullet is about 2700 ft./sec. If air resistance is neglected, determine the maximum height h to which the bullet could be fired. $Ans.$ $h = 21.4$ mi.

618. The average car can decelerate at the maximum rate of $0.8g$ on dry, clean, level pavement.   Find the total emergency stopping distance s, measured from the point where the driver first sights the danger, for a car traveling at a speed of 60 mi./hr.   The reaction time for a good driver is about ¾ sec. from the instant he sights the danger until he is actually applying the brakes.   (Note carefully the magnitude of the answer.) $Ans.$ $s = 216$ ft. (72 yd.)

619. The velocity of a point moving with rectilinear translation is given by $v = 8 - 2t^2$, where v is in feet per second and t is in seconds.   Determine the total distance D traveled by the point and the net displacement s both during the first 4 sec.

620. A balloon ascends vertically at the constant rate of 10 ft./sec.   When an altitude of 50 ft. is reached, a small weight is released.   Find the time t required for the weight to reach the ground and its final velocity v.

$Ans.$ $t = 2.10$ sec., $v = 57.6$ ft./sec.

621. A particle which moves in a straight line has an initial velocity at the origin of 40 ft./sec. to the right in the positive x-direction and a constant acceleration to the left.   If the particle returns to the origin in 4 sec., determine the acceleration a_x and the greatest distance s away from the origin reached by the particle.

622. An object moves in a straight line with the accelerations shown. If the velocity is 4 ft./sec. in the positive x-direction when $t = 0$, draw the v–t curve and determine the distance s traveled by the object in the 8 sec.

Ans. $s = 96$ ft.

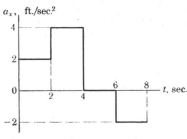

PROB. 622

623. The rate of change of velocity v with displacement s for a particle moving with rectilinear translation is 6 (ft./sec.)/ft. at an instant when the velocity is 30 ft./sec. What is the acceleration a of the particle at this instant?

624. A car accelerates uniformly from rest to 60 mi./hr. and then immediately decelerates uniformly until it stops. If the elapsed time is 20 sec., determine the distance s traveled. *Ans.* $s = 880$ ft.

625. A car starts from rest on a straight level road and moves with constant acceleration until it reaches a velocity of 60 ft./sec., which is then maintained. If the car is going 40 ft./sec. after 6 sec., find the time t required to cover a total distance of 1000 ft.

626. The displacement of a point which moves along a straight line is given by $s = 2t^3 + t^2 + 6$, where s is in feet and t is in seconds. Determine the displacement Δs of the point during the time the velocity changes from 8 ft./sec. to 28 ft./sec., and find the acceleration a when the velocity reaches 60 ft./sec.

Ans. $\Delta s = 17$ ft., $a = 38$ ft./sec.^{2}

627. A train passes a control tower with a velocity v_0 and is accelerating uniformly. At ½ mi. beyond the tower the velocity is 30 mi./hr., and at 1 mi. beyond the tower the velocity is 40 mi./hr. Find v_0.

628. A man stands in an open-top elevator which is descending at the constant rate of 10 ft./sec. and throws a ball vertically up with a velocity of 30 ft./sec. relative to the elevator. What is the downward velocity v of the ball relative to the earth when it returns to the man? *Ans.* $v = 40.0$ ft./sec.

629. A train accelerates from rest at the rate of 6 ft./sec.^{2} until it reaches its maximum permissible speed of 90 mi./hr. After running at this speed for a certain period, the train decelerates at the rate of 4 ft./sec.^{2} until it comes to a stop. If the train has traveled a total distance of 3 mi., find the time t required for the trip.

630. A body moves in a straight line with a decreasing velocity whose square is linear

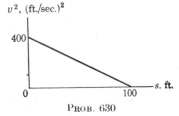

PROB. 630

with s as shown. Find the time t required for the body to travel the 100 ft. and the distance Δs traveled during the last 2 sec. before coming to rest.

Ans. $t = 10$ sec., $\Delta s = 4$ ft.

631. Experimental data for the acceleration of a point moving with rectilinear motion are obtained as a function of the displacement as shown in the graph. The velocity of the point is 6 ft./sec. when $s = 3$ ft. By using the graph, estimate the velocity v when $s = 10$ ft.

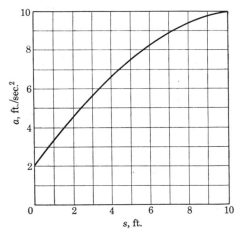

Prob. 631

632. A particle moves in a straight line with constant acceleration. The displacement s is measured from some position of the particle at which the time t is not zero. When $t = 10$ sec., $s = 30$ ft., and when $t = 20$ sec., $s = 50$ ft. Also the velocity v is 1 ft./sec. when $t = 0$. Find the acceleration a and the distance Δs traveled by the particle during the first 5 sec.

Ans. $a = 0.0667$ ft./sec.^{2}, $\Delta s = 5.83$ ft.

633. A particle moves along a straight line with constant acceleration. The displacement measured from a convenient position is $+4$ ft. at the time $t = 0$ and is zero when $t = 10$ sec. Furthermore the velocity is zero when $t = 6$ sec. Determine the velocity v when $t = 10$ sec.

634. The displacement of a point which moves in a straight line is given by $s = bt^3 - ct$, where s is in feet, t is in seconds, and b and c are positive constants. When $t = 2$ sec., the acceleration is 24 ft./sec.^{2} in the positive s-direction, and at the same time the velocity is 8 ft./sec. in the negative s-direction. Find the total time t required for the point to move away from and return to the origin at $s = 0$.

Ans. $t = 4$ sec.

635. Car A accelerates uniformly from rest on a straight road. Car B starts from rest at the same position 10 sec. later, accelerates uniformly, and overtakes A. When the cars pass, A is traveling 40 mi./hr. and has gone a distance of $\frac{1}{2}$ mi. from rest. Find the velocity of B at the time of passing.

636. A balloon ascends vertically at the constant rate of 10 ft./sec. A rock is thrown vertically up from the launching site 5 sec. after release of the balloon. Determine the required initial velocity of the rock in order that it just touch the balloon. Neglect air resistance on the rock. (*Hint:* The balloon and rock have the same velocity at contact.)

637. A faucet leaks at the rate of four drops each second. If air resistance is neglected, find the vertical separation h between two consecutive drops after the lower one has fallen 20 ft. *Ans.* $h = 7.97$ ft.

638. A particle starts from rest and moves along a straight line with a variable acceleration as shown. Draw the v–t curve for this motion and determine the displacement of the particle when $t = 10$ sec.

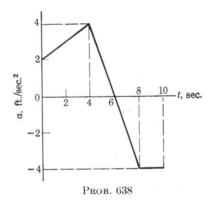

PROB. 638

639. Determine the velocity v and acceleration a of the bucket as functions of x if the velocity v_B of the jeep is constant. When $x = 0$, ends A and B are coincident at C.

$$Ans. \quad v = \frac{xv_B}{\sqrt{H^2 + x^2}}, \quad a = \frac{H^2 v_B^2}{\sqrt{(H^2 + x^2)^3}}$$

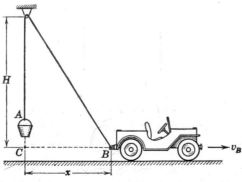

PROB. 639

640. For the given position of the symmetrical linkage each of the pins marked A has a velocity v_A directed toward the other and an acceleration a_A away from the other. Determine the velocity v_y and acceleration a_y of pin B at this position.

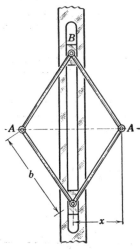

PROB. 640

641. The cam A with the shape indicated moves to the right with a constant velocity v and controls the motion of pin B in the fixed vertical slot. Find the velocity v_y and acceleration a_y of the pin as functions of x. Neglect the pin diameter compared with a and b.

$$Ans. \quad v_y = \frac{\pi b v}{a} \sin \frac{\pi x}{a}, \; a_y = -\frac{\pi^2 b v^2}{a^2} \cos \frac{\pi x}{a}$$

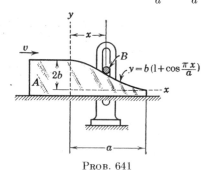

PROB. 641

* 642. A point moves on a straight line with an acceleration $a = -9s$, where a is in the units, in./sec.², and s is in inches. When $t = 0$, $v = 0$ and $s = 4$ in. Determine s, v, and a as functions of the time t, and find the value of s when $t = 1$ sec. *Ans.* $s = -3.96$ in.

* 643. The resistance to the motion of a projectile in air is approximately proportional to the square of its velocity v for speeds not exceeding about 500 ft./sec.

Thus the deceleration may be equated to Kv^2, where K is taken to be a constant whose numerical value depends on the prevailing air conditions and the projectile shape, roughness, and mass. If a projectile which moves in a horizontal straight line is fired with an initial velocity v_0 (less than 500 ft./sec.), find the velocity v and distance s at a time t after firing.

$$Ans. \quad v = \frac{v_0}{1 + Kv_0 t}, \quad s = \frac{1}{K} \log (1 + Kv_0 t)$$

* 644. A projectile moves in a straight line with a deceleration due to fluid resistance equal to Kv^n, where K and n are constants and n is greater than unity. If the projectile is fired with an initial velocity v_0 at $t = 0$, determine the velocity v and the distance s as functions of the time t after firing.

$$Ans. \quad v = [v_0^{1-n} + (n - 1)Kt]^{\frac{1}{1-n}},$$

$$s = \frac{1}{(n - 2)K} [v_0^{1-n} + (n - 1)Kt]^{\frac{n-2}{n-1}} - \frac{v_0^{2-n}}{(n - 2)K}$$

* 645. An object is dropped from rest at $t = 0$ from a high altitude. The acceleration at the start is g, but because of air resistance it decreases by the amount cv^2, where c is a constant and v is the downward velocity. Determine v and the distance h which the object falls as functions of the time t. What is the maximum velocity $v_{\max}$ which the object can attain?

$$Ans. \quad v = \sqrt{\frac{g}{c}} \tanh \sqrt{gc}\, t, \quad h = \frac{1}{c} \log \cosh \sqrt{gc}\, t, \quad v_{\max} = \sqrt{\frac{g}{c}}$$

PART *B*. CURVILINEAR TRANSLATION

71. Rectangular Components. The curvilinear translation of a rigid body is described by the motion of any point in the body. Thus, as in the case of rectilinear translation, attention will be directed to the motion of a point or particle. In this article curvilinear translation will be described in rectangular coordinates. Although the most general formulation would involve a path defined by x-, y-, and z-coordinates, most problems are two-dimensional, so that motion in the x–y plane only will be discussed.

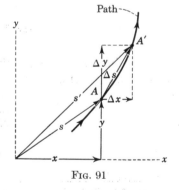

Fig. 91

Consider the motion of a particle along any plane curve such as shown in Fig. 91. The path may be described directly as $y = f(x)$ or else may be expressed parametrically in terms of the time t as $y = f_1(t)$ and $x = f_2(t)$. The displacement of the particle at any position such as A is the vector s measured from a convenient location

such as the origin. As the particle moves to A' its displacement becomes s', and the change in displacement is Δs. This change is clearly
independent of the choice of origin for the measurement of s. The
displacement at A and the change in displacement may be expressed by
the vector equations

$$s = x \not{+} y,$$

and

$$\Delta s = \Delta x \not{+} \Delta y.$$

The displacement of the particle between points A and A' is the vector Δs, whereas the *distance* traveled by the particle is the length of the
path measured along the arc between A and A' and is a scalar quantity.

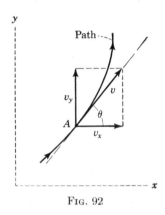

FIG. 92

The average velocity between A and A' is

$$v_{\text{av.}} = \frac{\Delta s}{\Delta t} = \frac{\Delta x}{\Delta t} \not{+} \frac{\Delta y}{\Delta t},$$

and the instantaneous velocity at A is the limit of this expression as
Δt approaches zero. Thus

$$\frac{ds}{dt} = \frac{dx}{dt} \not{+} \frac{dy}{dt},$$

or

$$v = v_x \not{+} v_y. \tag{54}$$

The direction of the vector v is along the tangent to the curve as shown
in Fig. 92. It is clear that

$$v^2 = v_x{}^2 + v_y{}^2 \qquad \text{and} \qquad \tan \theta = \frac{v_y}{v_x}.$$

The velocity of the particle is a vector quantity, whereas the *speed* of the particle along the path is the magnitude of the velocity and, hence, is a scalar quantity.

The change in velocity between A and A' is the vector difference Δv, shown in Fig. 93, which may be represented by the equation

$$\Delta v = \Delta v_x \leftrightarrow \Delta v_y.$$

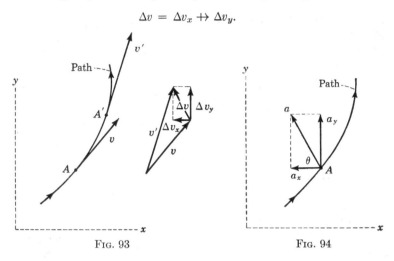

FIG. 93   FIG. 94

The average acceleration between A and A' is

$$a_{\text{av.}} = \frac{\Delta v}{\Delta t} = \frac{\Delta v_x}{\Delta t} \leftrightarrow \frac{\Delta v_y}{\Delta t},$$

and the instantaneous acceleration at A is the limit of this expression as Δt approaches zero. Thus

$$\frac{dv}{dt} = \frac{dv_x}{dt} \leftrightarrow \frac{dv_y}{dt},$$

or

$$a = a_x \leftrightarrow a_y. \tag{55}$$

The components may also be expressed as $a_x = d^2x/dt^2$ and $a_y = d^2y/dt^2$. The acceleration and its components are indicated in Fig. 94. The angle θ made by a with the x-direction is

$$\tan \theta = \frac{a_y}{a_x}.$$

The acceleration is, in general, *not* along the tangent to the path since $(d^2y/dt^2)/(d^2x/dt^2)$ is not equal to $(dy/dt)/(dx/dt)$ except for motion along a straight line or at a point of inflection in a curved path.

From the foregoing discussion it should be recognized that plane curvilinear translation is merely the superposition of the coordinates of two simultaneous rectilinear translations in the x- and y-directions.

SAMPLE PROBLEM

646. A projectile is fired with a muzzle velocity u at an angle θ with the horizontal. Neglect the effect of air resistance and determine the equations of the trajectory, the range R on a horizontal plane, and the maximum altitude h reached in flight.

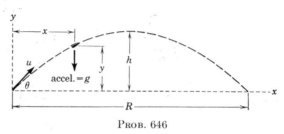

PROB. 646

Solution: With the neglect of air resistance the only force acting on the projectile is its weight, and the acceleration at all times is g directed vertically down. Thus $a_x = 0$ and $a_y = -g$. The resulting motion, then, is a superposition of two rectilinear motions with constant acceleration. With zero acceleration in the x-direction the horizontal distance traveled equals the constant horizontal component of velocity multiplied by the time. Thus

$$[s = v_0 t] \qquad\qquad x = ut \cos \theta.$$

The y-coordinate of the projectile is given by Eq. (52) for constant acceleration and is

$$[s = v_0 t + \tfrac{1}{2}at^2] \qquad\qquad y = ut \sin \theta - \tfrac{1}{2}gt^2.$$

These two expressions for x and y are the equations for the motion of the projectile in terms of the parameter t. The equation of the trajectory is obtained by eliminating t between the expressions and is

$$y = x \tan \theta - \frac{gx^2}{2u^2 \cos^2 \theta}. \qquad\qquad Ans.$$

From the form of the equation the curve is seen to be a parabola with vertical axis as shown in the figure.

The range R is obtained by equating to zero either of the two expressions for y. The second equation gives

$$0 = x \left(\tan \theta - \frac{gx}{2u^2 \cos^2 \theta} \right)$$

which has two solutions. The solution $x = 0$ is of no concern, but the other value is

$$x = R = \frac{2u^2 \sin \theta \cos \theta}{g} = \frac{u^2 \sin 2\theta}{g}. \qquad Ans.$$

The maximum range occurs for $\sin 2\theta = 1$ or $\theta = 45$ deg. and is

$$R_{\text{max.}} = \frac{u^2}{g}.$$

The time of flight for the range R may be obtained by equating y to zero in the second of the two parametric expressions. Thus

$$0 = t\left(u \sin \theta - \frac{1}{2} gt\right), \qquad \text{and} \qquad t = \frac{2u \sin \theta}{g}.$$

By symmetry the time of flight to the apex of the parabola is one half that for the complete journey. Substitution of this time into the expression for y gives a maximum altitude of

$$h = y = \frac{u^2 \sin^2 \theta}{g} - \frac{g}{2}\left(\frac{u^2 \sin^2 \theta}{g^2}\right), \qquad h = \frac{u^2 \sin^2 \theta}{2g}. \qquad Ans.$$

Accurate calculations for trajectories must account for the effect of air resistance, which is appreciable at high velocities. Wind velocity and direction as well as the rotation and curvature of the earth may also become important.

PROBLEMS

Except where indicated, neglect air resistance in the problems involving projectile motion.

647. The curvilinear motion of a particle is described by $x = 2t^3 - 3t$ and $y = 4t^2$, where x and y are in inches and t is in seconds. Determine the velocity v and acceleration a of the particle when $t = 2$ sec.

$\qquad Ans.$ $v = 26.4$ in./sec., $a = 25.3$ in./sec.^{2}

648. A particle moves on the curved path $y = x^2/4$ with a constant x-component of velocity of 2 ft./sec. Determine the total velocity v when $x = 2$ ft. and find the acceleration a for any position.

649. A bomber is flying horizontally at an altitude of 10,000 ft. with a speed of 300 mi./hr. Find the proper angle θ with the vertical made by the line of sight from the bomber to the target for a direct hit. $\qquad Ans.$ $\theta = 47° 37'$

650. A particle moves along the positive branch of the curve $x = 4y^2$ such that $y = t^3/3$, where x and y are measured in inches and t is in seconds. Determine the velocity v and acceleration a of the particle when $t = \frac{1}{2}$ sec.

651. The x-coordinate of a particle which moves with curvilinear motion is $x = 40t + 4t^3$, where x is in inches and t is in seconds. When $t = 2$ sec., the total acceleration is 64 in./sec.^{2} If the acceleration in the positive y-direction is constant and the particle starts from the origin with $v_y = 0$ at $t = 0$, determine the velocity v of the particle when $t = 4$ sec. $\qquad Ans.$ $v = 287$ in./sec.

652. Find the target lead L which a dive-bomber pilot must allow when releasing a bomb from an altitude $h = 2000$ ft. The flight angle is $\theta = 45$ deg., and the bomber is traveling 600 mi./hr.

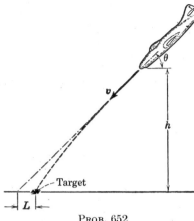

PROB. 652

653. The time of flight for a projectile with a horizontal range of 30,000 yd. is 90 sec. Determine the muzzle velocity u.   *Ans.* $u = 1760$ ft./sec.

654. An airplane pulls out of a dive and climbs with a velocity of 300 mi./hr. at an angle of 15 deg. from the horizontal. A small bomb is released when an altitude of 500 ft. is reached. Find the total horizontal distance x traveled by the bomb from the point of release and the velocity v with which it strikes the ground.

655. A battleship which moves at 20 knots (1 knot corresponds to 1.152 mi./hr.) parallel to a coast is 15,000 yd. offshore. The muzzle velocity of its 14 in. guns is 2600 ft./sec. Determine the proper time for firing a broadside by specifying the angle α which the line of sight to the coastal target makes with the athwartship direction of the guns, and the corresponding firing elevation θ. Assume that the target is at the same height above the water as the muzzle of the gun.   *Ans.* $\alpha = 0° 45'$, $\theta = 6° 11'$

656. A long-range rifle at A is aimed at an angle of 45 deg. with the horizontal, and its shell is just able to clear the mountain peak at the top of its trajectory. Determine the muzzle velocity u, the height h of the mountain above sea level, and the range R to the sea.

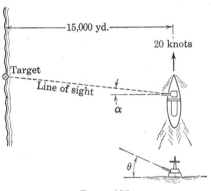

PROB. 655

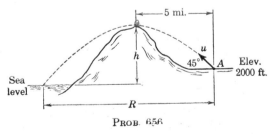

PROB. 656

657. Find the initial velocity u of a ball thrown down the slope as shown.

Ans. $u = 68.3$ ft./sec.

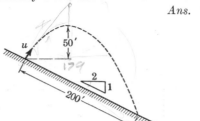

Prob. 657

658. The muzzle velocity for a certain gun is 2000 ft./sec. The target and gun are on the same horizontal plane, and the range is 5000 yd. Find the two values of the angle θ made by the barrel with the horizontal for which a direct hit can be scored.   Ans. $\theta = 3° 28'$ or $\theta = 86° 32'$

* **659.** The following data were taken from a test firing of a German V-2 rocket. The horizontal distance x and the vertical distance y are given in thousands of feet from the launching site along with the corresponding elapsed time t of flight in seconds. Plot these data and determine (*a*) the velocity v of the rocket at $t = 100$ sec. and (*b*) the final velocity v_f when the rocket returns to earth at the same elevation as the launching site. Indicate the procedure for finding the acceleration of the rocket at any time.

t	x	y	t	x	y
0	0	0	225	173	519
25	1	19	250	194	508
50	10	68	275	215	480
75	28	160	300	236	435
100	53	280	325	258	369
125	79	374	350	278	280
150	105	441	375	300	170
175	130	488	400	320	57
200	152	515	413	332	0

Ans.   (a) $v = 3200$ mi./hr.,
(b) $v_f = 3100$ mi./hr.

* **660.** Show that the acceleration of a point moving on the arc of the circle $x^2 + y^2 = r^2$ with a velocity of constant magnitude v is equal to v^2/r and is directed toward the center of the circle. Prove by considering the x- and y-components of acceleration.

* **661.** Find the range R for a projectile fired onto the inclined plane shown. What is the maximum value of R for a given muzzle velocity u?

$$Ans. \quad R = \frac{2u^2 \cos \theta \sin (\theta - \alpha)}{g} \cdot \frac{1}{\cos^2 \alpha}, \quad R_{\text{max.}} = \frac{u^2}{g(1 + \sin \alpha)}$$

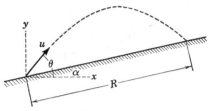

PROB. 661

* **662.** Find the equation of the envelope a to the parabolic trajectories of an anti-aircraft gun which fires at any angle but has a constant muzzle velocity u. (*Hint:* Substitute $m = \tan \theta$ in the equation of the trajectory. The two roots m_1 and m_2 of this relation give the firing angles for the two trajectories shown such that the shells pass through the same point A. Point A approaches the curve a when the two roots approach equality.)

$$Ans. \quad y = \frac{u^2}{2g} - \frac{gx^2}{2u^2}, \text{ a vertical parabola}$$

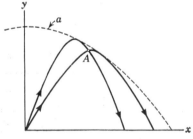

PROB. 662

72. Normal and Tangential Components of Acceleration.

The acceleration of a point which has curvilinear motion will be described in terms of its components in the directions of the normal n and tangent t to the curved path. Consider a particle moving along a plane curve, Fig. 95, such that its velocity changes both in magnitude and in direction from the vector v at A to $v + dv$ at A' during the time dt. The vector change of velocity during the differential interval is the difference dv in the velocities at A and A'. The acceleration of the particle is $a = dv/dt$. It should be recalled that the derivative of a vector will account not only for change in magnitude but also for change in direction. In the present case these two effects are separated by considering the components of dv in both the n- and t-directions. This separation is shown in Fig. 95 and may be stated by the vector equation

$$dv = (dv)_n + (dv)_t.$$

The acceleration a, then, has two components and is

$$\frac{dv}{dt} = \frac{(dv)_n}{dt} + \frac{(dv)_t}{dt},$$

$$a = a_n + a_t. \tag{56}$$

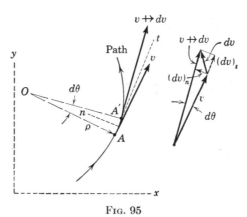

Fɪɢ. 95

The normal acceleration component a_n depends on $(dv)_n$ and is therefore due to the *change in direction* of the velocity. From the velocity diagram in Fig. 95 the vector $(dv)_n$ may be considered in the limit as a differential length of arc of radius v with a subtended angle $d\theta$. Thus $(dv)_n = v\,d\theta$, and the normal component of acceleration becomes

$$a_n = \frac{(dv)_n}{dt} = v\frac{d\theta}{dt}.$$

The arc length on the path between A and A' is $ds = \rho\,d\theta$, so that $d\theta/dt = (1/\rho)(ds/dt) = v/\rho$. Consequently the normal acceleration is

$$a_n = \frac{v^2}{\rho}. \tag{57}$$

This result is extremely important and must be thoroughly understood. It should be carefully noted that the direction of the normal component of acceleration is *always toward the center of curvature.*

The tangential component of acceleration is obtained from $(dv)_t$, which is the change in the magnitude of the velocity. Thus

$$a_t = \frac{(dv)_t}{dt} = \frac{d|v|}{dt} = \frac{d^2s}{dt^2}, \tag{58}$$

where s here is the scalar distance measured along the curve. It may be observed from Eq. (58) that, as long as all measurements of the motion are made in a direction along the curve, the distance s, the speed $|v|$, and the tangential acceleration a_t bear the same relationships as were discussed in Art. 70 and expressed in Eqs. (48), (49), and (50) for rectilinear translation. The tangential component of acceleration may also be expressed in terms of the radius of curvature ρ and the angle θ by introducing $v = \rho(d\theta/dt)$. Thus

$$a_t = \frac{d|v|}{dt} = \frac{d}{dt}\left(\rho\,\frac{d\theta}{dt}\right) = \rho\,\frac{d^2\theta}{dt^2} + \frac{d\rho}{dt}\frac{d\theta}{dt}.$$

The second term will be zero when $d\rho/dt = 0$, which occurs when ρ is constant, as for a circle or at points which represent a maximum or minimum radius of curvature.

The total or resultant acceleration is the vector sum of its two components as given by Eq. (56). In Fig. 96a is shown a schematic repre-

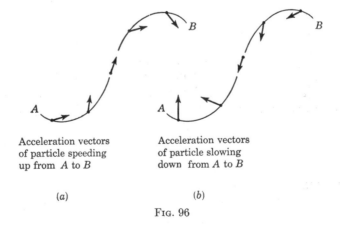

Acceleration vectors
of particle speeding
up from A to B

Acceleration vectors
of particle slowing
down from A to B

(a)   (b)

Fig. 96

sentation of the variation of the total acceleration vector a for a particle moving with increasing speed along the curve from A to B. In Fig. 96b is represented the acceleration of the particle when its speed is decreasing in going from A to B. In both cases the acceleration has a normal component directed toward the center of curvature.

SAMPLE PROBLEM

663. A projectile is fired at an angle of $\theta = 30$ deg. above the horizontal and with a muzzle velocity of 2000 ft./sec. Determine the radius of curvature of its path 10 sec. after firing. Neglect air resistance.

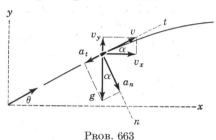

PROB. 663

Solution: As seen from Eq. (57) the radius of curvature ρ may be determined if the velocity v and normal acceleration a_n are known. The velocity may be found from its x- and y-components. Thus

$$[v = v_0 + at] \qquad v_x = 0.866 \times 2000 = 1732 \text{ ft./sec.,}$$

$$v_y = 0.5 \times 2000 - 32.2t = 678 \text{ ft./sec. for } t = 10 \text{ sec.}$$

The velocity v and the angle α made by the tangent of the trajectory to the horizontal at this instant of time are shown in the accompanying figure and are

$$[v = \sqrt{v_x{}^2 + v_y{}^2}\,] \qquad v = \sqrt{(1732)^2 + (678)^2} = 1860 \text{ ft./sec.,}$$

$$\left[\tan \alpha = \frac{v_y}{v_x}\right] \qquad \tan \alpha = \frac{678}{1732} = 0.391, \alpha = 21°\, 22'.$$

The total acceleration of the projectile at all times is g, so that the normal component of acceleration at the position considered is seen from the figure to be

$$a_n = g \cos \alpha = 32.2 \times 0.931 = 30.0 \text{ ft./sec.}^2$$

Thus Eq. (57) gives

$$\left[a_n = \frac{v^2}{\rho}\right] \qquad \rho = \frac{(1860)^2}{30.0} = 115{,}300 \text{ ft.} \qquad \qquad Ans.$$

PROBLEMS

664. A baseball is thrown horizontally with a velocity of 100 ft./sec. What is the radius of curvature of its path as it leaves the pitcher's hand?

665. At the bottom of a loop an airplane has a normal acceleration of $4g$ and a velocity of 500 mi./hr. Find the radius ρ of the loop.

Ans. $\rho = 4170$ ft.

666. For the projectile in Sample Prob. 663 determine the radius of curvature of the trajectory at its highest point.

667. A particle moves with a constant speed of $v = 10$ ft./sec. on the circular path shown. During the movement from A to B the velocity undergoes a vec-

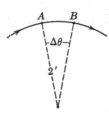

tor change. Divide this change by the time interval between the two points to obtain the average normal acceleration for (a) $\Delta\theta = 30$ deg., (b) $\Delta\theta = 15$ deg., and (c) $\Delta\theta = 5$ deg. Compare the results with the instantaneous normal acceleration.

PROB. 667

668. A point on the rim of a flywheel has a peripheral speed of 10 ft./sec. at an instant when this speed is increasing at the rate of 30 ft./sec. each second. If the total acceleration of the point at this condition is 50 ft./sec.^{2}, find the radius r of the flywheel. *Ans.* $r = 2.5$ ft.

669. A brake is applied to a flywheel 18 in. in diameter to bring it to rest with a constant deceleration. If the total acceleration of a point on the rim makes an angle of 1 deg. with the radial direction when the brake first begins to act, find the time t required to bring the wheel to a stop from a peripheral speed of 30 ft./sec.

670. The rim speed of a flywheel 12 in. in diameter increases uniformly from 20 ft./sec. to 40 ft./sec. during 10 rev. of the wheel. If the speed continues to increase at the same time rate, find the normal acceleration a_n of a point on the rim after the wheel has turned through another 10 rev.

          Ans. $a_n = 5600$ ft./sec.^{2}

671. The position of a point on the rim of a wheel 8 in. in diameter is specified by $s = t^3 - 4t^2 + 4$, where s is the distance of the point, measured in inches along the circular periphery, from a convenient origin and t is the time in seconds. Find the total acceleration a at the instant when the tangential acceleration is 4 in./sec.^{2}

672. A train enters a section of curved track at a speed of 60 mi./hr. and slows down at a uniform rate to 30 mi./hr. in 11 sec. while rounding the curve. An accelerometer, which is a delicate instrument for measuring acceleration, is mounted inside the train and records a horizontal acceleration of 5 ft./sec.^{2} when the train is 6 sec. past the beginning of the curve. Find the radius of curvature ρ of the track for this position of the train.

    Ans. $\rho = 1365$ ft.

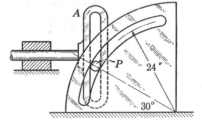

PROB. 673

673. The slotted guide A is moving to the right with a constant velocity. At the position shown the acceleration of the pin P has a magnitude of 36 ft./sec.^{2} Determine the velocity v of P along the circular slot at this position.

674. A projectile is fired with a muzzle velocity of 2000 ft./sec. at an angle of 45 deg. with the horizontal. Find the radius of curvature ρ of the trajectory at a point where the direction of flight makes an angle of 30 deg. with the horizontal. *Ans.* $\rho = 95,600$ ft.

675. The pin P moves along a curved path and is controlled by the motions of the slotted links A and B.   At the instant shown A has a velocity of 12 ft./sec. and an acceleration of 10 ft./sec.^{2}, both to the right, while B has a velocity of 16 ft./sec. and an acceleration of 5 ft./sec.^{2}, both vertically up.   Find the radius of curvature ρ of the path of P at this position.

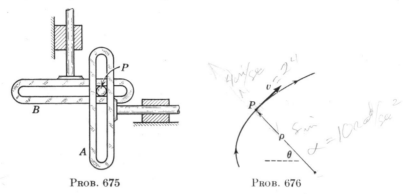

<table>
<tr><td>Prob. 675</td><td>Prob. 676</td></tr>
</table>

* **676.** A particle P is moving on the curved path shown.   The radius of curvature of the path for the position of the particle at any time is ρ and makes an angle θ with a fixed horizontal line.   As the particle passes the position shown, $\rho = 8$ in. and is increasing at the rate of 4 in./sec.   Also the velocity at this position is $v = 24$ in./sec., and $d\theta/dt$ is increasing at the rate of 10 rad./sec. each second.   Find the total acceleration of P at this instant.

Ans. $a = 117$ in./sec.^{2}

* **677.** A particle starts from rest at the origin and moves along the positive branch of the curve $y = 2x^{3/2}$ such that the distance s in inches measured along the curve varies with the time t in seconds according to $s = 2t^3$.   Find the total acceleration a of the particle when $t = 1$ sec.   (Recall that the radius of curvature ρ is given by $\rho = [1 + (dy/dx)^2]^{3/2}/(d^2y/dx^2)$.)   *Ans.* $a = 12.17$ in./sec.^{2}

* **678.** The path of a fluid particle in the centrifugal pump with straight vanes shown is to be approximated by the spiral $r = r_0 e^{b\theta}$, where b is a dimensionless constant.   The angular position of both the fluid particle and the pump impeller is given by θ, and the radial distance to the particle is specified by r.   If the pump turns with constant speed so that $d\theta/dt = K$, a constant, find the total acceleration of the fluid particle as it leaves the impeller by considering the acceleration components normal and tangent to the curve.   In polar coordinates the radius of curvature ρ is

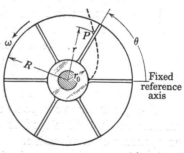

Prob. 678

$$\rho = [r^2 + (dr/d\theta)^2]^{3/2}/[r^2 + 2\,(dr/d\theta)^2 - r\,(d^2r/d\theta^2)].   \quad Ans.   \quad a = K^2(1 + b^2)R$$

73. Polar Coordinates. The third method of describing plane curvilinear motion utilizes polar coordinates. This description finds limited but important use. The position of the particle at some point A on its curved path, Fig. 97a, is specified by the coordinates r and θ. During

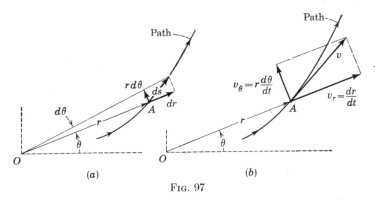

FIG. 97

an infinitesimal movement ds along the path the coordinates change by dr and $d\theta$, and the vector relation

$$ds = dr + r\,d\theta$$

may be seen from the figure. The velocity of the particle is along the path and is obtained by dividing ds by dt. Thus

$$\frac{ds}{dt} = \frac{dr}{dt} + r\frac{d\theta}{dt},$$

or

$$v = v_r + v_\theta. \tag{59}$$

These velocity components are shown in Fig. 97b.

The acceleration is not easily obtained by direct differentiation of Eq. (59) since the changes in both magnitude and direction of each of the two terms must be accounted for. These changes are shown in Fig. 98a, where the motion of the particle from A to A' during time dt is accompanied by the change in velocity from v to v'. Each of these velocity vectors is divided into its r- and θ-components as shown, and the changes in these components during motion are treated in the same manner as that developed in Art. 72 for the normal and tangential components of acceleration.

Consider first the change in the radial component v_r of the velocity between A and A'. The difference dv_r between v_r and v_r' is shown in the vector sketch in Fig. 98b, where the scale has been increased for clarity.

This change dv_r will have two components, a radial one $(dv_r)_r$ and a transverse one $(dv_r)_\theta$. The radial component is merely the increase in the magnitude of v_r, and the acceleration due to this change is

$$\frac{(dv_r)_r}{dt} = \frac{d|v_r|}{dt} = \frac{d^2 r}{dt^2} \qquad \text{[plus } r\text{-direction]}.$$

From Fig. 98b it is seen that the transverse component of the change in radial velocity may be expressed in the limit as the differential circu-

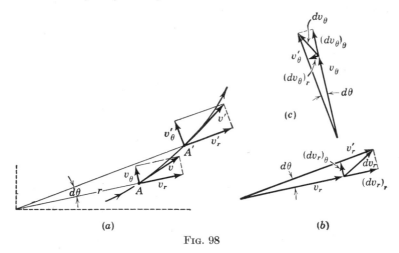

(c)

(a)

(b)

Fig. 98

lar arc of radius v_r with subtended angle $d\theta$. Hence $(dv_r)_\theta = v_r\, d\theta$, and the acceleration due to this change is

$$\frac{(dv_r)_\theta}{dt} = v_r \frac{d\theta}{dt} = \frac{dr}{dt}\frac{d\theta}{dt} \qquad \text{[plus } \theta\text{-direction]}.$$

The change dv_θ in the transverse velocity component is similarly treated and is shown in Fig. 98c. Again it is clear from the diagram that this vector has components in both the θ- and r-directions. The change in the θ-direction is the change in magnitude of v_θ or $(dv_\theta)_\theta = d|v_\theta| = d\left(r\frac{d\theta}{dt}\right)$. The acceleration due to this change is

$$\frac{(dv_\theta)_\theta}{dt} = \frac{d\left(r\dfrac{d\theta}{dt}\right)}{dt} = r\frac{d^2\theta}{dt^2} + \frac{dr}{dt}\frac{d\theta}{dt} \qquad \text{[plus } \theta\text{-direction]}.$$

It should be noted that this portion of the acceleration is due to the change in magnitudes of both r and $d\theta/dt$.

Finally the radial change $(dv_\theta)_r$ must be accounted for. Figure 98c shows that, in the limit, $(dv_\theta)_r = v_\theta \, d\theta$. The acceleration due to this change is then

$$\frac{(dv_\theta)_r}{dt} = v_\theta \frac{d\theta}{dt} = r\left(\frac{d\theta}{dt}\right)^2 \qquad \text{[minus } r\text{-direction]}.$$

The components of acceleration just computed in each of the two directions may now be combined. Thus the resultant r- and θ-components are

$$a_r = \frac{d^2r}{dt^2} - r\left(\frac{d\theta}{dt}\right)^2,$$

$$a_\theta = r\frac{d^2\theta}{dt^2} + 2\frac{dr}{dt}\frac{d\theta}{dt}.$$

$$(60)$$

The second component may be written in more compact form as

$$a_\theta = \frac{1}{r}\frac{d}{dt}\left(r^2\frac{d\theta}{dt}\right),$$

the equivalence of which is verified easily by differentiation.

When the radius r is constant, the motion is circular, and the origin and center of curvature are coincident. Equations (60) then reduce to the expressions obtained in Art. 72 for the case of circular motion, namely,

$$-a_r = a_n = r\left(\frac{d\theta}{dt}\right)^2 = \frac{v^2}{r},$$

$$a_\theta = a_t = r\frac{d^2\theta}{dt^2} = \frac{d^2s}{dt^2}.$$

SAMPLE PROBLEM

679. The slotted arm OB carries a small pin A of negligible diameter whose position in the slot is determined by the rotation of the arm about the fixed circular cam. If OB rotates at a constant rate $d\theta/dt = K$ for a certain interval, find the total acceleration of A.

Solution: The motion of A may be expressed in polar coordinates r and θ. The equation of the circular cam surface relative to the pole O is $r = 2b \cos \theta$. The velocity of A along the arm is

$$\frac{dr}{dt} = -2b \sin \theta \frac{d\theta}{dt} = -2Kb \sin \theta.$$

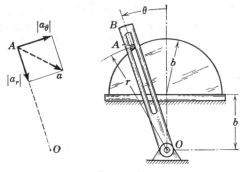

PROB. 679

The second time derivative of r is only a part of the radial acceleration and is

$$\frac{d^2r}{dt^2} = -2Kb \cos\theta \frac{d\theta}{dt} = -2K^2b \cos\theta.$$

Substitution of these derivatives together with $d\theta/dt = K$ and $d^2\theta/dt^2 = 0$ into Eqs. (60) gives

$$a_r = \frac{d^2r}{dt^2} - r\left(\frac{d\theta}{dt}\right)^2 = -4K^2b \cos\theta,$$

$$a_\theta = r\frac{d^2\theta}{dt^2} + 2\frac{dr}{dt}\frac{d\theta}{dt} = -4K^2b \sin\theta.$$

The total acceleration is

$$a = \sqrt{a_r{}^2 + a_\theta{}^2} = 4K^2b \qquad\qquad Ans.$$

and is in the direction shown.

PROBLEMS

680. The arm OB revolves in a horizontal plane at a constant clockwise rate of 100 rev./min. The velocity of the slider block A outward along the arm has a constant magnitude of 12 in./sec. Find the acceleration a of the block when it is 4 in. from O. *Ans.* $a = 506$ in./sec.^{2}

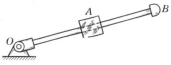

PROB. 680

681. Show that the components of acceleration in the x- and y-directions may be expressed as $a_x = -x(d\theta/dt)^2 - y(d^2\theta/dt^2)$ and $a_y = -y(d\theta/dt)^2 + x(d^2\theta/dt^2)$ for the case of circular motion with the center of the circle at the pole.

682. The slotted arm OB forces the small pin to move in the spiral guide defined by $r = k\theta$. If OB rotates with a constant angular speed $d\theta/dt = K$, find the total acceleration of the pin in terms of its angular position θ.

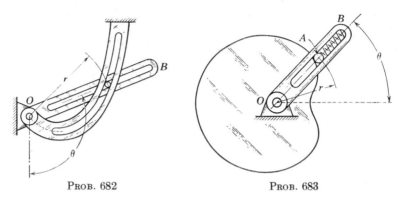

PROB. 682   PROB. 683

683. The fixed cam shown has a shape such that the center of the roller A which follows the contour moves on the limaçon defined by $r = b - c \cos \theta$, where $b > c$. If the slotted arm OB rotates at the angular rate $d\theta/dt = K$, a constant, determine the radial and transverse components of acceleration, a_r and a_θ, of the center of the roller for any value of θ.

Ans. $a_r = K^2(2c \cos \theta - b)$, $a_\theta = 2K^2c \sin \theta$

684. If the slotted arm OB in Prob. 683 remains fixed and the cam revolves at the constant angular rate of $d\theta/dt = K$, find the acceleration of the roller A.

685. If the arm OB in Prob. 683 increases its angular rate about the fixed cam according to $d\theta/dt = kt$, where k is a constant, find the radial and transverse components of acceleration, a_r and a_θ, of the center of the roller A at any time t.

686. By the method of this article solve for the fluid acceleration a just before exit for the centrifugal pump of Prob. 678.

* **687.** If the arm OB in Prob. 683 is revolving counterclockwise at the constant rate of 20 rev./min. and the cam is revolving clockwise at the constant rate of 40 rev./min., determine the acceleration of the center of the roller A when the arm and cam are in the relative positions for which $\theta = 90$ deg. The dimensions of the curve are $b = 4$ in. and $c = 2$ in. *Ans.* $a = 55.5$ in./sec.²

* **688.** The centrifugal pump with radial vanes shown with Prob. 678 rotates at the constant rate $d\theta/dt = K$. An element of the fluid being pumped will be considered here as a smooth particle P which is introduced at the radius r_0 without radial velocity and which moves outward along the vane without friction. There is no force on the particle in the direction along the vane, so that it has zero acceleration in this direction. Under these conditions determine the equation of the path of the particle if the time t is zero for $r = r_0$.

Ans. $r = r_0 \cosh \theta$

PART *C*. ROTATION

74. Defining Relations. Rotation is described
by the angular motion of a line. The *angular dis-*
placement θ of any line, such as *AB* in Fig. 99, is
the angle made by this line with any convenient
fixed reference axis in the same plane. The
angular velocity ω and *angular acceleration α* of

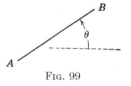

Fig. 99

a line are, respectively, the first and second time derivatives of its
angular displacement *θ*. These definitions give

$$\omega = \frac{d\theta}{dt},$$

$$\alpha = \frac{d^2\theta}{dt^2} = \frac{d\omega}{dt}, \qquad (61)$$

$$\omega \, d\omega = \alpha \, d\theta.$$

The third relation is obtained by eliminating *dt* from the first two. In
each of these relations the positive direction for *ω* and *α*, clockwise or
counterclockwise, is the same as that chosen for *θ*. Equations (61)
should be recognized as analogous to the definitions for the linear motion of
a point expressed by Eqs. (48), (49), and (50).
In fact all relations which were described for
rectilinear translation in Art. 70 apply to the
case of rotation if the linear quantities *s*, *v*,
and *a* are replaced by their respective equivalent angular quantities *θ*, *ω*, and *α*.

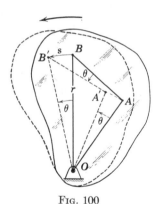

When a rigid body rotates about a fixed
bearing, Fig. 100, each line in the body
which is in a plane normal to the axis of
rotation revolves through the same angle in
the same time. Thus during the rotation
shown each leg of the triangle *OAB* revolves
through the same angle *θ*. The distance *s*

Fig. 100

along the circular arc described by any point
such as *B* is given by the product of the radius *r* and the subtended
angle *θ* expressed in radian measure. This relation and its two time
derivatives give

$$s = r\theta,$$

$$v = r\omega, \qquad (62)$$

$$a_t = r\alpha.$$

The second equation gives the magnitude of the linear velocity of the point B, and the third equation gives the magnitude of its tangential component of acceleration a_t. The normal component of acceleration of the point B may be written in any one of three equivalent forms by combining the second of Eqs. (62) with Eq. (57). These are

$$a_n = \frac{v^2}{r} = r\omega^2 = v\omega. \tag{63}$$

For rotation with *constant* angular acceleration α, Eqs. (61) may be integrated directly. The initial and final conditions which determine the limits of integration will be chosen in the same way as for rectilinear translation. Thus it will be assumed that $\theta = 0$ when $t = 0$ and that $\omega = \omega_0$ when $t = 0$. The integration is mathematically identical with that for rectilinear motion treated in Art. 70, and the results are

$$\omega = \omega_0 + \alpha t,$$
$$\theta = \omega_0 t + \tfrac{1}{2}\alpha t^2, \tag{64}$$
$$\omega^2 = \omega_0^2 + 2\alpha\theta.$$

The reader should perform the indicated integrations and compare these results with Eqs. (51), (52), and (53).

For rotation with variable angular acceleration, Eqs. (64) ·*cannot* be used, and the differential relations, Eqs. (61), must be integrated and account of the variation in α taken.

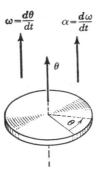

$$\omega = \frac{d\theta}{dt} \qquad \alpha = \frac{d\omega}{dt}$$

The graphical representation of the relations between θ, ω, α, and t will be found useful for problems in rotation with constant or variable angular acceleration in the same manner as the equivalent motion curves were found useful for linear motion.

Angular motion may be represented vectorially. The angular displacement θ of the disk in Fig. 101 may be represented by the free vector θ with the aid of the right-hand rule to establish the positive sense. The vector θ is not restricted to the axis of the disk since the angular movement is the same for every line in

Fig. 101

the plane of the disk. Thus the rotation vector is a free vector. Likewise the angular velocity ω and the angular acceleration α are free vectors, and their positive sense is taken to be that of θ. As long as rotation is confined to a single plane these rotation vectors will be parallel to each other. Thus nothing is gained by the vector description, and θ, ω, and α may be considered scalar quantities. The algebraic sign is sufficient to account for either sense of the vector.

The foregoing description applies only to plane rotation, which is rotation about a fixed axis. A more general treatment would describe the rotation of a rigid body about a point, such as with a spinning top. Here there are components of angular motion about the three mutually perpendicular axes through the pivot point, and vector representation is particularly useful. This problem will be treated briefly in the discussion of gyroscopic motion in Chapter XIII. Fortunately most machine movements are plane motions, and a two-dimensional analysis is sufficient.

SAMPLE PROBLEM

689. A flywheel which is turning freely at 1800 rev./min. clockwise is subjected to a constant counterclockwise torque which produces a uniform counterclockwise angular acceleration of 24 rad./sec.[2] Determine the angular velocity in revolutions per minute 10 sec. after the torque is applied. Also find the total number of revolutions (clockwise turns plus counterclockwise turns) through which the wheel rotates during this interval.

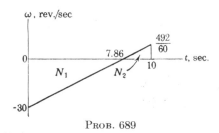

PROB. 689

Solution: Since the angular acceleration is constant, Eqs. (64) may be used. With the counterclockwise sense as positive the new angular velocity is

$$[\omega = \omega_0 + \alpha t] \qquad \omega = -\frac{1800 \times 2\pi}{60} + 24 \times 10 = 51.5 \text{ rad./sec.,}$$

or

$$\omega = \frac{51.5 \times 60}{2\pi} = 492 \text{ rev./min.} \qquad \qquad Ans.$$

If desired, the time could be expressed in minutes and the acceleration as $(24/2\pi)(60)^2$ rev./min.[2] The formula would then give the angular velocity directly in revolutions per minute.

A plot of the angular speed in revolutions per second against the time in seconds discloses the angular displacements which are represented by the area under the curve. The time at which the wheel reverses its motion is

$$[\omega = \omega_0 + \alpha t] \qquad 0 = -\frac{1800 \times 2\pi}{60} + 24t, \qquad t = 7.86 \text{ sec.}$$

From the areas on the diagram the total clockwise displacement is

$$N_1 = \tfrac{1}{2} \times 30 \times 7.86 = 117.9 \text{ rev.},$$

and the counterclockwise displacement is

$$N_2 = \tfrac{1}{2} \times \tfrac{492}{60} \times (10 - 7.86) = 8.78 \text{ rev.}$$

Thus the total number of turns is

$$N = N_1 + N_2 = 126.7 \text{ rev.} \qquad\qquad \textbf{\textit{Ans.}}$$

PROBLEMS

690. The rotor of a turbine which operates at 10,000 rev./min. requires 5 min. to come to rest after the steam is shut off. Compute the average deceleration α.

691. A braking torque causes a flywheel to slow down at the uniform rate of 20 rev./min. during each second. If the wheel comes to rest from a speed of 1800 rev./min., find the number of revolutions N made during this interval.

Ans. $N = 1350$ rev.

692. In the hoisting rig shown the pinion A reaches a speed of 900 rev./min. in 10 sec. from rest with constant acceleration. Determine the acceleration a of the load W.

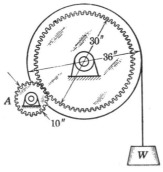
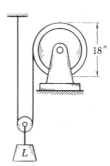

PROB. 692   PROB. 693

693. The load L is lowered 100 ft. from rest in 10 sec. with constant acceleration. Determine the angular velocity ω of the hoisting drum 6 sec. after the load starts.   *Ans.* $\omega = 32$ rad./sec.

694. The angular velocity of a gear is controlled according to $\omega = 6 - 3t^2$, where ω, in radians per second, is positive in the clockwise sense, and where t is in seconds. Find the net angular displacement θ from the time $t = 0$ to $t = 3$ sec.

695. The angular displacement of a wheel is given by $\theta = 2t^3 + 3t^2 + 2$, where θ is in radians, clockwise, and t is in seconds. Find the angular displacement $\Delta\theta$ during the time ($t > 0$) that the velocity is changing from 12 to 72 rad./sec., both clockwise.

696. Experimental data for a rotating control element reveal the relation between angular velocity ω and angular displacement θ shown. Determine the angular acceleration α of the element when $\theta = 5$ rad.

Ans. $\alpha = 4.3$ rad./sec.^{2}

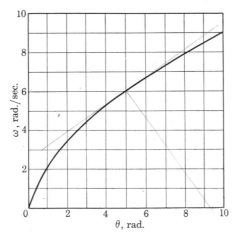

ω, rad./sec.

θ, rad.

PROB. 696

697. Line AB is scribed on the face of the rotating disk as shown. The angle θ made by this line with a fixed reference direction increases at the rate of 150 deg./sec. If the normal acceleration of a point on the rim is 6 ft./sec.^{2}, find the radius r of the disk. *Ans.* $r = 0.874$ ft.

PROB. 697

698. A shaft is accelerated from rest to a speed of 1200 rev./min. and then decelerated immediately to rest again in a total time interval of 12 sec. If both accelerations are constant, find the total number of revolutions N through which the shaft turns.

699. A flywheel is rotating at a uniform clockwise speed of 2 rad./sec. when a variable torque is applied to it at time $t = 0$. As a result there is a clockwise angular acceleration α which increases in direct proportion to the angle θ through which the wheel turns from the instant $t = 0$. After 16 complete turns from this time the angular acceleration is 4 rad./sec.^{2} Determine the angular velocity ω of the wheel at this instant. *Ans.* $\omega = 20.2$ rad./sec.

700. The motion of a rotating element in a mechanism is controlled so that the rate of change of angular velocity ω with angular displacement θ is a constant k. If the angular velocity is ω_0 when both θ and the time t are zero, determine θ, ω, and the angular acceleration α as functions of t.

701. A gear, which turns with constant angular acceleration, has a displacement of 4 rad. when $t = 0$. After 10 sec. it has a displacement of zero, and, when $t = 4$ sec., the gear reverses the direction of its motion. Find the angular velocity ω when $t = 10$ sec.   *Ans.* $\omega = -2.4$ rad./sec.

702. The elements of a wheel-and-disk type mechanical integrator are shown in the figure. The integrator wheel A turns about its fixed axis and is driven by friction from disk B without slippage tangent to its rim. The distance y is a variable and can be controlled at will. Show that the angular displacement of the integrator wheel shaft is given by $z = (1/b)\int y\,dx$, where x is the angular displacement of the disk.

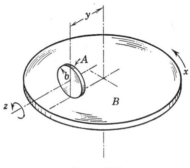

PROB. 702

703. A cable is wound around a shaft against the face of a disk so that the cable forms a spiral as shown. If the radius of the coil at any instant is r and is large compared with the cable diameter D, find the vertical acceleration a of the load L if the shaft is turning at a constant speed ω.

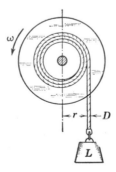

PROB. 703

* **704.** In rewinding the film for the moving-picture projector shown, the lower reel is turned by the motor at a constant angular velocity ω_0. At any instant when the radii of the driving and driven rolls of film are r_0 and r, respectively, find the angular acceleration α of the driven reel. The thickness of the film is b.

$$Ans. \quad \alpha = \frac{b\omega_0^2}{2\pi r}\left(1 + \frac{r_0^2}{r^2}\right)$$

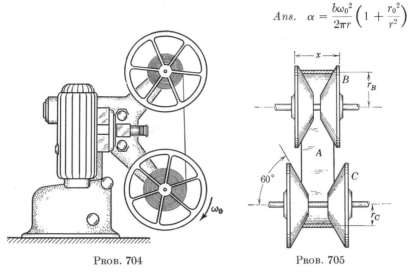

PROB. 704   PROB. 705

* **705.** A variable-speed friction drive consists of the steel ring A, shown in section, which bears against the two identical pairs of rotating conical disks. By synchronizing the motions of the cones along their shafts contact with sufficient pressure may be maintained on the ring. If the driving cones B turn at the constant speed of 600 rev./min. and are separated at the constant rate of $dx/dt = 1$ in./sec., determine the angular acceleration α of the cones C while they are brought together at this same rate for the position where $r_B = 3$ in. and $r_C = 2$ in. $\qquad Ans. \quad \alpha = -68.0$ rad./sec.^{2}

PART *D*. PLANE MOTION

75. Plane Motion. A rigid body executes plane motion when each point in the body remains at a constant distance from a fixed reference plane. Thus all points in the body move in parallel planes. The plane which contains the center of gravity is known as the *plane of motion*. A rolling wheel and the connecting rod of a stationary reciprocating engine are examples of bodies which have plane motion. This type of motion may be described by linear and angular measurements made with respect to a fixed coordinate system (absolute motion analysis) or with the aid of linear and angular measurements made with respect to a moving coordinate system (relative motion analysis). The first method lends itself readily to a direct mathematical solution, whereas the second method is more easily handled by graphical representation. Emphasis will be placed on the relative motion approach with the accompanying graphical analysis, since a visual representation will be found particularly useful in analyzing the various motions.

76. Relative Linear Displacement.   Consider the motions of any two points in a plane.   These points need not be connected, as would be the case if they were attached to a rigid body.   In Fig. 102a one point A moves to A' at the same time that the other point B moves to B'.   The

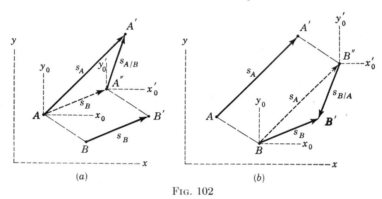

Fig. 102

displacements of A and B are the vectors s_A and s_B measured in the fixed x–y reference frame.   Now consider the displacement of A, which would be measured from a moving but nonrotating reference system x_0–y_0 which has the same motion as point B.   Since displacements are free vectors, s_B may be represented as the parallel vector from A to A'', and the x_0–y_0 origin may be considered as moving from A to A''.   Thus the displacement of A measured from or relative to the moving coordinate system is the vector $s_{A/B}$, which is read "the displacement of A relative to B."   The triangle $AA'A''$ is expressed by the vector equation

$$s_A = s_B +\!\!\!\!\!\!+ s_{A/B}. \tag{65}$$

In words Eq. (65) states that the displacement of any point A equals the displacement of a second point B plus (vectorially) the displacement of A relative to B.   This relation holds for finite movements or for infinitesimal movements.   If the motion of B is measured from a set of axes having the motion of A, Fig. 102b, the vector $s_{B/A}$ would result from the equation $s_B = s_A +\!\!\!\!\!\!+ s_{B/A}$.   The two figures show that $s_{B/A} = -s_{A/B}$, and therefore the relative displacement equation may also be written as

$$s_A = s_B \;\longrightarrow\; s_{B/A}.$$

When the two points are fixed to a rigid body having plane motion, an additional requirement holds. In Fig. 103a the rigid body undergoes an infinitesimal movement from the full to the dotted position. Any two points on the body, such as A and B a fixed distance r apart, will move to the new positions A' and B'. The line AB will have a movement which may be considered as composed of two parts, first, a *translation ds_B* to the position $B'A''$, and, second, a *rotation $d\theta$* about B' to

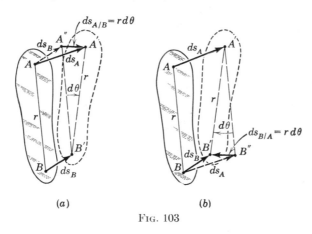

(a)   (b)

FIG. 103

the final position. The differential triangle $AA'A''$ is expressed by Eq. (65) in differential form. Thus

$$ds_A = ds_B \rightarrow ds_{A/B} \quad \text{where} \quad ds_{A/B} = r\, d\theta.$$

The term $r\, d\theta$ is the displacement of A relative to B and is the arc movement due to the rotation about B. Consequently this relative component is perpendicular to AB.

The motion of line AB may be considered equally well as the translation ds_A plus a rotation $d\theta$ about A as shown in Fig. 103b. In this case the relation

$$ds_B = ds_A \rightarrow ds_{B/A} \quad \text{where} \quad ds_{B/A} = r\, d\theta$$

holds. The vector $ds_{B/A}$ is equal and opposite to $ds_{A/B}$, but both rotations are, of course, in the same clockwise sense.

It is important to recognize clearly the two components of plane motion of a rigid body, translation and rotation. It is necessary to see that the term $ds_{A/B}$ in the relative displacement equation is determined by considering point B to be fixed and measuring the movement of A due to the rotation about B.

77. Relative Linear Velocity. If Eq. (65) is differentiated with
respect to the time, there results

$$v_A = v_B \mathbin{+\!\!\!\!+} v_{A/B}. \tag{66}$$

In words Eq. (66) states that the velocity of point A equals the velocity
of point B plus (vectorially) the velocity of A measured relative to B.
It should be emphasized that this relative velocity $v_{A/B}$ is the measurement from a set of nonrotating axes which has the same velocity as

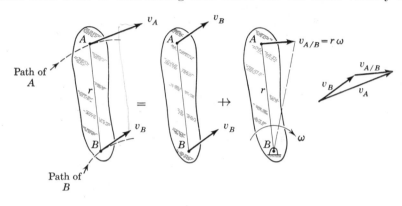

(Plane motion) = (Translation) $\mathbin{+\!\!\!\!+}$ (Rotation)

Fɪɢ. 104

does B. The directions of v_A and v_B coincide with the directions of the
corresponding increments ds_A and ds_B and are, consequently, tangent
to the respective paths of the points.

When the two points A and B are on a rigid body having general
plane motion, the relative velocity term becomes

$$v_{A/B} = \frac{ds_{A/B}}{dt} = r\frac{d\theta}{dt} = r\omega. \tag{67}$$

It should be noted in this relation that the *relative* linear velocity $v_{A/B}$
is determined by the *absolute* angular velocity ω. This relative velocity
is the velocity which would be measured from a nonrotating station
attached to point B, and, consequently, only the rotation of A about
B is observed. The combination of translational velocity and relative
rotational velocity is illustrated in Fig. 104. The vector representation
of Eq. (66) for this motion is shown at the right side of the
figure. It is necessary to recognize that the relative velocity term $v_{A/B}$
is *perpendicular* to the line AB. This is always the case for a rigid body
when the length of the line does not change with time.

The velocity relations shown in Fig. 104 are based on rotation about B. The same results are achieved by considering the relative velocity of B due to rotation about A. In this event the equation is

$$v_B = v_A \leftrightarrow v_{B/A}.$$

The reader should draw the figure corresponding to that in Fig. 104 and verify that $v_{B/A} = -v_{A/B}$ and that the direction of the angular velocity is the same for either reference point.

Equation (66) is a vector equation which is equivalent to the two scalar equations

$$(v_A)_x = (v_B)_x + (v_{A/B})_x,$$

$$(v_A)_y = (v_B)_y + (v_{A/B})_y.$$

Thus there are these six components to the vector equation with the three terms. The six components may also be considered as the magnitude and direction of each of the three vector terms in the vector equation. It becomes apparent that a single vector equation in two dimensions is sufficient for the solution of *two* unknown scalar quantities.

SAMPLE PROBLEMS

706. A wheel of radius r is rolling to the left on the straight path without slipping. If the velocity of the center O is v_O at the instant considered, determine the velocity of any point in the wheel.

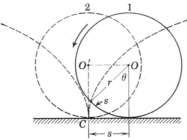 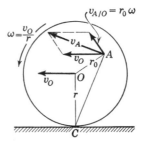

PROB. 706

Solution: The relation between the linear velocity v_O and the angular velocity ω of the wheel will be established first. As the wheel rolls from position 1 to position 2 shown in the figure, the center O has moved a distance s. This distance equals the length $r\theta$ along the arc upon which the wheel rolls if there has been no slipping. Hence

$$s = r\theta,$$

and the time derivative of this equation gives

$$v_O = r\omega$$

for the velocity of the center O in terms of the rolling radius r and the angular velocity ω of the wheel. It should be noted that the angular velocity of every line in the wheel is the same.

The equation of relative velocity may be written for any point A in terms of the velocity of O. Thus

$$v_A = v_O \,\text{+\!\!+}\, v_{A/O}.$$

The velocity of O is $r\omega$. The velocity of A with respect to O depends on the distance r_0 between the two points and the angular velocity of line AO, which is ω. Thus by Eq. (67)

$$v_{A/O} = r_0\omega.$$

The direction is perpendicular to the line AO and is up and to the left as shown, since the rotation with respect to O is counterclockwise. The vector addition of $v_O = r\omega$ and $v_{A/O} = r_0\omega$ is shown on the sketch and gives the velocity of A in both magnitude and direction.

A second method for determining the velocity of A is worth noting. The point on the rim of the wheel in contact with the ground is C, and its path describes a cycloid, shown by the dotted lines in the first figure. In the position shown C has zero velocity, so that the use of this point for reference results in

$$v_A = v_{A/C}.$$

Since the relative velocity of two points on a rigid body is normal to the line joining the points, the velocity v_A is normal to AC. Also the magnitude of the velocity of A is

$$v_A = v_{A/C} = \overline{AC}\omega_{AC} = \overline{AC}\omega = \frac{\overline{AC}}{r}\,v.$$

The magnitude and direction of the velocity of any point on the wheel may be determined easily by using C as the reference point. The magnitude of this velocity will vary linearly with the distance of the point from C. Instantaneously the wheel is pivoted about C, and the direction and magnitude of the velocities of all points may be determined as though the wheel were rotating about C as a momentary fixed point.

707. The rotating slotted arm OC causes the pivoted slider blocks to move in both slots. Determine the velocity of the pin A at the instant shown for which OC has a counterclockwise angular velocity of 4 rad./sec.

Solution: A point B considered to be on the arm OC and coincident with A for the position shown is chosen as a reference point for determining the velocity of A. The relative velocity equation is

$$v_A = v_B \,\text{+\!\!+}\, v_{A/B}.$$

In this case, contrary to the preceding sample problem, the two points selected are *not* attached to the same rigid body. The velocity of B is easily computed and is

$$[v = r\omega] \qquad\qquad v_B = \frac{9}{\cos 20°} \times 4 = 38.3 \text{ in./sec.}$$

in a direction perpendicular to OC. The direction of the velocity of A with respect to B is along the arm OC. This direction may be seen from the diagram at the right side of the figure, where the positions of A and B are shown an instant before and an instant after coincidence. From a vantage point attached to B it is seen that, as the arm OC turns counterclockwise, point A approaches B from a direction along the arm and moves away from B radially outward along the slot in OC. Thus $v_{A/B}$ is a vector parallel to OC with a sense from O to C.

At this point it should be noted that only two quantities remain unknown in the relative velocity equation, namely, the magnitude of v_A and the magnitude of $v_{A/B}$. The velocity v_B is completely known, and the direction of v_A is, of

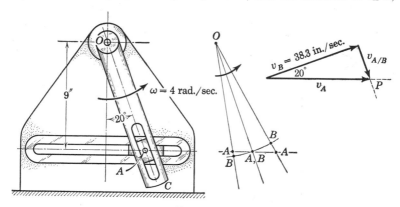

PROB. 707

course, along the horizontal slot. Thus the solution can now be made. The vector v_B is laid off to scale as shown in the diagram, and the directions of $v_{A/B}$ and v_A are drawn through the ends of v_B. The intersection occurs at point P, and the unknown magnitudes may be scaled from the figure. In the case of such a simple figure, the vector diagram may be used to determine the algebraic relations which govern the solution. Thus,

$$v_A = \frac{v_B}{\cos 20°} = \frac{38.3}{0.940} = 40.8 \text{ in./sec.} \qquad Ans.$$

708. Determine the velocity of the piston and the angular velocity of the connecting rod of the reciprocating engine shown for the conditions of $\theta = 60$ deg., $r = 5$ in., $l = 14$ in., and for a clockwise crank speed of 1500 rev./min.

Solution: Points A, B, and O are first located in their proper positions for the given values as shown in the diagram to the right of the engine. The velocity of B is easily found, so that B is used as the reference point for determining the velocity of A. Thus

$$v_A = v_B \leftrightarrow v_{A/B}.$$

The crank-pin velocity v_B is

$$[v = r\omega] \qquad v_B = \frac{5}{12} \times \frac{1500 \times 2\pi}{60} = 65.4 \text{ ft./sec.}$$

and is perpendicular to the crank BO as shown.   The direction of v_A is, of course, along the cylinder axis, and the direction of $v_{A/B}$ must be perpendicular to the line AB, as explained in the present article for the case of two points on a rigid body.   Thus the magnitudes of v_A and $v_{A/B}$ are the only remaining unknowns, and the vector equation can therefore be solved for these two quantities.

The vector v_B is first drawn to scale as shown.   Next a line with the direction of $v_{A/B}$ is drawn through the head of v_B.   This line is perpendicular to the rod AB.   Finally, the known direction of v_A is established through the tail of v_B, and

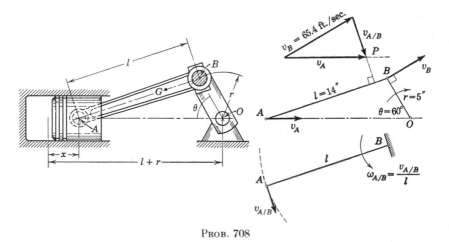

PROB. 708

the intersection P gives the solution of the equation.   Vectors v_A and $v_{A/B}$ are labeled with the proper sense such that v_A equals the vector sum of v_B and $v_{A/B}$. Their magnitudes are scaled off the diagram and are

$$v_{A/B} = 34.4 \text{ ft./sec.}, \qquad v_A = 67.3 \text{ ft./sec.} \qquad\qquad Ans.$$

The angular velocity of AB is due to the rotation of A about B (or B about A). Thus from a station on B (B considered as fixed) A appears to rotate around B with the tangential velocity $v_{A/B}$ as shown in the bottom view in the figure. Therefore the absolute angular velocity of the rod is

$$\left[\omega = \frac{v}{r}\right] \qquad \omega_{AB} = \frac{v_{A/B}}{l} = \frac{34.4}{14/12} = 29.5 \text{ rad./sec., counterclockwise.} \quad Ans.$$

The problem may also be analyzed by considering the motion of B relative to A.   The student should sketch the solution by this procedure.

If an algebraic solution is desired, the trigonometry of the velocity triangle may be used to indicate the necessary relations.   Thus the law of sines could be used to solve for v_A or $v_{A/B}$ provided the angles of the velocity triangle were first obtained.   The calculation of these angles, however, usually involves more work than that accompanying a graphical solution from which satisfactory accuracy can be obtained.

PROBLEMS

709. In the design of the blades for an impulse turbine it is essential that
there be a minimum of turbulence when the op-
erating fluid hits the blade. This problem is met
by designing the blade entrance angle θ so that
the fluid from the nozzle enters at this angle relative
to the blade. Find the proper angle θ for a turbine
designed to operate with a peripheral blade speed of
500 ft./sec., a nozzle angle of 20 deg., and a fluid
velocity of 1000 ft./sec. at the nozzle exit.

Ans. $\theta = 52° 7'$

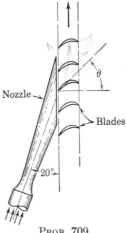

PROB. 709

710. Two ships are heading on straight but non-
parallel courses. The captain of ship A takes a
bearing on ship B, that is, measures the angle between the line of sight to B and the north direction.
After a reasonable interval of time, when ship B appears closer, he takes a second bearing and records
the same angle as previously measured. If both
ships maintain their respective speeds and courses,
what can be said regarding the risk of collision?

711. Determine the velocity of C for the position of the linkage shown. Link
OA is revolving clockwise with a velocity of 15 rad./sec.

Ans. $v_C = 15.0$ ft./sec.

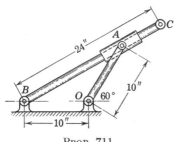

PROB. 711

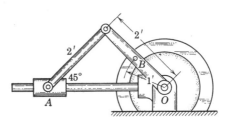

PROB. 712

712. The slider A moves back and forth along the fixed rod because of an
oscillation of the wheel. Determine the angular velocity of the wheel and attached arm OB if the slider A has a velocity of 20 ft./sec. to the left in the position shown.

713. A certain airplane can fly 200 mi./hr. in still air. The pilot desires to
fly to an airport 300 mi. directly north. If a 30 mi./hr. wind is blowing from
the southwest, find his proper compass heading θ (angle measured clockwise
from the north direction) and the time t required to fly the 300 mi.

Ans. $\theta = 353° 55'$, $t = 1$ hr. 22 min.

714. When a sailboat tacks to windward, the minimum angle between the
direction of the apparent wind (relative to the boat) and the direction in which

the boat is heading is about 45 deg. If a north wind is blowing at 15 mi./hr. and the boat is tacking at 5 mi./hr., find the acute angle θ between the direction which the boat is heading and the north direction.

715. A passenger on a ship traveling north at 10 knots notices that the wind appears to come from the west. The ship increases its speed to 20 knots, and the wind appears to come from the northwest. Find the magnitude and direction of the actual wind velocity v_W. *Ans.* $v_W = 10\sqrt{2}$ knots from southwest

716. Determine the velocity of the upper end C of the oscillating arm of the quick-return mechanism for the position shown if the driving pinion is turning clockwise at 200 rev./min. *Ans.* $v_C = 3.18$ ft./sec.

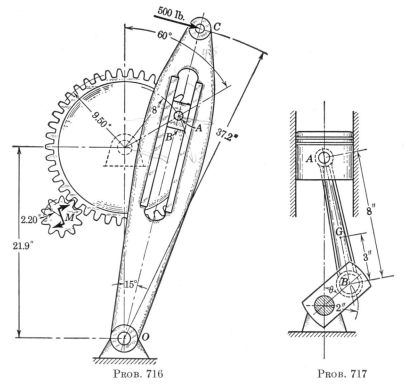

PROB. 716   PROB. 717

717. The piston, connecting rod, and crankshaft of an automobile engine are shown in the figure. Determine the velocity v_A of the piston and the angular velocity ω_{AB} of the connecting rod for a clockwise engine speed of 2700 rev./min. and a crank angle of $\theta = 30$ deg.

718. Use the conditions and solution of Sample Prob. 708 to determine the velocity of the center of gravity G of the connecting rod if G is 4 in. from the crank pin. *Ans.* $v_G = 64.1$ ft./sec.

719. Work Prob. 717 for $\theta = 240$ deg. and also find the velocity of a point M midway between A and B.

720. The drum D rotates clockwise with a velocity of 20 rev./min. and winds up the cable which is also wrapped around the disk. Determine the velocities of points O and A on the integral disk and gear unit for the position shown.

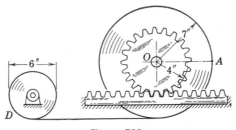

PROB. 720

721. The gear is rolling on the rack with a velocity of 10 rad./sec. counterclockwise at the instant represented. Determine the angular velocity of AB.

Ans. $\omega_{AB} = 3.08$ rad./sec. counterclockwise

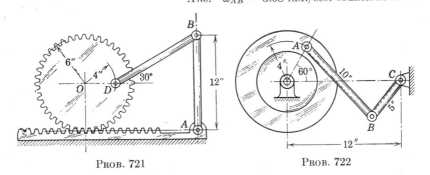

PROB. 721   PROB. 722

722. Find the angular velocities of the links CB and AB for the position shown if the wheel is turning momentarily at a clockwise speed of 60 rev./min.

Ans. $\omega_{CB} = 4.84$ rad./sec. counterclockwise,
$\omega_{AB} = 0.424$ rad./sec. clockwise

723. The wheel shown is rolling counterclockwise and slipping at the same time. The center has a velocity of 10 ft./sec. to the left, and point A has a total velocity of 20 ft./sec. in the position indicated. Determine the angular velocity ω of the wheel.

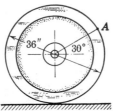

PROB. 723

724. The motion of the slider block A is controlled by the movement of the gear along the rack. If the center of the gear has a velocity of 3 ft./sec. to the left at the instant shown, find the velocity of A.   *Ans.* $v_A = 5$ ft./sec.

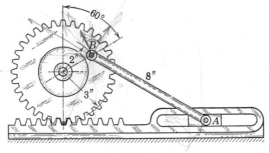

PROB. 724

725. At the instant shown the distance x between blocks B and C is decreasing at the rate of 10 ft./sec. Determine the instantaneous velocity of block C.

Ans. $v_C = 25.1$ ft./sec. to the left

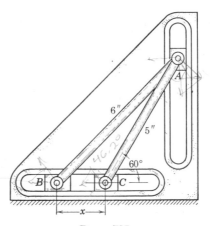

PROB. 725

78. Instantaneous Center. In Art. 77 the velocity problem for the plane motion of a rigid body was solved by considering the motion in terms of a velocity due to translation and a velocity due to rotation (relative velocity). In the present article the problem will be solved by considering the body to be in pure rotation at any instant about a certain axis, normal to the plane of motion, which is momentarily at rest. This axis is called the *instantaneous axis* of zero velocity, and the intersection of this axis with the plane of motion is known as the *instantaneous center* of zero velocity.

The existence of the instantaneous center is easily shown. For the body in Fig. 105a let it be assumed that the directions of the velocities of any two points A and B are known and are not parallel. If there is a point about which A has absolute circular motion at the instant considered, this point must lie on the normal to v_A through A. Similar reasoning applies to B, and the intersection C of these perpendiculars fulfills the requirement for an absolute center of rotation *at the instant considered*. Point C is the instantaneous center and may lie on or off the body. The instantaneous center is *not* a fixed point in the body or a

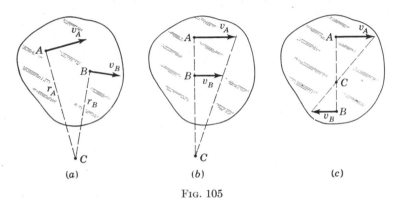

Fig. 105

fixed point in the plane. The motion of the instantaneous center is often very complicated, and, in general, it does *not* have zero acceleration.

If the magnitude of the velocity of one of the points, say, v_A, is also known, the angular velocity ω of the body and the linear velocity of every point in the body are easily obtained. Thus the angular velocity of the body, Fig. 105a, is

$$\omega = \frac{v_A}{r_A},$$

which is also the angular velocity of *every* line in the body. Therefore the velocity of B is $v_B = r_B\omega = (r_B/r_A)v_A$. Once the instantaneous center is located, the direction of the instantaneous velocity of every point in the body is readily found since it is perpendicular to the radial line joining the point in question with C.

If the velocities of two points in a body having plane motion are parallel, Fig. 105b or c, the line joining the points is perpendicular to the direction of the velocities, and the instantaneous center C is located by direct proportion as shown.

The method of instantaneous centers is particularly useful for the graphical determination of velocities in plane motion. The instantaneous center of velocity does not, in general, have zero acceleration and, therefore, *cannot* be used for a similar determination of *acceleration*.

SAMPLE PROBLEM

726. Arm OB of the linkage shown has a counterclockwise angular velocity of 10 rad./sec. in the position shown. Determine the velocity of A, the velocity of D, and the angular velocity of the link AB at this instant.

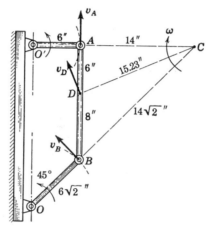

PROB. 726

Solution: The directions of the velocities of A and B are tangent to their circular paths about the fixed centers O' and O as shown. The intersection of the two perpendiculars to the velocities from A and B locates the instantaneous center C for the link AB. The distances AC, BC, and DC, shown on the diagram, are scaled off the drawing or are computed as desired. The angular velocity of BC, which is equal to the angular velocity of AC, DC, and AB, is

$$\left[\omega = \frac{v}{r}\right] \qquad \omega = \frac{v_B}{BC} = \frac{\overline{OB}\omega_{OB}}{\overline{BC}} = \frac{6\sqrt{2}}{14\sqrt{2}} \times 10 = 4.29 \text{ rad./sec. clockwise.}$$

Thus the velocities of A and D are

$$[v = r\omega] \qquad\qquad v_A = \frac{14}{12} \times 4.29 = 5.00 \text{ ft./sec.,} \qquad\qquad Ans.$$

$$v_D = \frac{15.23}{12} \times 4.29 = 5.44 \text{ ft./sec.} \qquad\qquad Ans.$$

in the directions shown.

PROBLEMS

Solve the following problems by the method of the instantaneous center of zero velocity.

727. Show that it is impossible for the two points A and B on the same rigid body to have the parallel velocities shown.

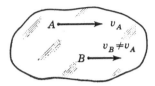

Prob. 727

728. Prob. 717.

729. Prob. 719.   *Ans.* $v_A = 35.6$ ft./sec., $\omega_{AB} = 36.2$ rad./sec. clockwise, $v_M = 39.9$ ft./sec.

730. The collar at A has a velocity of 2 in./sec. to the right when $\theta = 30$ deg. Find the angular velocity ω of arm OB at this position.

Ans. $\omega = 0.151$ rad./sec. counterclockwise

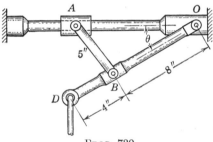

Prob. 730

731. Prob. 721.

732. Prob. 724.

733. The link OA slides in the fixed guide G and has a velocity of 4 ft./sec. to the right in the position shown.   Find the angular velocity ω of the wheel at this instant.   *Ans.* $\omega = 8.97$ rad./sec. counterclockwise

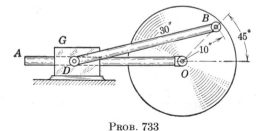

Prob. 733

734. Determine the angular velocity ω of the ram head AE of the rock crusher in the position shown if the crank OB has a clockwise angular velocity of 90 rev./min. When B is at the bottom of its circle, D and E are on a horizontal line through F, and lines BD and AE are vertical. The dimensions are $OB =$ 3 in., $BD = 30$ in., $ED = DF = 15$ in., $AE = 16$ in.

        Ans. $\omega = 0.65$ rad./sec. clockwise

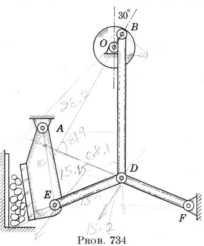

PROB. 734

735. Rack A has a velocity of 6 ft./sec. to the right, and rack B has a velocity of 4 ft./sec. to the left. Find the distance d of the instantaneous center for the gear from O and the velocity of the point D in the position shown.

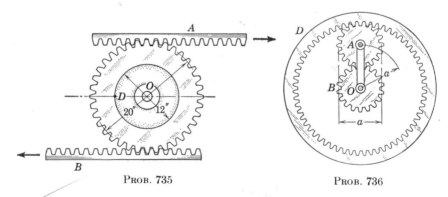

      PROB. 735   PROB. 736

736. A shaft at O drives the arm OA at a speed of 60 rev./min. counterclockwise about a fixed bearing at O. Determine the speed of gear B if (a) gear D does not rotate, (b) gear D rotates clockwise at a speed of 40 rev./min. about O.

      Ans. (a) $\omega_B = 240$ rev./min.,

             (b) $\omega_B = 360$ rev./min.; both counterclockwise

* **737.** The gear B is turning 30 rad./sec. counterclockwise, and the arm OA is turning 12 rad./sec. clockwise. Locate the instant center of gear D and find the angular velocity of D. *Ans.* $1\frac{1}{2}$ in. left of A, $\omega_D = 96$ rad./sec. clockwise

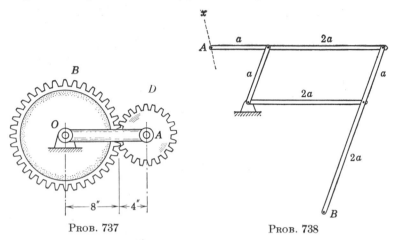

PROB. 737   PROB. 738

* **738.** The pantograph shown is a device for reproducing a drawing to a different scale. If the tracer point A is given a small movement in the arbitrary x-direction, what are the magnitude and direction of the movement of the pencil at B? Answer the question by graphical use of instantaneous centers for any position of the pantograph.

79. Relative Linear Acceleration. If the relative velocity relation, Eq. (66), is differentiated with respect to the time, there results

$$a_A = a_B \leftrightarrow a_{A/B}. \qquad (68)$$

In words Eq. (68) states that the acceleration of a point A equals the acceleration of a second point B plus (vectorially) the acceleration of A measured relative to B. As in the case of relative velocity the relative acceleration term $a_{A/B}$ is the acceleration which would be measured from a set of nonrotating axes whose origin has the same acceleration as point B. Contrary to velocities the accelerations, a_A and a_B, are, in general, *not* tangent to the paths described by points A and B when these paths are curvilinear.

Equation (68) has greatest use when applied to two points on the same rigid body where the distance between the points remains fixed. The relative acceleration term $a_{A/B}$ then becomes the acceleration of A measured from a station B on the same body. Since this relative measurement would in no way disclose the motion of B, it follows that $a_{A/B}$ is the acceleration which A would appear to have if it executed a pure rotation about B considered a fixed point.

The interpretation of Eq. (68) is shown in Fig. 106, where the rigid body has any general motion in the plane of the figure. Points A and B are a fixed distance r apart and move on the paths indicated. Each point has an absolute acceleration as shown in the left-hand view. Equation (68) states that the acceleration of A equals the acceleration of B, as shown in the middle view, plus (vectorially) the relative acceleration due to rotation about B considered a fixed point, as shown in the right-hand view. As in the case of any rotation with both angular

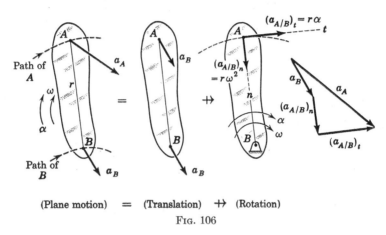

(Plane motion)   =   (Translation)   +> (Rotation)

Fig. 106

velocity and angular acceleration there will be both a normal acceleration component due to the change in the direction of the velocity and a tangential component due to the change in the magnitude of the velocity. The normal component of the relative acceleration is, by Eq. (63),

$$(a_{A/B})_n = \frac{(v_{A/B})^2}{r} = r\omega^2.$$

In this relation it must be understood that ω is the *absolute* angular velocity of the body which is determined by the *relative* linear velocity $v_{A/B}$ as shown in Art. 77. This normal component of relative acceleration is always directed from A to B, and is not influenced by the direction of ω, clockwise or counterclockwise.

The tangential component of relative acceleration is due to the angular acceleration α of the line AB and by Eq. (62) is

$$(a_{A/B})_t = r\alpha.$$

Again it must be understood that α is the *absolute* angular acceleration of the body.

For two points on a rigid body Eq. (68) may be written directly as

$$a_A = a_B + (a_{A/B})_n + (a_{A/B})_t, \qquad (69)$$

where the n- and t-directions are as explained and shown in Fig. 106. If point B happens to have curvilinear motion, then both the normal and tangential components of the absolute acceleration of B must be combined to yield the term a_B.

This sum of the three acceleration components is shown symbolically at the extreme right in Fig. 106. Attention is again called to the fact that plane motion may be analyzed as the superposition of the components of translation and the components of pure rotation.

The polygon which represents the sum of the several acceleration components is usually best solved graphically, although if preferred it may be used to indicate the trigonometric relations necessary for an algebraic solution. The relative acceleration equation is, of course, a vector equation which is equivalent to two scalar equations for a two-dimensional problem in plane motion. Thus there may be as many as, but no more than, two unknown quantities in the equation for solution. These unknowns may be any combination of the magnitude or direction of the acceleration vectors. In solving Eq. (69) graphically it should be pointed out that the known vectors should be drawn first.

SAMPLE PROBLEMS

739. The wheel rolls to the left without slipping, and at the instant considered the center O has a velocity v_O and an acceleration a_O to the left. Determine the acceleration of points A and C on the wheel.

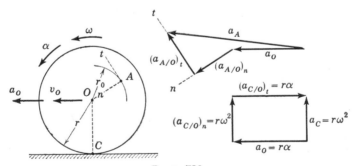

PROB. 739

Solution: The acceleration of A will be expressed directly in terms of the known acceleration of O by the relation

$$a_A = a_O + a_{A/O}.$$

The relative term $a_{A/O} = (a_{A/O})_n \mathbin{+\!\!\!+} (a_{A/O})_t$ depends on the angular velocity, $\omega = v_O/r$, and the angular acceleration, $\alpha = a_O/r$. Thus

$$(a_{A/O})_n = r_0\omega^2 \qquad \text{(directed from } A \text{ to } O\text{),}$$

$$(a_{A/O})_t = r_0\alpha \qquad \text{(directed normal to } AO\text{).}$$

The absolute acceleration of A is the sum of its three components as indicated in the upper of the two symbolic acceleration polygons. In a numerical problem the polygon may be drawn to scale and the answer measured from the figure; or an approximate sketch of the polygon may be made and used to determine a_A algebraically by computing, say, its horizontal and vertical components.

The acceleration of C, the instantaneous center of velocity, is found by a similar process. Thus

$$a_C = a_O \mathbin{+\!\!\!+} a_{C/O} = a_O \mathbin{+\!\!\!+} (a_{C/O})_n \mathbin{+\!\!\!+} (a_{C/O})_t.$$

The last two terms are found by computing the acceleration due to rotation of C about O. The first is

$$(a_{C/O})_n = r\omega^2 \qquad \text{(directed from } C \text{ to } O\text{),}$$

and the second is

$$(a_{C/O})_t = r\alpha = a_O \qquad \text{(directed to the right).}$$

Addition of the three components produces $a_C = r\omega^2$ in the direction from C to O as shown in the lower acceleration polygon. Thus, although the instantaneous center has zero velocity, it does *not* have zero acceleration.

740. Determine the acceleration of the piston A and the angular acceleration of the connecting rod AB for the engine described in Prob. 708 with $\theta = 60$ deg. if the crank speed is constant. Also find the acceleration of the center of gravity G of the rod if G is 4 in. from B.

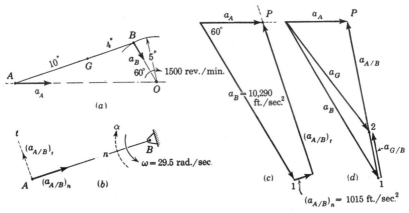

PROB. 740

Solution: The acceleration of A may be expressed in terms of the acceleration of the crank pin B. Thus

$$a_A = a_B \rightarrowtail (a_{A/B})_n \rightarrowtail (a_{A/B})_t.$$

Point B moves in the arc of the 5 in. crank circle with a constant speed, so that it has a normal acceleration equal to

$$[a_n = r\omega^2] \qquad a_B = \frac{5}{12} \times \left(\frac{1500 \times 2\pi}{60}\right)^2 = 10{,}290 \text{ ft./sec.}^2$$

in the direction from B to O.

The normal component of relative acceleration $(a_{A/B})_n$ is calculated by considering B as fixed and therefore depends on the angular velocity of the rod AB and the length of AB. From Prob. 708 this angular velocity was found to be 29.5 rad./sec. counterclockwise, corresponding to the relative linear velocity $v_{A/B} = 34.4$ ft./sec. Using this velocity gives

$$[a_n = r\omega^2] \qquad (a_{A/B})_n = \tfrac{14}{12} \times (29.5)^2 = 1015 \text{ ft./sec.}^2$$

in the direction from A to B as indicated on the separate diagram of the rod in the b-part of the figure, which shows B as fixed for the purpose of visualizing the relative acceleration. The alternate relation, $a_n = v^2/r$, may also be used for calculating the relative normal acceleration provided the relative velocity $v_{A/B}$ is used for v. The equivalence is easily seen when it is recalled that $v_{A/B} = r\omega$.

It may be observed now that there are only two unknowns remaining in the relative acceleration equation, the magnitude of a_A and the magnitude of $(a_{A/B})_t$. Thus the solution may be obtained. The known vectors are laid off by first starting with a_B as indicated in the c-part of the figure. Next $(a_{A/B})_n$ is added, and then the direction of the component $(a_{A/B})_t$ is drawn through the head of this last known vector. The solution of the equation is obtained by constructing the correct direction of the sum a_A through the starting point. This direction is, of course, along the axis of the cylinder in which A slides. The intersection point P on the polygon enables the correct magnitude of the two unknowns to be determined either by measurement from the scale drawing or by algebraic solution of the acceleration polygon. The results are

$$a_A = 3320 \text{ ft./sec.}^2 \qquad \text{and} \qquad (a_{A/B})_t = 9040 \text{ ft./sec.}^2 \qquad Ans.$$

in the directions shown.

It is not until the magnitude and sense of the component $(a_{A/B})_t$ are found that the angular acceleration of the rod may be determined. The quantities $(a_{A/B})_t$ and α were indicated by dotted lines in the b-portion of the illustration because their magnitude and sense were unknown until the solution point P was found. Now it can be seen that, since $(a_{A/B})_t$ is up and slightly to the left, the angular acceleration must be clockwise for this position of the rod. The magnitude is

$$\left[\alpha = \frac{a_t}{r}\right] \qquad \alpha = \frac{9040}{\tfrac{14}{12}} = 7750 \text{ rad./sec.}^2 \qquad Ans.$$

The acceleration of G may be determined in terms of the acceleration of either A or B. Using B gives

$$a_G = a_B \nleftrightarrow a_{G/B}.$$

The relative term is

$$a_{G/B} = (a_{G/B})_n \nleftrightarrow (a_{G/B})_t = \overline{GB}\omega^2 \nleftrightarrow \overline{GB}\alpha.$$

This expression is the same as that for $a_{A/B}$ except that $\overline{GB}$ replaces $\overline{AB} = r$. Thus the two relative acceleration terms have the same direction and are related by direct ratio, or

$$a_{G/B} = \frac{\overline{GB}}{\overline{AB}} a_{A/B} = \frac{4}{14} a_{A/B}.$$

The acceleration polygon is redrawn in the d-part of the figure, and the vector from point 1 to P is the term $a_{A/B}$. Point 2 is therefore located $\frac{4}{14}$ of the distance from point 1 to P. The acceleration of G is then drawn to point 2 and is found to be

$$a_G = 7870 \text{ ft./sec.}^2 \qquad\qquad Ans.$$

in the direction shown. It should be noted that a point close to B will have an acceleration nearly that of B, while a point close to A will have an acceleration nearly that of A.

PROBLEMS

741. An automobile with standard 28 in. diameter tires accelerates uniformly from rest to a speed of 30 mi./hr. in a distance of 80 ft. Determine the acceleration a of a point on the top of the wheel as the car reaches the speed of 10 mi./hr.

742. The cable is wrapped around the inner hub of the wheel and pulled to the right with a constant velocity of 0.5 ft./sec. If the wheel does not slip, determine the velocity and acceleration of point A. (Which way does the wheel roll?) *Ans.* $v_A = 2$ ft./sec. to the right, $a_A = 1$ ft./sec.^{2} down

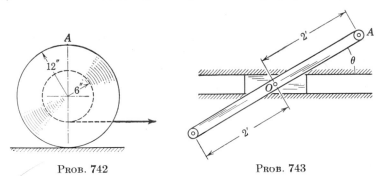

PROB. 742   PROB. 743

743. The bar OA is pivoted on the moving slider block at O and has a constant clockwise angular velocity of 2 rad./sec. Determine the acceleration of point A when it passes the position $\theta = 30$ deg. if (a) the velocity of the block is constant and (b) the acceleration of the block is 4 ft./sec.^{2} to the right.

744. Assume the bar OA in Prob. 743 has a counterclockwise angular acceleration of 5 rad./sec.^{2} and a clockwise angular velocity of 2 rad./sec. as the bar passes the position shown. Determine the total acceleration of A at this instant if the slider block has an acceleration of 4 ft./sec.^{2} to the right at this same time. *Ans.* $a_A = 9.20$ ft./sec.^{2}

745. The elements of a steam locomotive drive are shown in the sketch. If the locomotive is traveling at a constant speed of 60 mi./hr. to the right, determine the acceleration of the crosshead A when it is at the extreme left end of its stroke. *Ans.* $a_A = 911$ ft./sec.^{2}

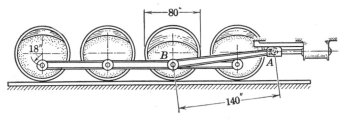

PROB. 745

746. The circular disk turns about its center O with a constant clockwise angular acceleration of 4 rad./sec.^{2} The bar revolves clockwise about O so that OA overtakes a radial line scribed on the disk once every 3 sec. during the entire period of the acceleration of the disk. In addition O has a uniform acceleration of 3 ft./sec.^{2} horizontally to the right. Determine the acceleration of the end A of the rod at the instant shown, for which the angular velocity of the disk is 2 rad./sec. clockwise.

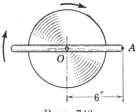

Ans. $a_A = 5.74$ ft./sec.^{2}

747. Find the acceleration of the piston A and the center of gravity G of the connecting rod for the automobile engine described in Prob. 717 for the crank angle of $\theta = 30$ deg. and a constant clockwise engine speed of 2700 rev./min.

PROB. 746

748. The acceleration of pin A is 6 ft./sec.^{2} down and to the right, and its velocity is 3 ft./sec. up and to the left as the link passes the horizontal. For this position determine the angular acceleration α_{AB} of the link.

Ans. $\alpha_{AB} = 8.75$ rad./sec.^{2} clockwise

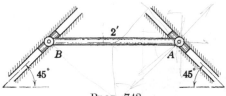

PROB. 748

749. If the link AB shown with Prob. 748 has an angular velocity of 3 rad./sec. and a counterclockwise angular acceleration of 5 rad./sec.^{2}, find the larger of the accelerations of the two ends.

750. The locomotive of Prob. 745 is traveling 60 mi./hr. to the right with no acceleration. Determine the angular acceleration α of the main rod AB when in the position shown.   *Ans.* $\alpha = 90.3$ rad./sec.^{2} clockwise

751. The link OA in the mechanism shown with Prob. 733 has a constant velocity of 4 ft./sec. to the right when in the position shown. Determine the angular acceleration α of the wheel at this instant.

752. At the instant shown rack A has a velocity of 6 ft./sec. to the right and an acceleration of 19 ft./sec.^{2} to the left. Also at this instant rack B has a velocity of 3 ft./sec. to the left and an acceleration of 4 ft./sec.^{2} to the left. Determine the acceleration of point C on the two integral gears.

Ans. $a_C = 41.2$ ft./sec.^{2}

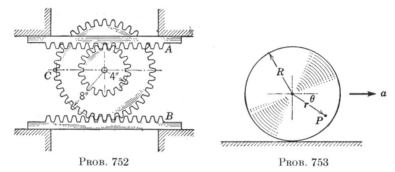

PROB. 752   PROB. 753

753. The wheel rolls to the right without slipping, and its center has an acceleration a. A point P on the wheel is at a fixed distance r from the center. Determine the value of θ and the corresponding velocity v of the center in order that the acceleration of P be equal to zero.

$$Ans. \quad \theta = \sin^{-1}\frac{r}{R}, \quad v = \sqrt{\frac{aR}{r}}\sqrt{R^2 - r^2}$$

754. In the linkage shown with Prob. 730 the vertical component of the total acceleration of D is 4 ft./sec.^{2} down, and the vertical component of the velocity of D at the instant shown is 2 ft./sec. also down. Determine the acceleration of the slider A for the position of $\theta = 30$ deg.

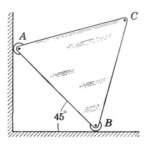

PROB. 755

755. The plate ABC is in the form of an equilateral triangle 12 in. on a side and moves so that the rollers at A and B are in contact with the vertical and horizontal surfaces. Find the acceleration of C in the position shown if B has an acceleration of 4 ft./sec.^{2} to the right and a velocity of 2 ft./sec. at this instant.

Ans. $a_C = 12.02$ ft./sec.^{2}

756. The sliding collar B has a constant velocity of 10 ft./sec. vertically down on the fixed shaft during an interval of its motion. Determine the angular acceleration α_{OA} of the wheel at the instant represented.

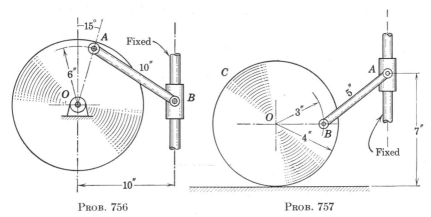

PROB. 756   PROB. 757

757. The wheel C rolls back and forth over a short distance on the horizontal surface without slipping, and the connecting link causes the collar A to slide up and down on the fixed vertical shaft. When A passes the position shown, the center O of the wheel has a velocity of 0.4 ft./sec. to the right and no acceleration. Determine the acceleration a_A of the collar at this position.

Ans. $a_A = 2.26$ ft./sec.^{2} down

* 758. Wheel A has a clockwise angular acceleration of 12 rad./sec.^{2} and a counterclockwise angular velocity of 4 rad./sec. at the instant represented. Determine the angular acceleration α of wheel B for this position.

Ans. $\alpha = 19$ rad./sec.^{2} clockwise

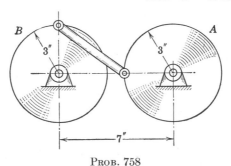

PROB. 758

* 759. The circular disk is coupled to the shaft of the electric motor A such that with the arm OB stationary the disk revolves at 24 rev./min. clockwise when viewed from above. The arm OB is set in motion with an angular acceleration of 20 (rev./min.)/sec. clockwise when viewed from above. The current supplied to the motor is not changed, so that a point on the disk still crosses the arm OB

with the same frequency. Determine the velocity v_C and acceleration a_C of the point C if it is in the position shown when OB has reached a speed of 12 rev./min.

Ans. $v_C = 1.831$ ft./sec., $a_C = 4.81$ ft./sec.^{2}

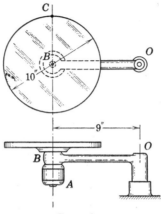

PROB. 759

* **760.** The spider A and central gear B are independently mounted on the shaft at O. At the instant shown $\omega_A = 2$ rad./sec. clockwise and $\alpha_A = 12$ rad./sec.^{2} counterclockwise. Also $\omega_B = 4$ rad./sec. counterclockwise and $\alpha_B = 10$ rad./sec.^{2} clockwise. Determine the angular acceleration α_D of the ring gear D and the acceleration a_C of point C on the intermediate gear. The pitch diameter of each of the five small gears is 6 in.

Ans. $a_C = 14.50$ ft./sec.^{2}, $\alpha_D = 19.33$ rad./sec.^{2} counterclockwise

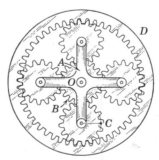

PROB. 760

80. Absolute Determination of Motion. In the preceding three articles the determination of the velocities and accelerations in plane motion has been accomplished with the aid of the equations of relative motion. This type of problem may also be solved by a direct calculation of the absolute motions desired. Such calculation will involve the first and second time derivatives of displacement to obtain velocity and acceleration, respectively. The method is best illustrated by a sample problem.

SAMPLE PROBLEM

761. End A of the link is given a constant velocity of 4 ft./sec. to the right during a short interval of its motion. When $\theta = 30$ deg., find the angular velocity and acceleration of AB and the linear velocity and acceleration of end B.

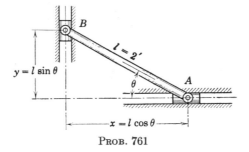

PROB. 761

Solution: The velocity of A is the time rate of change of x, or

$$v_A = \frac{dx}{dt} = \frac{d}{dt}(l\cos\theta) = -l\sin\theta\frac{d\theta}{dt}.$$

The angular velocity of the bar is, then,

$$\omega_{AB} = \frac{d\theta}{dt} = -\frac{v_A}{l}\csc\theta,$$

and for $\theta = 30$ deg.,

$$\omega_{AB} = -\frac{4}{2}\times 2 = -4 \text{ rad./sec.} \qquad Ans.$$

The minus sign indicates that the angular velocity is counterclockwise since θ is measured clockwise.

The angular acceleration is obtained by differentiation of ω_{AB}. Thus

$$\alpha_{AB} = \frac{d^2\theta}{dt^2} = -\frac{v_A}{l}\frac{d}{dt}\csc\theta = +\frac{v_A}{l}\operatorname{ctn}\theta\csc\theta\frac{d\theta}{dt} = -\frac{v_A{}^2}{l^2}\operatorname{ctn}\theta\csc^2\theta.$$

For $\theta = 30$ deg. this becomes

$$\alpha_{AB} = -\frac{4^2}{2^2}\sqrt{3}\times 2^2 = -27.7 \text{ rad./sec.}^2 \qquad Ans.$$

Again the negative sign indicates that α_{AB} is counterclockwise since θ and its derivatives are positive in a clockwise sense.

The linear motion of B is obtained by differentiation of the dimension y. Thus

$$v_B = \frac{dy}{dt} = \frac{d}{dt}(l\sin\theta) = l\cos\theta\frac{d\theta}{dt} = -v_A\operatorname{ctn}\theta,$$

and for $\theta = 30$ deg.,

$$v_B = -4\times\sqrt{3} = -6.93 \text{ ft./sec.} \qquad Ans.$$

The minus sign shows that the velocity of B is actually down in the sense opposite to that for positive measurement of y and its derivatives.

By differentiation the acceleration of B is

$$a_B = \frac{d^2y}{dt^2} = -v_A \frac{d}{dt} \operatorname{ctn} \theta = +v_A \csc^2 \theta \frac{d\theta}{dt} = -\frac{v_A{}^2}{l} \csc^3 \theta.$$

For $\theta = 30$ deg. this becomes

$$a_B = -\frac{4^2}{2} \times 2^3 = -64 \text{ ft./sec.}^2 \qquad\qquad Ans.$$

As before, the minus sign indicates that the acceleration is opposite to the positive direction for the measurement of y and is therefore down.

PROBLEMS

762. The circular disk is mounted eccentrically and turns about the shaft at O with a constant angular velocity ω. Find the acceleration a, measured positive to the right, of the plunger for any angle θ of the circular cam.

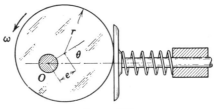

PROB. 762

763. Show that the expressions $v = r\omega$ and $a_t = r\alpha$ hold for the motion of the center O of the wheel which rolls on the circular arc, where ω and α are the absolute angular velocity and acceleration, respectively, of the wheel.

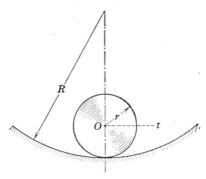

PROB. 763

764. The two slotted links are caused to rotate about their fixed bearings by the movement of the connecting pin in the vertical slot. If the pin has a constant upward velocity v, find the angular acceleration α of the links in terms of θ.

$$Ans. \quad \alpha = -\frac{v^2}{b^2}\sin 2\theta \cos^2\theta$$

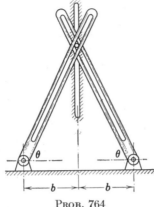

PROB. 764

765. The wheel rolls to the right with a constant velocity v. Determine the angular acceleration α of the bar for any value of θ.

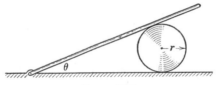

PROB. 765

766. A device to produce oscillation of the shaft at A is shown in the figure. The eccentric circular cam rotates with a constant clockwise angular velocity ω_0. Determine the angular velocity ω of the fork in terms of the cam angle θ.

$$Ans. \quad \omega = \frac{b\cos\theta - e}{b^2 - 2be\cos\theta + e^2}e\omega_0$$

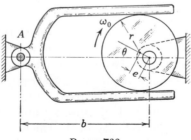

PROB. 766

* **767.** Determine by direct computation the velocity v, measured positive to the right, of the piston A in the reciprocating engine in Sample Prob. 708 in terms of r, l, and θ if the engine speed is $\omega = d\theta/dt$.

$$Ans. \quad v = r\omega \left[\sin \theta + \frac{r \sin 2\theta}{2l \sqrt{1 - \left(\frac{r}{l} \sin \theta\right)^2}} \right]$$

81. Rotating Axes; Coriolis Acceleration.

In Arts. 77 and 79 the motion of a point was described relative to the motion of another point wherein the coordinate system which moves with the reference point has no rotation. There are certain problems where it is convenient to refer the motion of a point to a rotating coordinate system.

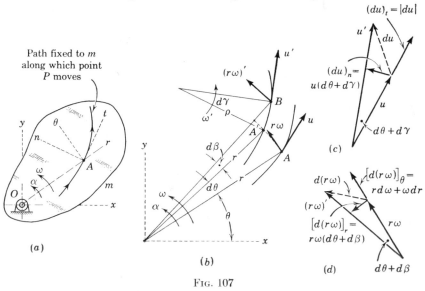

Fig. 107

Consider a body which rotates about a fixed point O with an angular velocity ω and an angular acceleration α as shown in Fig. 107a. A radial line on the body constitutes the rotating reference frame. The motion of a point P along any curved path which is fixed to the rotating body will be described in terms of the motion of the point A, which is fixed on the path and coincident with P, and in terms of the motion of the point P with respect to the path considered as not rotating. It may be visualized, for example, that such a description will fit the problem of a fluid particle moving along the curved vane of a centrifugal pump.

When the particle is at A, Fig. 107b, its absolute velocity may be represented in terms of the velocity of A, which is $r\omega$, and the velocity relative to A, which is labeled u and is along the path fixed in the body.

During an infinitesimal rotation $d\theta$ of the body the point moves to B, and its new absolute velocity is represented by the sum of the velocity of B, denoted by $(r\omega)'$, and the velocity relative to B, denoted by u'. The acceleration of P is found by evaluating the changes in these two velocity components.

In Fig. 107c the change in the velocity relative to the path is shown. It should be noted that the angle between u and u' is the rotation $d\theta$ of the path plus the rotation $d\gamma$ relative to the path. From the figure it is seen that du is expressed by the sum $\left| du \right| \leftrightarrow (u\,d\theta + u\,d\gamma)$. The acceleration corresponding to this change in the relative velocity u is obtained by dividing the components of the increment du by dt and therefore may be written as the vector sum

$$\overset{(t)}{\frac{du}{dt}} \leftrightarrow \overset{(n)}{u\omega} \leftrightarrow \overset{(n)}{u\omega'}.$$

The direction of each term is indicated above the term as a reminder. In this expression the absolute angular velocity of the path is $\omega = d\theta/dt$, and the angular velocity of the radius of curvature relative to the path is $\omega' = d\gamma/dt$. The term du/dt is the time rate of change of the magnitude of u and is merely the acceleration of P tangent to the path measured from the path considered as fixed.

In Fig. 107d is shown the difference in the velocities of the reference points A and B coincident with P. The angle between $r\omega$ and $(r\omega)'$ is the rotation $d\theta$ of the path plus the rotation $d\beta$ due to the changed position along the path. From the figure it is seen that $d(r\omega)$ may be expressed as the vector sum $(r\,d\omega + \omega\,dr) \leftrightarrow (r\omega\,d\theta + r\omega\,d\beta)$. The acceleration due to this differential change in velocity of the reference points on the path is obtained by dividing the components of the increment $d(r\omega)$ by dt and therefore may be written as the vector sum

$$\overset{(\theta)}{r\alpha} \leftrightarrow \overset{(\theta)}{\omega\frac{dr}{dt}} \leftrightarrow \overset{(-r)}{r\omega^2} \leftrightarrow \overset{(-r)}{r\omega\frac{d\beta}{dt}}.$$

Again the direction of each term is indicated as a reminder by the symbol above it. In this expression the substitutions $\alpha = d\omega/dt$ and $\omega = d\theta/dt$ have been made.

The absolute acceleration a of P is the vector combination of the two summations obtained, and the terms are regrouped to give

$$a = (\overset{(\theta)}{r\alpha} \leftrightarrow \overset{(-r)}{r\omega^2}) \leftrightarrow \left(\overset{(t)}{\frac{du}{dt}} \leftrightarrow \overset{(n)}{u\omega'}\right) \leftrightarrow \overset{(n)}{u\omega} \leftrightarrow \omega\left(\overset{(-r)}{r\frac{d\beta}{dt}} \leftrightarrow \overset{(\theta)}{\frac{dr}{dt}}\right).$$

The arc length ds from A' to B may be expressed as $ds = r\,d\beta \mathbin{+\!\!\!+} dr$, and, consequently, the velocity u along the curve (relative to the curve) is

$$u = \frac{ds}{dt} = r\frac{d\beta}{dt} \mathbin{+\!\!\!+} \frac{dr}{dt}.$$

Thus the two terms in the last parenthesis of the expression for a have the magnitude of u. The direction of the sum of these terms is, however, not along the path but normal to the path in the n-direction, as may be seen by adding them together, using the proper direction for each term. Consequently

$$\omega\left(\overset{(-r)}{r\frac{d\beta}{dt}} \mathbin{+\!\!\!+} \overset{(\theta)}{\frac{dr}{dt}} \right) = \overset{(n)}{u\omega}.$$

The acceleration of P may now be written as

$$a = a_m \mathbin{+\!\!\!+} a_p \mathbin{+\!\!\!+} 2u\omega. \tag{70}$$

In this equation the expression $a_m = r\alpha \mathbin{+\!\!\!+} r\omega^2$ is the acceleration of the point A on body m and is the acceleration that P would have if it were fixed to the path and rotated with the path. The term $a_p = du/dt \mathbin{+\!\!\!+} u\omega'$ is the acceleration which P would have if the path were fixed and the motion of P along the path were observed. This fact may be seen more readily when it is observed that the tangential component along the path considered as fixed is du/dt and the normal component is $u\omega' = \rho\omega'^2 = u^2/\rho$. The term $2u\omega$ is called the *supplementary* or *Coriolis acceleration*. The acceleration given by Eq. (70) expresses the so-called *theorem of Coriolis*. The direction of $2u\omega$ is always perpendicular to the velocity u of the point relative to the path. If the vector u is rotated about its tail in the direction of ω, the tip of the vector u will move in the proper sense of the vector $2u\omega$.

The analysis of acceleration in mechanisms which involve sliding contact along rotating members may be solved by the method of this article.

SAMPLE PROBLEM

768. Determine the angular acceleration of the link AB in the position shown if OC has a constant counterclockwise velocity of 4 rad./sec.

Solution: Link OC will be considered as the rotating reference body, and the acceleration of B will be analyzed by Eq. (70). Let D be the point on OC coincident with B at this instant. The first term in this equation is the acceleration of the coincident point on the rotating reference frame and is $a_m = a_D = \overline{OB}(\omega_{OB})^2$. Point D has no tangential acceleration in this problem. The second term is the acceleration of B along the path considered as not rotating. Since the path is a straight line, this acceleration is merely $a_p = d^2x/dt^2$. The last term or Coriolis acceleration is $2u\omega$, where $u = dx/dt = v_{B/D}$.

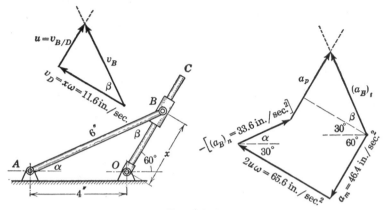

PROB. 768

It should be apparent that the velocities involved must be obtained first. From the geometry of the triangle AOB and from the solution of the equation $v_B = v_D \not\rightarrow v_{B/D}$ shown in the figure, the following values are obtained:

$$x = 2.90 \text{ in.}, \quad u = v_{B/D} = 8.20 \text{ in./sec.}, \quad v_B = 14.20 \text{ in./sec.}$$

From these values the following computations may now be made:

$$(a_B)_n = \frac{v_B^2}{\overline{AB}} = \frac{(14.20)^2}{6} = 33.6 \text{ in./sec.}^2 \text{ from } B \text{ to } A,$$

$$a_m = a_D = x\omega^2 = (2.90)(4)^2 = 46.4 \text{ in./sec.}^2 \text{ from } B \text{ to } O,$$

$$2u\omega = (2)(8.20)(4) = 65.6 \text{ in./sec.}^2 \text{ in the direction of } v_D.$$

The magnitudes of the term $(a_B)_t$ normal to AB and the term $a_p = d^2x/dt^2$ are unknown. Substituting the values just obtained into Eq. (70) and solving for $(a_B)_t$ give

$$(a_B)_t = 46.4 \not\rightarrow 65.6 \rightarrow 33.6 \not\rightarrow a_p.$$

The solution of this equation is shown by the acceleration polygon in the figure and results in the values

$$(a_B)_t = \overline{AB}\alpha_{AB} = 56.6 \text{ in./sec.}^2,$$

and

$$\alpha_{AB} = \frac{56.6}{6} = 9.4 \text{ rad./sec.}^2 \text{ counterclockwise} \qquad Ans.$$

PROBLEMS

769. When the disk shown is at rest, the pin A moves in the circular slot at the constant counterclockwise rate of 4 rad./sec. If the pin continues to move in the slot at this same rate relative to the disk, while the disk accelerates counterclockwise from rest at the rate of 32 rad./sec.², determine the acceleration of the pin when the disk reaches a velocity of 8 rad./sec. Solve by Eq. (70) and also by direct consideration of the absolute rotation about O.

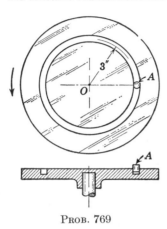

770. Assume that the fluid particle P in Prob. 678 moves with a constant velocity u measured out along the radial vane of the centrifugal pump, which turns with a constant angular velocity ω. Determine the acceleration a of the particle when it is a distance r from the axis of rotation. (Compare solution by Eq. (70) with solution by Eqs. (60).)

PROB. 769

$$Ans. \quad a = \omega\sqrt{r^2\omega^2 + 4u^2}$$

771. Assume that the pump impeller of Prob. 678 has a diameter of 15 in. and turns at the constant speed of 1800 rev./min. If the total acceleration of the fluid particles is tangent to the rim just before they leave the rim, find the acceleration a_p of the particles along and relative to the blades at this position. $Ans. \quad a_p = 22,200$ ft./sec.²

772. An airplane flies north along a meridian at a constant speed of 600 mi./hr. Determine the Coriolis component of the acceleration of the airplane when a latitude of 45 deg. north is reached. The radius of the earth is very nearly 3960 mi., the angular velocity of the earth is 0.729×10^{-4} rad./sec., and the axis of the earth may be considered fixed in space. (*Hint:* Consider the projection of the motion of the airplane on a plane of rotation of the earth.)

Ans. $2u\omega = 0.0907$ ft./sec.² directed west

* **773.** The slotted disk shown rotates with a constant counterclockwise angular velocity of 10 rad./sec. During a short interval of time the arm OA is made to rotate counterclockwise so that its angle θ with the radial line OB fixed on the disk increases at the constant rate of 4 rad./sec. Determine the total acceleration of C when $\theta = 30$ deg.

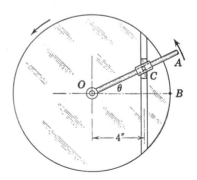

PROB. 773

* **774.** Find the angular acceleration of link AB in Prob. 768 for the 60 deg. position shown if OC has a clockwise angular velocity and acceleration of 4 rad./sec. and 8 rad./sec.², respectively, at this instant.

$Ans. \quad \alpha_{AB} = 4.70$ rad./sec.² counterclockwise

* 775. The figure shows one of the vanes of a centrifugal pump impeller which turns with a constant clockwise speed of 300 rev./min. The fluid particles are observed to have an absolute velocity whose component in the r-direction is 10 ft./sec. at discharge from the vane. Furthermore, the magnitude of the velocity of the particles measured relative to the vane is increasing at the rate of 80 ft./sec.^{2} just before they leave the vane. Determine the total acceleration a of a fluid particle an instant before it leaves the impeller. The radius of curvature ρ of the vane at its end is 8 in. *Ans.* $a = 360$ ft./sec.^{2}

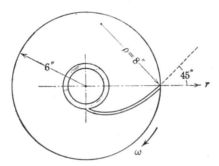

PROB. 775

CHAPTER X

Principles of Kinetics

82. Introduction. When a body is subjected to a force system which is unbalanced, the body is not in equilibrium and therefore has accelerated motion. *Kinetics* is a study of the relations between unbalanced force systems and the changes in motion which they produce. The properties of forces were defined and illustrated in Part I on statics, and the relations between displacement, velocity, acceleration, and time were covered in Chapter IX. The remainder of the book concerns the laws which govern the combination of the two ingredients of kinetics, force and motion. The basic concepts and definitions presented in Chapter I are fundamental to the development of kinetics, and a review of this introduction is strongly recommended before proceeding.

83. The Fundamental Experiment. The basic connection between force and acceleration is stated by Newton's second law of motion. The validity of this law is entirely experimental, and the fundamental meaning of the law will be described by an ideal experiment in which force and acceleration are assumed to be measured without error. Any particle is isolated in the primary inertial system * and is subjected to the action of a single force F_1. The acceleration a_1 of the particle is measured, and the ratio F_1/a_1 will be some number C_1 whose value depends on the units used for measurement of force and acceleration. The experiment is now repeated by subjecting the same particle to a different force F_2 and measuring the corresponding acceleration a_2. Again the ratio F_2/a_2 will produce a number C_2. The experiment is repeated as many times as desired. Two important conclusions may be drawn from the results. First, the ratios of applied force to corresponding acceleration will all equal the same number, provided the units for measurement are not changed in the experiments. Thus

$$\frac{F_1}{a_1} = \frac{F_2}{a_2} = \cdots = \frac{F}{a} = C, \text{ a constant.}$$

* The primary inertial system or astronomical frame of reference is an imaginary set of reference axes attached to the mean position of the so-called "fixed" stars. See Art. 3, Chapter I.

The constant C is a measure of some property of the particle which does not change. This property is the *inertia* of the particle which is the *resistance* to change in velocity. Thus for a particle with high inertia (large C) the acceleration will be small for a given force F, and, conversely, if the inertia is small, the acceleration will be large. The *mass m* is used as the quantitative measure of inertia, and, therefore, the expression

$$C = km$$

may be written, where k is a constant to account for the units used. Thus the experimental relation becomes

$$F = kma, \tag{71}$$

where F is the resultant force acting on a particle of mass m, and a is the resulting acceleration of the particle.

The second conclusion from the ideal experiments is that the acceleration is always in the direction of the applied force. Thus Eq. (71) is a *vector* equation which expresses equality of direction as well as magnitude.

Although an actual experiment cannot be performed in the ideal manner described, the conclusions are inferred from the measurements of countless accurately performed experiments where the results are correctly predicted from the hypothesis of the ideal experiment. The most accurate check undoubtedly lies in the precise account of the motions of planets based on Eq. (71).

It should be understood that the results of the fundamental experiment may be obtained only if measurements are made relative to the "fixed" primary inertial system.* Thus, if the experiment described were performed on the surface of the earth and all measurements were made relative to a reference system attached to the earth, the measured results would show a slight discrepancy upon substitution into Eq. (71). This discrepancy would be due to the neglect of the components of acceleration of the earth, and would disappear when these components were accounted for. The corrections due to the acceleration of the earth are negligible † for almost all practical engineering purposes.

---

* The theory of relativity demonstrates that there is no such thing as a preferred primary inertial system and that experiments conducted in reference systems moving with constant velocity relative to one another will yield exactly the same results. See the footnote on p. 342 for the numerical magnitude of a relativity effect.

† Equation (71) may be rewritten as

$$F = m(a_r + \kern-0.8em+\ a_e),$$

in which k is taken as unity and the absolute acceleration a is replaced by the vector

Thus accelerations measured on the earth's surface may be treated as "absolute," and Eq. (71) may be applied with negligible error to experimental measurements made on the surface of the earth.

84. Units. It is customary to take k equal to unity in Eq. (71), which puts the relation in the usual form of Newton's second law

$$F = ma. \qquad (1)$$

A system of units for which k is unity is known as a *kinetic* system. Thus for a kinetic system the units of force, mass, and acceleration are not independent. Also, the engineer uses a *gravitational* kinetic system in which the units of force, length, and time are considered fundamental and the units of mass are derived from these three. The British gravitational system of units, listed in the table accompanying Art. 6 of Chapter I, is the system used universally by engineers in English-speaking countries. This table should be studied carefully before proceeding.

The pound is used frequently as a unit of mass as well as a unit of force. The legal pound in the United States is defined as 0.4535924277 times the mass of the international kilogram. A one pound *force* is required to support this portion of the standard kilogram at the standard conditions of sea level and 45 deg. N latitude or, more precisely, any location at which $g = 32.1740$ ft./sec.^{2} At any other location the force is slightly different because of the variation in the earth's attraction. For all practical purposes, however, it may be said that a body which "weighs" one pound on the surface of the earth has a mass of one pound. The British pound is the mass of a certain platinum cylinder kept at the Standards Office in London and is essentially identical with the United States pound.

A second example of the accepted use of the word pound as a unit of mass occurs in the expression for the heat or energy content of a unit quantity of matter. Thus the available energy of fuel is expressed as so many "B.t.u./lb." and means the number of available units of heat

---

sum of the acceleration a_r of the particle measured relative to the earth, and the acceleration a_e of a point on the earth's surface in the primary system.

In the case of a body falling from rest from an altitude h the rotation of the earth gives rise to an eastward acceleration (Coriolis acceleration), and, neglecting air resistance, it may be shown that the body falls to the ground a distance

$$x = \frac{2}{3} \omega \sqrt{\frac{2h^3}{g}} \cos \gamma$$

east of the point on the ground directly under that from which it was dropped. The angular velocity of the earth is $\omega = 0.729 \times 10^{-4}$ rad./sec., and the latitude, north or south, is γ. At a latitude of 45 deg. and from a height of 200 ft., the eastward deflection is $x = 0.291$ in.

energy (British thermal units) per *pound* of mass (not pound of force). This double standard for the term pound is unfortunate but unavoidable. The symbols *lbf.* and *lbm.* are sometimes used to distinguish between pound-force and pound-mass, respectively. In the British absolute system the pound is the unit of mass and the poundal is the unit of force. This system finds little use because the poundal (1/32.2 times the pound force) is too small a unit for convenience.

85. Motion of a Particle. Consider a particle of mass m subjected to the action of the concurrent forces F_1, F_2, F_3, $\cdots$ whose vector sum is ΣF. Equation (1) becomes

$$\Sigma F = ma, \tag{72}$$

which is a vector equation with the components

$$\Sigma F_x = ma_x,$$
$$\Sigma F_y = ma_y, \tag{73}$$
$$\Sigma F_z = ma_z,$$

where $\Sigma F = \sqrt{(\Sigma F_x)^2 + (\Sigma F_y)^2 + (\Sigma F_z)^2}$ and $a = \sqrt{a_x^2 + a_y^2 + a_z^2}$. Equation (72) is said to be the *equation of motion* for the particle, and Eqs. (73) are the three equivalent scalar equations of motion. In applying Eqs. (73) the reference axes may be oriented in any convenient manner. Thus, if the x-axis is chosen to coincide with the direction of the resultant acceleration a, Eqs. (73) become $\Sigma F_x = ma$, $\Sigma F_y = 0$, $\Sigma F_z = 0$. The particle may then be said to be in equilibrium in so far as motion in the y- and z-directions is concerned. The equation of motion may also be considered a differential equation. Thus for motion in the x-direction the first of Eqs. (73) may be written as

$$\Sigma F_x = m \frac{d^2 x}{dt^2}.$$

This form of the motion equation may be used to describe a problem in which ΣF_x is given as a function of x or t and where integration of the equation is necessary to obtain the relationship between x and t.

In applying the equations of motion to a particle it is *absolutely necessary* to account for *all* forces acting on the particle. The only forces which may be neglected are those whose magnitudes are negligible compared with other forces acting. The forces of mutual attraction between particles or bodies (except that of the earth) may be neglected. The vector sum ΣF in Eq. (72) and the corresponding scalar sums in Eqs. (73) refer to *all* forces acting *on* the particle in question. The only reliable way to account accurately for every force is to isolate the body or particle under consideration by drawing its complete and correct *free-body diagram* where every force, known and unknown, which acts on the particle is represented. Only after this vital step has been completed should the application of the equations of motion be attempted. The free-body diagram serves the same key purpose in kinetics as it does in statics. This purpose is simply to establish a *thoroughly reliable method* for the correct evaluation of the resultant of all real forces acting on the body in question. In statics this resultant was equated to zero, while in kinetics it is equated to the product of mass and acceleration. If the student recognizes that the equations of motion must be taken literally, and if he respects the exact meaning of the equals sign, very little difficulty will arise.

86. D'Alembert's Principle. Equation (72) for the motion of a particle may be rewritten as

$$\Sigma F - ma = 0,$$

which has the same form as the force equilibrium equation, where the sum of a number of terms equals zero. Thus, if a fictitious force equal to ma is applied to the particle in the direction opposite to the acceleration, the particle may be considered to be in equilibrium, and the equation $\Sigma F = 0$ may be used where one of the terms is the fictitious ma force. This hypothetical force which, if applied, would provide equilibrium with the actual forces is known as the *inertia force*, since it is proportional to the mass or inertia of the particle. This artificial state of equilibrium is known as *dynamic equilibrium*. The resultant of the actual forces is equal to ma and is known as the *effective force* for the particle. Hence the equal and opposite inertia force is often called the

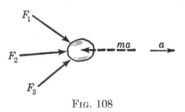

FIG. 108

reversed *effective force*. This viewpoint is due to D'Alembert, and the transformation of a problem in dynamics to an equivalent problem in statics is known as *D'Alembert's principle*.

If the inertia-force method is used, the fictitious force should be indicated by a dotted line to distinguish it from the actual forces. This representation is shown in Fig. 108 for the particle of mass m subject to the action of three actual forces and having an acceleration a.

D'Alembert's principle as applied to the motion of a particle offers no advantage over the straightforward application of the equation of motion, Eq. (72), where the real forces only are involved. The dynamic equilibrium method does offer advantage in some instances for describing the motions of a body (not a particle) under the action of an unbalanced nonconcurrent force system.   D'Alembert's principle, explained here for a particle, will be extended to the cases of rigid body motion in the chapter which follows.

87. Motion of a System of Particles.   The principle of motion for a single particle will now be extended to cover a system or discrete number of particles.   No restriction will be placed on the manner in which the particles are connected, and the analysis which follows will apply equally well to the motion of a solid body, a liquid body, or a defined system of gas molecules.   Such a general system subjected to certain external forces is represented schematically in Fig. 109, where the dotted envelope

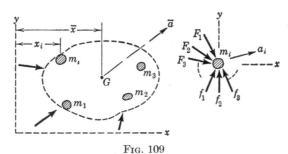

FIG. 109

encompasses and defines the system at the instant under consideration. Several particles only of the system are shown.   The particle of mass m_i will be selected as a representative particle of the system. The free-body diagram of m_i is drawn to the right of the system and shows the particle under the action of forces F_1, F_2, F_3, $\cdots$, which are applied from sources external to the envelope, and forces f_1, f_2, f_3, $\cdots$, which are applied from sources internal to the envelope.

As a result of the forces acting on m_i the particle has an acceleration component in the x-direction at the instant considered, and the first of Eqs. (73) requires

$$F_{1_x} + F_{2_x} + F_{3_x} + \cdots + f_{1_x} + f_{2_x} + f_{3_x} + \cdots = m_i a_{i_x}.$$

Similar equations may be written for *all* particles of the system, and, when added together, they give

$$\Sigma F_x + \Sigma f_x = \Sigma m_i a_{i_x}.$$

The symbol ΣF_x stands for the algebraic sum of the x-components of *all* forces applied externally to the envelope or system.   This sum of external forces includes not only mechanically applied contact forces but also all body forces applied by remote action such as gravity forces (weights) or electrical and magnetic forces.   The term Σf_x is the algebraic sum of the x-components of all internal forces. This latter sum vanishes since, by Newton's third law, each internal action on one particle is accompanied by an equal and opposite internal reaction on its neighboring particle, and the net effect for each and all such pairs of forces is zero. The expression $\Sigma m_i a_{i_x}$ represents the algebraic sum of the products of the mass of each particle and its corresponding x-component of acceleration. The remaining relation is now

$$\Sigma F_x = \Sigma m_i a_{i_x}.$$

This equation may be interpreted by introducing the position of the center of mass G of the system. The x-coordinate of G is $\bar{x}$ and is located by the principle of moments which requires that

$$m\bar{x} = m_1 x_1 + m_2 x_2 + m_3 x_3 + \cdots = \Sigma m_i x_i.$$

The total mass of the system is $m = \Sigma m_i$. Two successive differentiations with respect to the time yield

$$m\frac{d^2\bar{x}}{dt^2} = \Sigma m_i \frac{d^2 x_i}{dt^2} \qquad \text{or} \qquad m\bar{a}_x = \Sigma m_i a_{i_x}.$$

The symbol $\bar{a}_x$ is the x-component of the acceleration of the center of mass G. This last summation is identical with that in the combined motion equations so that $\Sigma F_x = m\bar{a}_x$. Similar analyses in the y- and z-directions hold, and therefore the three resulting equations are

$$\Sigma F_x = m\bar{a}_x,$$
$$\Sigma F_y = m\bar{a}_y, \tag{74}$$
$$\Sigma F_z = m\bar{a}_z.$$

These equations express the fact that the resultant in any direction of all external forces acting on the system equals the total mass of the system times the component of the acceleration of the mass center in that direction. Equations (74) are the three scalar components of the single vector equation

$$\Sigma F = m\bar{a}. \tag{75}$$

Equation (75) states that the vector resultant of all external forces acting on the system equals the total mass of the system times the acceleration of the center of mass and that the acceleration is in the direction of the resultant force. This statement, or the equivalent ones for Eqs. (74), constitutes the *principle of motion of the mass center*. This principle is one of the most important of the derived relations in mechanics because it finds direct and repeated use in most of the problems that follow. Equation (75), although identical in form with Eq. (1) for a particle, may not be inferred from Eq. (1) but must be proved.

Equation (75) is a vector equation, and, hence, the equals sign signifies equality in magnitude and direction. It must not be assumed, however, that the resultant force ΣF passes through the center of mass G. There is no step in the foregoing proof which depends on the position of ΣF or any of its components, and, therefore, it must be assumed that, in general, ΣF does not pass through G. The location of ΣF for the various types of rigid body motion will be established in the following chapter.

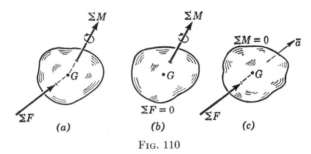

Fig. 110

It should be recalled from the principles of statics (see Chapter II of *Part I: Statics*) that the most general force system may be expressed in terms of the resultant force ΣF applied at any point and the corresponding resultant couple ΣM whose magnitude and direction depend on the line of action chosen for ΣF. The general force system may be considered, then, as the resultant force ΣF acting through G and a corresponding resultant couple ΣM as represented in Fig. 110a. If $\Sigma F = 0$, Fig. 110b, there can be no acceleration $\bar{a}$ of the mass center G, and the effect of ΣM is to govern the rotational motion about G. Conversely, if $\Sigma M = 0$, with ΣF passing through G, Fig. 110c, there will be a translational acceleration $\bar{a}$ of the system as a whole. If both ΣF and ΣM are zero, the system is in complete external equilibrium, whereas, if neither ΣF nor ΣM is zero, both linear and angular motion of the system will result. Although these conclusions hold for any material system, they are more easily visualized and find more ready application for the motion of solid bodies.

The principles developed in this chapter will now be applied to the various types of rigid body motion in the chapter which follows.

CHAPTER XI

Force, Mass, and Acceleration

88. Introduction. In this chapter the equation of motion for a particle and the principle of motion of the mass center for a system of particles, which were discussed in Chapter X, will be used to describe the translation, rotation, and plane motion of rigid bodies. The order in which these motions will be described is identical with the order used in Chapter IX, where the kinematics of these motions was developed. The procedure to be used in all problem work which follows was developed in the work in statics. (Refer to *Part I* of *Mechanics* and to Art. 10, Chapter I, in particular.) In this procedure it should be emphasized that the isolation of the body in question, or the group of connected bodies considered as a single body, by means of a complete *free-body diagram* is *essential* to the application of the equations of motion.

PART *A*. RECTILINEAR TRANSLATION

89. Analysis as a Particle. When the forces acting on a body having translation are concurrent at its center of mass, the dimensions of the body will not be involved. Therefore Newton's second law of motion

$$\Sigma F = ma \tag{72}$$

or the equivalent scalar components, Eqs. (73), may be applied directly to the body. It should be noted that a is the *absolute* acceleration in this fundamental equation, and that ΣF and a are both measured positive in the same sense.

If the forces are constant, the acceleration of the translating body will also be constant, and, hence, the kinematical relations given by Eqs. (51), (52), and (53) may be applied as needed to find the velocity and displacement. If the forces are not constant but are functions of the time or displacement, for example, then it will be necessary to integrate Eq. (72) written in the form of a differential equation. A common type of motion which involves variable force occurs in periodic vibrations, which are discussed in Chapter XIV.

When two or more accelerating bodies are connected, and if it is not desired to find the forces in the connections, it is often convenient to consider the bodies and their connections as a single system, thus eliminating any reference to the forces in the connections, which then become internal forces.

SAMPLE PROBLEMS

776. A 161 lb. man stands on a platform scale in an elevator. For the first 3 sec., starting from rest, the scale reads 181 lb. Find the velocity of the elevator at the end of the 3 sec. and the tension T in the supporting cable for the elevator during the acceleration period. The total weight of elevator, man, and scale is 1610 lb.

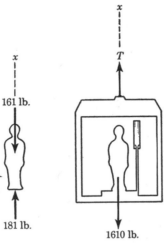

PROB. 776

Solution: The vertical distance traveled and the cable tension will depend on the initial acceleration. This acceleration is obtained by considering the two forces acting on the man during the first 3 sec. The free-body diagram of the man is first drawn as indicated. Next the equation of motion is applied which is

$$[\Sigma F_x = ma_x] \qquad 181 - 161 = \frac{161}{32.2}\,a_x, \qquad a_x = 4 \text{ ft./sec.}^2 \text{ up.}$$

The velocity reached at the end of the 3 sec. is

$$[v = at] \qquad\qquad v = 4 \times 3 = 12 \text{ ft./sec.} \qquad\qquad Ans.$$

The tension in the cable is obtained from the free-body diagram of the elevator and its contents considered together. Thus

$$[\Sigma F_x = ma_x] \qquad T - 1610 = \frac{1610}{32.2} \times 4, \qquad T = 1810 \text{ lb.} \qquad Ans.$$

777. Find the vertical distance s through which the 650 lb. weight has moved during 4 sec. following its release from rest and determine the tension T in the cable. The friction and weight of the pulleys are negligible.

Solution: The distance moved in the given time will depend on the acceleration, which is determined from the force analysis of each of the weights. The direction of movement of the 500 lb. block is not given so must be either assumed or determined. It may be determined by considering the system without friction, and in this event an additional force of $500 \sin 60° - (650/2) = 108$ lb. would be required on the block in the direction up the plane to hold it in equilib-

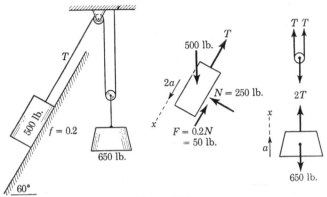

PROB. 777

rium. This force is greater than the friction force of $0.2N = 0.2 \times 500 \times 0.5 = 50$ lb., so that, if the supposed 108 lb. force is released, friction would be insufficient to prevent movement down the plane. Thus the direction of the friction force is established, and the correct free-body diagrams are drawn with the directions of the accelerations indicated. It should be clear that the acceleration of the 500 lb. weight is twice that of the 650 lb. weight. Also with negligible mass of the small pulleys and no appreciable friction in their bearings there is a negligible unbalance of forces and moments required for their accelerations. Hence the small pulleys may be treated as though they were in equilibrium.

The equation of motion for the 500 lb. block is

$$[\Sigma F_x = ma_x] \qquad 500 \sin 60° - 50 - T = \frac{500}{32.2} \times 2a,$$

and that for the 650 lb. weight is

$$[\Sigma F_x = ma_x] \qquad 2T - 650 = \frac{650}{32.2} a.$$

Solution of these two equations gives

$$a = 1.41 \text{ ft./sec.}^2 \qquad \text{and} \qquad T = 339 \text{ lb.} \qquad \textit{Ans.}$$

Thus in 4 sec. the 650 lb. weight moves

$$[s = \tfrac{1}{2}at^2] \qquad s = \tfrac{1}{2} \times 1.41 \times 4^2 = 11.28 \text{ ft. up.} \qquad \textit{Ans.}$$

PROBLEMS

778. In the position shown the link A of negligible weight is under a tension of 60 lb.   Find the acceleration a of the 50 lb. collar B along the fixed vertical shaft if the coefficient of friction is 0.20 and the collar is moving down the shaft.

Ans. $a = 6.19$ ft./sec.²

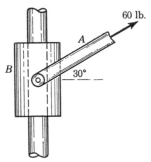

60 lb.

Prob. 778

779. A car left skid marks from all four wheels on a level road for a distance of 40 ft. before coming to a stop.   Determine the velocity v of the car when the brakes were applied.   The coefficient of kinetic friction between the tires and the pavement may be taken as 0.8.

780. The resultant horizontal force on a small object of weight W which moves in a straight line on a horizontal plane is 10 lb.   The displacement of the object is given by $s = 4 + 2t + 10t^2$, where s is in feet and t is in seconds. Determine W.   *Ans.* $W = 16.1$ lb.

781. The small ball is suspended by a cord from an object which moves with a constant acceleration a to the right.   Determine the angle θ assumed by the cord.

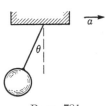

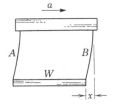

Prob. 781   Prob. 782

782. A linear accelerometer is an instrument for measuring linear accelerations.   One type, shown in the figure, consists of a bar of weight W attached at its ends to two small cantilever beams A and B whose weights are small compared with W.   If a static force k, applied to the end of the bar in the direction of the bar, causes unit deflection, determine the deflection x due to an acceleration a.

Ans. $x = \dfrac{Wa}{kg}$

783. The supporting cable for the 2000 lb. elevator is wrapped several times around the 3 ft. hoisting drum and leads to the counterweight, which also weighs 2000 lb.   If the motor supplies a starting torque of 600 lb. ft. in either direction to the drum, find the acceleration of the elevator.   Neglect the relatively small mass of the drum and any frictional resistance.

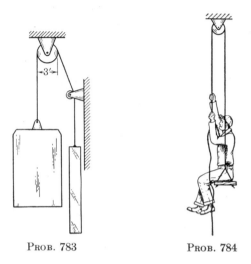

PROB. 783   PROB. 784

784. A 150 lb. man hoists himself on a bosun's chair as shown.   If, for a short interval, he exerts a pull of 80 lb. on the rope, find his acceleration.

Ans. $a = 2.15$ ft./sec.² up

785. Determine the necessary acceleration a to the left which the vertical plate A must have so that the slider B will remain in a fixed position relative to the smooth slot.

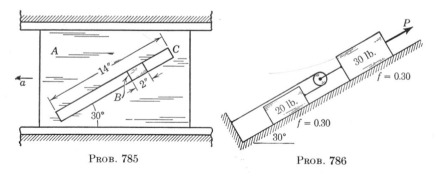

PROB. 785   PROB. 786

786. Find the constant force P necessary to give the 20 lb. block a velocity of 16 ft./sec. up the plane after 4 sec., starting from rest.   Neglect the weight of the pulley.   *Ans.* $P = 60.0$ lb.

787. The pulley is fixed so that it cannot rotate. Determine the larger of the two tensions T in the cable and the acceleration a of the blocks. The coefficient of kinetic friction for the cable and pulley is 0.15.

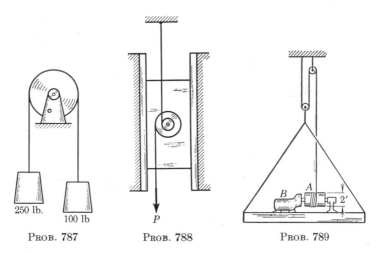

250 lb.

100 lb

P

PROB. 787   PROB. 788   PROB. 789

788. The 32.2 lb. sliding block moves in the smooth vertical guide under the action of a force P applied to the cable as shown. The separate cables are wound around the light pulleys, which are fastened together and which are perfectly free to turn about their common shaft. The diameter of the larger pulley is twice that of the smaller one. Determine the acceleration a of the block for (a) $P = 35$ lb. and (b) $P = 30$ lb. (*Hint:* The integral pulley may be treated as a body in equilibrium since its mass is negligible.)

$Ans.$ (a) $a = 2.8$ ft./sec.^{2} up,

(b) $a = 2.2$ ft./sec.^{2} down

789. A platform together with the load it carries weighs 600 lb. and is raised by winding the supporting cable around the drum A, which is driven by the motor and gear unit B. If this unit supplies a starting torque of 250 lb. ft. to the drum, find the initial acceleration a of the platform. The weight of the drum is small and may be neglected. $Ans.$ $a = 8.05$ ft./sec.^{2} up

790. The box car is accelerating down the inclined track under the action of its own weight and with negligible friction. Show that an object dropped from point A will strike the floor at point B regardless of the angle θ.

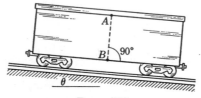

PROB. 790

791. A tank of water has a constant horizontal acceleration a. Determine the angle θ made by the surface with the horizontal. (*Hint:* Relate the forces acting on a small triangular element of the fluid at the surface to its known motion.)

792. Small objects leave the assembly line at the rate of one every second from a conveyor belt traveling at the lineal speed of 2 ft./sec. The objects enter the chute with this initial velocity and slide to the floor below where a second conveyor belt takes them to the shipping department. The coefficient of friction for the parts on the steel chute is found to be $\frac{1}{3}$. What would be the required velocity v of the lower conveyor in order that there be no slipping of the parts when they are deposited horizontally on the belt?

Ans. $v = 11.52$ ft./sec.

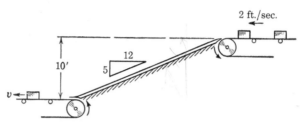

Prob. 792

793. A small block is given an initial velocity of 8 ft./sec. (absolute) up the moving belt from position A. The endless belt is traveling down with a speed of 2 ft./sec. If the coefficients of static and kinetic friction are both $\frac{1}{4}$, find the absolute velocity v of the block when it returns to position A. Assume the block does not reach the upper extremity of the belt.   Ans. $v = 5.83$ ft./sec.

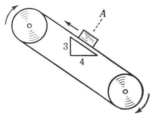

Prob. 793

794. The elevator in a vertical mine shaft weighs 3000 lb. loaded and requires 24 sec. to descend 300 ft. from rest until it stops at the bottom. The velocity of the elevator is 15 ft./sec. except during the starting and stopping periods. If the tension in the cable supporting the elevator is 2700 lb. during the starting period, what is its value during the stopping period, assuming constant deceleration?

795. In the Scotch yoke mechanism shown the 2 lb. piston and the 5 lb. connecting link are driven by the pin A in the flywheel. At the position shown the angular velocity and angular acceleration of the wheel are 18 rad./sec. and 72 rad./sec.², respectively, both counterclockwise. Determine the force A exerted by the pin on the link and find the total force B on the piston pin for this position.   *Ans.* $A = 9.67$ lb., $B = 2.76$ lb.

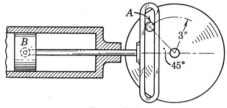

PROB. 795

796. A small steel block is "weighed" by a spring balance in the gondola of a balloon which is at rest at an altitude of 20 mi. above the earth, and a value of 1.200 lb. is recorded. The block is placed on a perfectly smooth horizontal surface in the gondola and subjected to a horizontal force of ½ lb. Find the acceleration a of the block. Take the radius of the earth to be 4000 mi. and the acceleration of gravity at the surface of the earth to be 32.17 ft./sec.²   *Ans.* $a = 13.26$ ft./sec.²

797. A small block is given an initial velocity v measured along the floor of an elevator moving with a downward acceleration a. Because of friction the block moves a distance s_1 measured along the floor before it stops sliding. The experiment is repeated with the same initial velocity relative to the floor when the elevator has an upward acceleration of the same magnitude a, and the block slides a shorter distance s_2. Determine the elevator accelerations a.

$$Ans. \quad a = g\,\frac{s_1 - s_2}{s_1 + s_2}$$

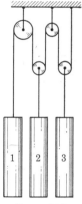

PROB. 798

798. Determine the acceleration of each of the identical metal cylinders if the pulleys and cables have negligible weight and friction is too small to be considered.

799. The resistance to motion of a boat varies directly as the square of its velocity through the water. When the sailboat shown is towed at a speed of 4 mi./hr. with sails furled, the towing line is under a tension of 22 lb. When the boat is sailing in the direction of the wind, the force P exerted on the sails is proportional to the effective sail area A and the square of the velocity v_r of the wind relative to the boat. This relation is $P = 0.0024Av_r^2$, where the terms are in foot-pound-second units. If the effective sail area is 200 ft.², what velocity does the boat reach on the course indicated in a 15 mi./hr. wind?

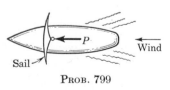

PROB. 799

Ans. $v = 7.0$ mi./hr.

800. The chain is released from rest in the position shown and slides on the smooth surface through the opening and over the edge. Determine the velocity

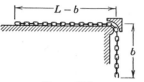

v of the chain when the last link has left the edge.

801. Assume that the surface on which the chain of Prob. 800 slides is not smooth and that the coefficient of friction is f. Determine the velocity v of the chain when the last link leaves the edge if the chain was started from rest with a sufficient number of links over the edge to overcome

PROB. 800

friction on the remaining links and barely initiate motion. Neglect friction at the edge.

$$Ans. \quad v = \sqrt{\frac{gL}{1+f}}$$

* 802. Assume that the plate in Prob. 785 is in the horizontal plane and that the slider block weighs 1.61 lb. If the plate is given an acceleration of 10 ft./sec.^{2} to the right, determine the force F exerted by the guide on the block and the time t required for the block to move across the smooth slot if it starts from C at rest relative to the plate.

* 803. The polishing disk shown rotates counterclockwise. A small metallic specimen is placed on the disk at A in the smooth slot of the fixed supporting rail and released from rest. Determine the velocity v of the specimen as it passes the vertical center line of the disk if the coefficient of friction between the specimen and the disk is f. Assume that ω is large so that the velocity of the point on the disk under the specimen is large compared with v and hence that the friction force is always normal to the radial line joining A with the center of the disk.

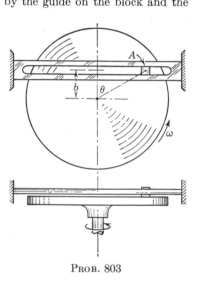

PROB. 803

$$Ans. \quad v = \sqrt{fgb \log \frac{1 + \sin \theta}{1 - \sin \theta}}$$

* 804. Pulley A is moved vertically down with a constant velocity v by the action of a variable force P. Determine P as a function of x. Neglect the weight and radius of the pulleys.

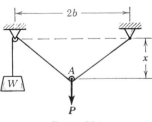

$$Ans. \quad P = 2Wx \left[\frac{2v^2b^2}{g(b^2 + x^2)^2} + \frac{1}{\sqrt{b^2 + x^2}} \right]$$

* 805. A small steel ball of weight W and diameter D is released from rest on a smooth horizontal surface with its center a distance s from the vertical pole face of a magnet. Determine

PROB. 804

the velocity v with which the ball strikes the face. The opposite pole of the magnet is assumed to be at a considerable distance from the ball so that the attractive force varies inversely as the square of the distance from the pole face to the center of the ball. Also, a force P, normal to the pole face, is required to dislodge the ball when it rests against the face.

$$Ans. \quad v = \sqrt{\frac{PDg}{2W}\left(2 - \frac{D}{s}\right)}$$

* 806. In theory an object projected vertically up from the surface of the earth with a sufficiently high velocity v can escape from the earth's field of influence. Calculate this velocity on the basis of the absence of an atmosphere to offer resistance due to air friction. The radius R of the earth is very nearly 4000 mi.

$$Ans. \quad v = \sqrt{2gR} = 6.98 \text{ mi./sec.}$$

* 807. A small steel ball of weight W is released from rest in a liquid which resists the fall with a force F proportional to the square of the velocity of the ball ($F = kv^2$). Determine the velocity of the ball after it has fallen a distance h.

$$Ans. \quad v = \sqrt{\frac{W}{k}\left(1 - e^{-2gkh/W}\right)}$$

* 808. The end of a coil of flexible rope of total length L and weight μ per unit length is run over a small pulley with negligible weight and bearing friction and brought down to a position very slightly below the coil. The small unbalance causes the rope to accelerate from rest and uncoil the remainder of the rope. Find the velocity v of the rope as the coiled end leaves the platform.

$$Ans. \quad v = \sqrt{2g\left(L - 2h + 2h \log \frac{2h}{L}\right)}$$

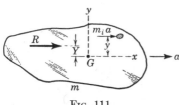

PROB. 808

90. Rectilinear Translation of a Rigid Body.

When a rigid body is translating under the action of a system of external forces whose lines of action are not concurrent, it is often necessary to consider the locations of the forces on the body. In this event treatment of the body as a moving particle is not sufficient.

It was shown in Art. 87, Chapter X, that, if the resultant moment of all external forces on a body is zero about any and every axis through the mass center G, the body has a translatory acceleration only, and the resultant of the external forces acting on the body passes through G. This important conclusion may be reached in another way by reference to the translating body shown in Fig. 111. The x-axis is chosen to coincide with the direction of the acceleration, and the external

FIG. 111

forces have been replaced by their resultant R, which is in the direction of a and whose line of action is assumed temporarily not to pass through G. The resultant (effective) force on any particle of mass m_i is $m_i a$, where a is the common acceleration of all particles. The resultant is $R = ma = \Sigma m_i a$, and the principle of moments about G gives

$$RY = \Sigma m_i a y = a \Sigma m_i y = a \bar{y} m = 0 \quad \text{since } \bar{y} = 0.$$

Hence $Y = 0$. In a similar manner Z, the z-distance of R from G, is zero, and the resultant therefore passes through G. Thus the resultant R of the external forces on a translating body, Fig. 112a, always passes

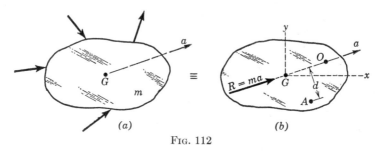

FIG. 112

through the center of mass, Fig. 112b. For translation in the x–y plane the equations of motion are seen from the latter figure to be

$$\Sigma F_x = ma_x,$$

$$\Sigma F_y = ma_y, \tag{76}$$

$$\Sigma \overline{M} = 0 \quad \text{or} \quad \Sigma M_O = 0 \quad \text{or} \quad \Sigma M_A = mad.$$

In the event that there are forces in the z-direction, then $\Sigma F_z = 0$ must also hold. The first two of Eqs. (76) need no further explanation. The third condition may be written in any one of the three ways. In the first of the three moment equations the bar refers to the center of mass G as the moment center. From Fig. 112b it is perfectly clear that the moment of all forces about any point O on the line of action of their resultant R must also equal zero. A point A not on the line of action of R may also be used as a moment center. In this event the sum of the moments of all external forces about A equals the moment of their sum, which is $Rd = mad$. For A below R the moment summation is positive in the clockwise sense, whereas for A above R the counterclockwise sense would be positive.

An alternative method for solving the translation problem by utilizing D'Alembert's principle may be employed. If a force ma equal and opposite to the resultant R were applied through G, the body would be in equilibrium. This force is represented by the dotted arrow on the free-body diagram of the body, Fig. 113, which had a translational acceleration a before the hypothetical force was applied. This fictitious force ma is known as the *inertia force* or *reversed effective force* for the body. With the inertia force represented on the free-body diagram the body may be considered to be in equilibrium, and the equations of equilibrium

$$\Sigma F_x = 0, \qquad \Sigma F_y = 0, \qquad \Sigma M = 0$$

may be applied. The inertia force appears in these equations the same as any other force, and the moment equilibrium equation may be evaluated about any moment center.

The fictitious state of equilibrium created by the addition of the inertia force is known as *dynamic equilibrium*. These two words are intrinsically contradictory, but are descriptive since the dynamics problem has been transformed into an equivalent statics problem. Before the method of dynamic equilibrium is used it is absolutely

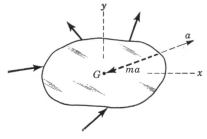

Fig. 113

essential to understand that the inertia force is *not* a real force. Consequently it is highly desirable that the inertia force be indicated by a dotted line to distinguish it from the gravity forces and all other forces actually applied.

The dynamic equilibrium method offers particular advantage for the solution of problems which involve interconnected bodies whose configuration depends on the acceleration. (See the mechanisms represented in Probs. 824, 827, and 830.) In such cases the fictitious inertia forces may be added to produce the equivalent equilibrium problem, and solution may be effected by the principle of virtual work. (See Chapter VIII of *Part I*.) In this way it becomes unnecessary to dismember the mechanism, and the internal forces of action and reaction in the connections are not involved directly.

It is recommended that ample practice with both methods of solution be gained in the problems which follow. If the translation is solved directly as a dynamics problem where the free-body diagram includes only the actual forces, then the principles which should be stated in the solution are those of Eqs. (76). On the other hand, if the body is placed in dynamic equilibrium with the addition of the inertia force, then the principles which should be stated are the equilibrium equations. The principles stated must agree with the free-body diagram.   A careless mixture of principles and method leads to difficulty.

SAMPLE PROBLEM

809. The 3220 lb. car shown has a forward acceleration on the level road of 16.1 ft./sec.^{2} Determine the normal reactions N_1 and N_2 under each pair of wheels and find the coefficient of friction f between the tires and the road if the rear wheels are on the verge of slipping.

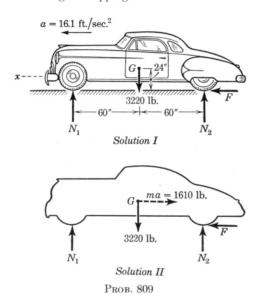

Solution I

Solution II

PROB. 809

Solution I: In this solution the equations of motion will be applied directly to the upper free-body diagram of the car, which shows only the actual forces acting on the car.   It will be assumed that the weight of the wheels is small compared with the total weight of the car; otherwise it would be necessary to consider the forces required to produce the angular acceleration of the wheels. The third of the alternative moment relations of Eqs. (76) will eliminate N_2 and F when applied about the rear wheel contact as a moment center.   The direction for positive ΣM is counterclockwise about this point since the resultant ma is directed to the left through G.   Thus

$[\Sigma M_{N_2} = mad]$ $3220 \times 5 - 10N_1 = 100 \times 16.1 \times 2,$ $N_1 = 1288$ lb.   *Ans.*

The remaining two principles give

$[\Sigma F_x = ma_x]$ $F = 100 \times 16.1 = 1610$ lb.,

$[\Sigma F_y = 0]$ $1288 + N_2 - 3220 = 0,$ $N_2 = 1932$ lb.   *Ans.*

If the rear wheels are on the verge of slipping, the friction force F is the limiting value, and, hence, the coefficient of friction is

$$f = \frac{F}{N_2} = \frac{1610}{1932} = 0.834. \qquad\qquad Ans.$$

Solution II: For the second method the car is put in dynamic equilibrium by the addition of the fictitious inertia force ma through the center of mass G and in the direction opposite to the acceleration as shown in the lower free-body diagram. With this supposed force in place the car would be in equilibrium. The principles of equilibrium are used to obtain

$$[\Sigma M_{N_2} = 0] \qquad 3220 \times 5 - 10N_1 - 1610 \times 2 = 0, \qquad N_1 = 1288 \text{ lb.},$$

$$[\Sigma F_x = 0] \qquad F - 1610 = 0, \qquad F = 1610 \text{ lb.},$$

$$[\Sigma F_y = 0] \qquad 1288 + N_2 - 3220 = 0, \qquad N_2 = 1932 \text{ lb.}$$

These resulting equations are identical with those in *Solution I*, and the equivalence of the two formulations of the problem should be recognized.

PROBLEMS

810. The end deflection of a uniform horizontal cantilever beam of weight W and length l is $\delta = Wl^3/8EI$, where E is the modulus of elasticity of the material and I is the moment of inertia of the beam section. If such a beam is given a vertical acceleration, find the end deflection.

$$Ans. \quad \delta = \frac{Wl^3}{8EI}\left(1 \pm \frac{a}{g}\right), \ + \text{ up}, \ - \text{ down}$$

811. One type of instrument for measuring accelerations is known as a classifying accelerometer and indicates whether an acceleration is greater or less than some prescribed value. The device shown may be used as such an instrument. When the acceleration to the left exceeds a certain critical value, the uniform bar of weight W rotates slightly against the spring and opens the electrical contacts. If the bar weighs 8 oz. and the spring has a stiffness of 20 lb./in., how many turns N of the adjusting screw from the position of initial contact of the spring with the bar are required to pre-set the device for an acceleration of $12g$? The screw has 40 single threads per inch.

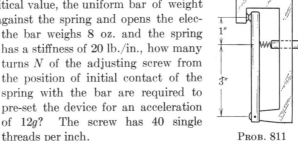

Prob. 811

812. A uniform rod of length l and weight W is clamped at its upper end as shown and given a linear acceleration a in a direction normal to its length. Determine the moment M exerted on the beam at the support.

Prob. 812

813. A stunt car, shown in the figure, which will turn a forward somersault when the brakes are applied, is to be built from an existing car by removing a section of the frame to produce a short wheel base b. If the center of gravity of the car is 3.5 ft. above the road and is midway between the wheels, and if the greatest dependable coefficient of friction between the tires and the road is 0.8, find the maximum permissible value of b. Neglect the weight of the wheels.

$Ans.$ $b = 5.6$ ft.

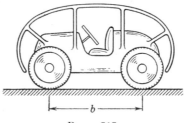

PROB. 813

814. Find the maximum velocity v which the bus can reach in a distance s from rest without slipping its rear driving wheels if the coefficient of friction between the tires and the road is f. Neglect the weight of the wheels.

$Ans.$ $v = \sqrt{\dfrac{fbgs}{b - fh}}$

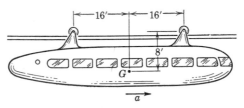

PROB. 814

815. The proposed overhead monorail car shown is to be driven by one of its two wheels. Select the one for which the acceleration of the car would be the greater without slipping the wheel and compute the corresponding maximum acceleration if the coefficient of friction between the wheels and the rail is 0.30. The center of gravity of the car is to be at G. Neglect the small part of the friction force necessary to give the wheels their angular acceleration.

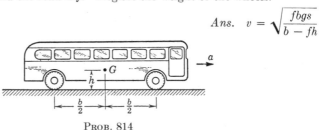

PROB. 815

816. Assume that the driver of the car shown with Sample Prob. 809 applies the brakes so that all four wheels slide when the car is going down a slope of 1 to 4. Find the total normal force N_1 under the front pair of wheels if the coefficient of friction between the tires and the road is 0.80.

Ans. $N_1 = 2060$ lb.

817. The angle θ shown is large enough to cause the homogeneous rectangular crate to slide. If the coefficient of friction is 0.20, find the acceleration a of the crate in terms of θ and find the distance x from the forward edge of the crate at which the resultant force between the incline and the crate acts.

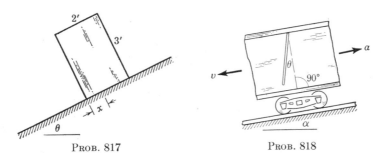

PROB. 817　　　　　　　PROB. 818

818. A straight rod is suspended from the ceiling of the railroad car shown so that the rod may swing freely in the vertical plane. As the train is going down a grade inclined an angle α with the horizontal, the brakes are applied, and the train has a uniform deceleration a. During this period the bar makes an angle θ with the perpendicular to the tracks. Find a.

$$Ans. \quad a = g\,\frac{\sin{(\theta - \alpha)}}{\cos{\theta}}$$

819. A water heater is placed on the horizontal bed of a truck. The base of the four legs forms a 12 in. square as shown, and the center of gravity of the heater is 3 ft. above its base. The coefficient of friction between the legs and the truck bed is 0.25. If the driver forgets to secure the heater with the ropes shown, find the forward acceleration a at which the heater tips or slips.

Ans. $a = 5.37$ ft./sec.^{2} tips

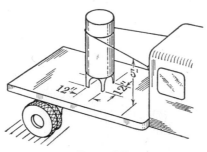

PROB. 819

820. With the water heater in Prob. 819 secured to the back of the cab of the truck with the rope in a horizontal plane as shown, find the acceleration a at which the heater would slip on the bed of the truck. The other data of Prob. 819 remain the same.

821. A 150 lb. force is applied to the homogeneous 100 lb. box as shown. The coefficient of friction is 0.30. Find the limiting values of h such that the box will slide without tipping about either the front edge or the rear edge.

Ans. $h_{max.} = 11.33$ in., $h_{min.} = 4.67$ in.

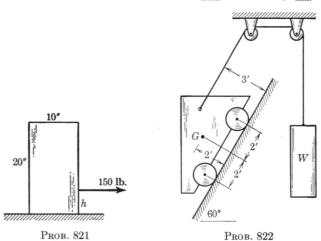

PROB. 821   PROB. 822

822. Determine the maximum counterweight W so that the empty 300 lb. skip with center of gravity at G will not overturn about its upper wheels. Neglect the weights of the pulleys and wheels and any friction in the bearings.

823. A 3000 lb. milling machine with center of gravity at G is to be hoisted on rollers from the position shown to the bed of the truck. When the power for the winch is applied, the cable tension is momentarily 50 per cent greater than that necessary to maintain equilibrium of the milling machine with both rollers on the incline. Determine the reactions on the rollers A and B at the instant of this maximum tension. Neglect friction on the rollers compared with the other forces acting. *Ans.* $A = 831$ lb., $B = 2530$ lb.

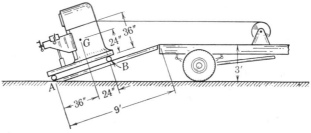

PROB. 823

824. Each of the two uniform and identical links has a weight W. Find the angle θ when they are accelerating under a constant force P. Neglect the weight of the wheels.

825. A chain of length L and weight μ per unit length is suspended at one end from a body which moves with constant horizontal acceleration a. Prove that the chain hangs in a straight line which makes an angle $\theta = \tan^{-1}(a/g)$ with the vertical.

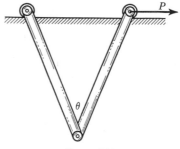

826. Each of the two identical bars shown weighs 2 lb., is uniform, and is freely pivoted on the moving frame A. The bars are connected by two light, flexible wires. Show that the angular position

PROB. 824

of the bars about their pivots is not influenced by any translational acceleration of A. Find the tension T in the tight wire if A has a horizontal acceleration of $2g$ and the bars are vertical. *Ans.* $T = 6$ lb.

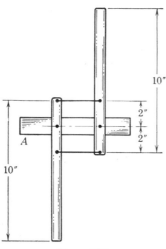

PROB. 826

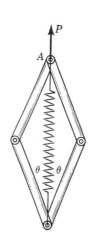

PROB. 827

* **827.** Each of the four identical links has a weight W and a length b. The connecting spring of stiffness k maintains an equilibrium position of $\theta = 45$ deg. when the linkage is suspended from A and is at rest. Determine the angle θ when the upward acceleration produced by a force P has been increased smoothly to an amount a. (*Suggestion:* Create dynamic equilibrium and apply the principle of virtual work.)

$$Ans. \quad \theta = \cos^{-1}\left[\frac{W\left(1 + \dfrac{a}{g}\right)}{kb} + \frac{1}{\sqrt{2}}\right]$$

* **828.** The supporting base A is given an acceleration of $3g$ in the direction shown. Determine the force acting on the connecting pin at B if the uniform angle BE weighs 8 lb. and the uniform link BC weighs 3 lb.

Ans. $B = 30.7$ lb.

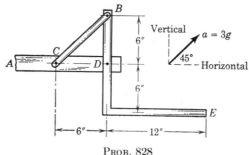

PROB. 828

* **829.** The road grader of Prob. 123 is shown again here. The tandem unit A weighs 6500 lb. and is freely pivoted to the motive unit B at O, which is also the center of gravity of A. Unit B alone weighs 22,000 lb. including wheels C, and its center of gravity is 54 in. above the road and 81 in. to the right of O. The diameter of each of the tires is 48 in. Find the minimum distance s in which the grader can stop when traveling on a level highway at 25 mi./hr. (blade retracted) so that the rear pair of wheels of the tandem unit A will not lift off the road.

Ans. $s = 27.1$ ft.

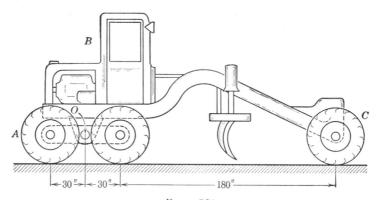

PROB. 829

* **830.** The device shown is in the horizontal plane and has the configuration indicated when at rest with no force in the spring. If the acceleration of A is increased gradually to the value a, each sector assumes a new angular position about the pivots marked O. Design the spring by specifying its modulus k so that the central rack moves 1 in. to the left relative to the frame under a constant acceleration of $a = 2g$. Each sector unit weighs 3 lb. with center of gravity at G, and the central rack weighs 2 lb. (*Suggestion:* Create dynamic equilibrium and use the method of virtual work.)   *Ans.* $k = 3.56$ lb./in.

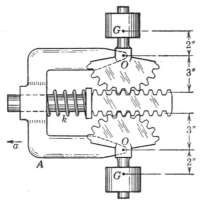

PROB. 830

PART *B*. CURVILINEAR TRANSLATION

91. Analysis as a Particle. In Art. 89 it was shown that a translating body subjected to a system of forces concurrent at the center of mass may be analyzed as though it were a particle. This condition holds for either type of translation, rectilinear or curvilinear. With rectilinear translation the resultant force on the body is in the constant direction of the acceleration. In curvilinear translation the direction of the resultant force will usually vary but always coincides with the direction of the resultant acceleration at every instant.

In Arts. 71, 72, and 73 of Chapter IX plane curvilinear translation was described in terms of rectangular components, normal and tangential components, and polar components. Regardless of the description, of course, the resultant force on the body (particle) is always given by

$$\Sigma F = ma$$

in both magnitude and direction. The most useful description is that of expressing the acceleration in terms of its component normal to the curve, $a_n = v^2/\rho$, and its component tangent to the curve, $a_t = d|v|/dt$, where the meaning of the symbols is the same as that established in Chapter IX. Thus, in terms of tangential and normal components of acceleration, the equations of motion for a particle having curvilinear translation are

$$\Sigma F_n = m a_n = m \frac{v^2}{\rho},$$

$$\Sigma F_t = m a_t = m \frac{d|v|}{dt}.$$

(77)

When the motion is circular and the radius of curvature ρ is the constant radius r of the circle, the tangential acceleration becomes $a_t = d|v|/dt = d(r\omega)/dt = r\alpha$.*

Equations (77) must be applied literally. The normal acceleration, $a_n = v^2/\rho$, is always directed *toward* the center of curvature, and, therefore, the summation ΣF_n must be taken in that *same* sense. Likewise the summation ΣF_t must be taken in the same sense as the time rate of change of the magnitude of the velocity along the curve.

SAMPLE PROBLEMS

831. *Conical Pendulum.* A small weight W is suspended by a light arm or wire of length l and made to revolve in a horizontal circle with a constant angular velocity ω. Locate the plane of the circular motion by finding h and calculate the tension T in the supporting member.

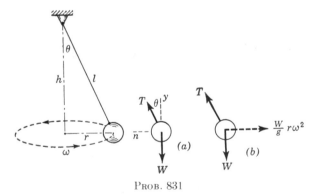

PROB. 831

Solution: For constant speed of rotation the conical pendulum will assume a position for which θ, h, and r will have fixed values. The free-body diagram (a) of the particle in this position discloses *only two real forces* acting on it, its weight

---

* This relation holds also at points on a curved path for which the radius of curvature is a maximum or a minimum given by $d\rho/dt = 0$. At all other points

$$a_t = \frac{d}{dt}\left(\rho \frac{d\theta}{dt}\right) = \rho \frac{d^2\theta}{dt^2} + \frac{d\rho}{dt}\frac{d\theta}{dt}.$$

W and the tension T. The first of Eqs. (77) and the equilibrium requirement for the vertical direction give

$$[\Sigma F_n = ma_n] \qquad\qquad T \sin \theta = \frac{W}{g} r\omega^2,$$

$$[\Sigma F_y = 0] \qquad\qquad T \cos \theta = W.$$

Substitution of $r = l \sin \theta$ into the first equation gives

$$T = \frac{W}{g} l\omega^2. \qquad\qquad Ans.$$

Division of the first equation by the second and substitution of $h = l \cos \theta$ give

$$h = \frac{g}{\omega^2}. \qquad\qquad Ans.$$

This last result shows that the distance h from the plane of rotation to the point of support is the same for all conical pendulums which rotate at the same rate, irrespective of their length l.

The term "centrifugal force" is often used (misused) in connection with this and similar problems of rotating bodies. Examination of the free-body diagram (a) of the particle discloses the two forces T and W only. Neither of these forces is centrifugal, which means "away from the center." The word "centripetal" means "toward the center," and, therefore, the component $T \sin \theta$ is properly known as a *centripetal force*. There is *no actual centrifugal force* acting on the particle.

If the particle is analyzed by D'Alembert's principle, then the fictitious inertia force, $ma_n = (W/g)r\omega^2$, is added in the direction opposite to the acceleration to produce dynamic equilibrium as shown by the dotted line in diagram (b). This hypothetical inertia force is away from the center of rotation and is referred to as the *centrifugal force*. It must be clearly understood that the so-called centrifugal force is *not* a real force. D'Alembert's principle offers no particular advantage in the analysis of this problem or other similar problems involving concurrent forces.

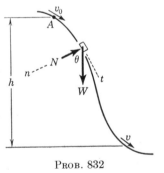

PROB. 832

832. A small object slides on a smooth vertical curve and has an initial velocity v_0 at a point A as shown. Determine the velocity v of the object after it has descended a vertical distance h and write the expression for the normal force acting on the particle.

Solution: The free-body diagram of the particle shows the weight W and the normal force N. The equation of motion in the tangential direction gives

$$[\Sigma F_t = ma_t] \qquad\qquad W \sin \theta = \frac{W}{g} a_t, \qquad a_t = g \sin \theta.$$

The velocity change along the path is given by

$$[v \, dv = a_t \, ds] \qquad\qquad v \, dv = g \, ds \sin \theta = g \, dh.$$

Integration between the appropriate limits gives

$$v^2 = v_0{}^2 + 2gh. \qquad\qquad Ans.$$

This equation shows that for a path without friction the velocity does not depend on the shape of the path but only on the vertical change in position.

The normal force is given by

$$[\Sigma F_n = ma_n] \qquad W \cos \theta - N = \frac{W}{g} \frac{v^2}{\rho}, \qquad N = W \left(\cos \theta - \frac{v^2}{g\rho} \right). \qquad Ans.$$

The value of N may be obtained in any particular problem where the radius of curvature ρ is known or can be computed. If friction is present, the problem is complicated considerably. (See Prob. 864.)

833. A small sphere of weight W is attached to one end of a light rod freely pivoted about the other end as shown. If the rod and sphere are released from rest in the vertical position, find the angle θ for which the force in the rod is zero, and determine the force in the rod when θ reaches 90 deg.

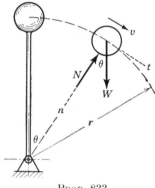

Solution: The free-body diagram of the sphere is shown for the general position θ. In addition to the weight W there is the force N which is exerted by the bar on the sphere. This force is along the bar since the bar, if light, may be considered a two-force member. The required answers may be determined when the expression for N as a function of θ is obtained. This expression will depend upon the equations of motion, which are

PROB. 833

$$[\Sigma F_n = ma_n] \qquad W \cos \theta - N = \frac{W}{g} \frac{v^2}{r}, \qquad N = W \left(\cos \theta - \frac{v^2}{gr} \right),$$

$$[\Sigma F_t = ma_t] \qquad W \sin \theta = \frac{W}{g} a_t, \qquad a_t = g \sin \theta.$$

The velocity v of the sphere depends on the tangential acceleration and its change with θ. Thus

$$[v \, dv = a_t \, ds] \qquad \int_0^v v \, dv = \int_0^\theta g \sin \theta \, r \, d\theta, \qquad v^2 = 2gr(1 - \cos \theta).$$

Substitution of this value for v^2 in the first equation of motion gives

$$N = (3 \cos \theta - 2)W.$$

The force in the rod is clearly zero when

$$\theta = \cos^{-1} \tfrac{2}{3}, \qquad \theta = 48° \, 11'. \qquad\qquad Ans.$$

When $\theta = 90$ deg., $\cos \theta = 0$ and

$$N = -2W. \qquad\qquad Ans.$$

Hence the force in the rod at this position is a tension equal to twice the weight of the sphere. The similarity between this problem and Prob. 832 should be noted.

PROBLEMS

834. The loaded bucket of a centrifuge weighs 1.5 lb., and its center of gravity G is located as shown in the figure for the rest position. Determine the force on the pin at A while the machine is revolving at a speed of 900 rev./min. At this speed the line AG will be practically horizontal.   *Ans.* $A = 552$ lb.

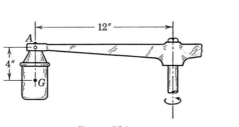

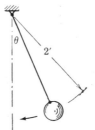

PROB. 834   PROB. 835

835. The simple pendulum weighs 4 lb. and is given an initial swing such that its velocity is 10 ft./sec. when $\theta = 30$ deg. Find the tension T in the supporting wire at this instant.

836. A small 4 lb. weight is swung in a vertical circle of 3 ft. radius with slowly increasing speed on the end of a light steel wire of 100 lb. breaking strength. Determine the velocity v of the weight when the wire breaks.

        Ans. $v = 48.2$ ft./sec.

837. The pendulum is held at rest in the position shown by the light horizontal string. If the string is suddenly cut, by what factor will the original tension in the wire OA be momentarily reduced?

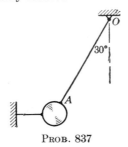

PROB. 837

838. A 3.22 lb. particle moves in the x–y plane according to $x = 2t^3 + 2t + 4$ and $y = 5t^2 + 8$, where x and y are in feet and t is in seconds. Find the resultant force F acting on the particle when $t = 2$ sec. *Ans.* $F = 2.6$ lb.

839. A small car starts from rest at A and rolls freely down the track and around the vertical loop. Determine the minimum height h such that the car does not leave the rails when upside down.

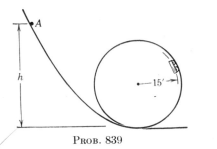

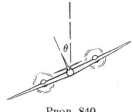

PROB. 839   PROB. 840

840. Determine the proper angle of bank θ for an airplane flying at 300 mi./hr. and making a horizontal turn of 1 mi. radius. *Ans.* $\theta = 48.7$ deg.

841. A small ball is dropped into the hemispherical bowl, shown in section, which rotates at a constant angular speed ω. Determine the angle θ when the ball stops moving relative to the bowl. *Ans.* $\theta = \cos^{-1}\dfrac{g}{r\omega^2}$

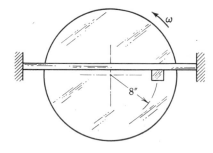

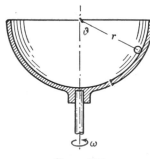

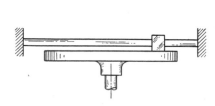

PROB. 841   PROB. 842

842. A small metallic specimen is placed on the slowly moving polishing disk against the fixed rail which is slightly above the disk. If the angular velocity of the disk is increased, what speed ω, if any, will cause the block to slide off the disk? The coefficient of friction for both pairs of contacting surfaces is 0.4.

843. At the bottom of a vertical loop the test pilot of an experimental airplane notices that his accelerometer indicates an absolute linear acceleration of the airplane of $5g$ normal to its path and that his speed is 600 mi./hr. If the pilot weighs 161 lb., find the radius of curvature ρ of the bottom of the loop and the force N exerted by the man on the seat.   *Ans.* $\rho = 4810$ ft., $N = 966$ lb.

844. A 3220 lb. car traveling at 30 mi./hr. passes over (*a*) a hump and (*b*) a dip in the road. If the radius of curvature of both the top of the hump and the bottom of the dip is 80 ft., determine the total normal force N between the tires and the road when the car passes over each contour.

845. Determine the speed of rotation N of the aerial ride at the amusement park when the angle θ is 60 deg.   *Ans.* $N = 17.6$ rev./min.

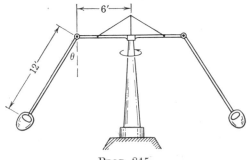

PROB. 845

846. The position of the small 1 lb. block in the smooth radial slot of the flywheel depends on the speed of rotation and is used as an activating device for the speed-control mechanism. If the axis of the flywheel is vertical and the block moves from a radius r of 6 in. to one of 7 in. while the speed changes slowly from 300 to 400 rev./min., find the constant k of the spring.

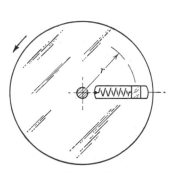

PROB. 846

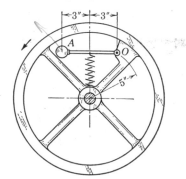

PROB. 847

847. An inertia type of speed governor on a flywheel with vertical axis consists of the small 1 lb. weight A attached to the light arm AO. The position of AO is used to activate the speed control, and this position depends on the speed of the flywheel and the stiffness k of the spring. Determine k if the governor is to assume the position shown where the spring is stretched ¾ in. for a constant speed of 600 rev./min.   *Ans.* $k = 109.0$ lb./in.

848. A spring scale is suspended from the ceiling of a railway mail car. A package is weighed while the car is rounding a curve of 600 ft. radius at 30 mi./hr., and the scale reads 9.20 lb. What is the true weight of the package? Neglect the mass of the moving parts of the scale.

849. A small block of weight W is placed on the horizontal surface of a circular disk at a radius r from the axis of rotation. If the coefficient of friction is f

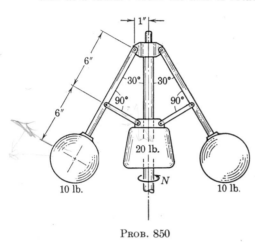

and the disk starts from rest with a constant angular acceleration α, find the angular velocity ω at which the block begins to slip.

$$Ans. \quad \omega = \left[\left(\frac{fg}{r} \right)^2 - \alpha^2 \right]^{\frac{1}{4}}$$

850. Determine the rotational speed N necessary to maintain the given configuration of the flyball governor. The weights of the links may be neglected.

851. A small steel ball is placed on a rotating conical dish at a distance b along the cone from the axis and given a tangential velocity equal to that of the dish at this point. If b is greater than a certain value, the

PROB. 850

ball will move out and up along the cone, and if b is less than this value, the ball will roll down and toward the center. Determine the location of this unstable position for a given speed ω and angle θ.

$$Ans. \quad b = \frac{g \cos \theta}{\omega^2 \sin^2 \theta}$$

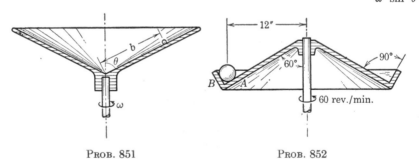

PROB. 851   PROB. 852

852. A rotor with the cross section indicated carries a 4 lb. steel ball in the position shown. Find the forces at A and B exerted by the rotor on the ball if the angular speed is 60 rev./min.   *Ans.* $A = 1.01$ lb., $B = 6.25$ lb.

853. A penny is placed on the surface of a rotating disk at a distance of 6 in. from the axis of rotation, which is tilted 10 deg. from the vertical. If the coefficient of friction is 0.30 and the speed of rotation is increased slowly, find the speed ω at which the penny slips.

854. Two small steel blocks have equal weights of 4 lb. and are connected 24 in. apart by a wire. If the blocks are placed on the horizontal surface of a rotating disk in the positions shown, find the angular velocity ω at which both blocks begin to slip as a unit and determine the tension T in the wire at this instant. The coefficient of friction is 0.30 for both blocks, and the angular acceleration is negligibly small. $Ans.$ $\omega = 5.38$ rad./sec., $T = 3.60$ lb.

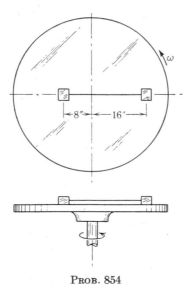

PROB. 854

855. If the pendulum of Prob. 835 is released from rest at $\theta = 90$ deg., find the tension T in the supporting wire when it passes the bottom position.

856. A small object is given an initial horizontal velocity v at the bottom of a smooth slope. The angle made by the slope with the horizontal varies according to $\sin \theta = ks$, where k is a constant and s is the distance measured along the slope from the bottom. Find the maximum distance s which the object slides up the slope.

$$Ans. \quad s = \frac{v}{\sqrt{kg}}$$

857. The small pin A weighs 1.61 lb. and is attached to the face of the wheel which rolls on a horizontal track. If the wheel has a constant angular acceleration of 2 rad./sec.² clockwise, find the force R exerted by the wheel on the pin after the wheel has rolled without slipping through ¼ turn from the rest position shown. $Ans.$ $R = 1.540$ lb.

PROB. 857

858. A tachometer of the centrifugal type measures engine speed by the horizontal movement of the collar B on the rotating shaft. This movement is caused by the centrifugal action of the small 8 oz. rotating weights marked A.

Collar C is fixed to the shaft. Determine the speed N of rotation for a reading of $\theta = 20$ deg. The spring has a constant of 4 lb./in. and is uncompressed at the position for which both α and θ are zero. The weights of the links may be neglected.

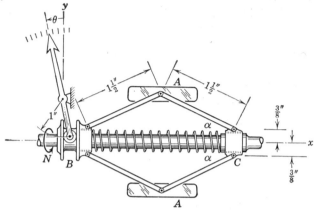

PROB. 858

859. A flat, flexible belt of weight μ per unit length drives the pulley at a constant high speed ω. The relation $T_2 = T_1 e^{f\beta}$ derived for the impending slippage of stationary belts must now be modified to account for the "centrifugal" effect. Derive this new relation between the tensions T_2 and T_1 in terms of the given quantities and the coefficient of friction f. (The resulting relation may be adapted to the case of V-belts by replacing f by $f/\sin (\alpha/2)$, where α is the angle of the V-section. See Art. 56 and Prob. 564 of *Part I*.)

$$Ans. \quad T_2 - \frac{\mu r^2 \omega^2}{g} = \left(T_1 - \frac{\mu r^2 \omega^2}{g} \right) e^{f\beta}$$

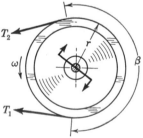

PROB. 859

* 860. The radius r of the earth is about 20.9×10^6 ft., and the distance R between the centers of the earth and the moon is 12.54×10^8 ft. Determine the period τ of the rotation of the moon about the earth considered as fixed.

$$Ans. \quad \tau = \frac{2\pi R}{r} \sqrt{\frac{R}{g}}, \ \tau = 27.2 \text{ days}$$

* 861. A 1 lb. particle P slides on a smooth curve in the vertical plane under the action of its own weight. The angular acceleration α of the radial line PO to the center of curvature O for this point on the curve is 4 rad./sec.^{2} counter-clockwise, and the radius of curvature to the moving particle is increasing at the rate of 3 ft./sec. Determine the angular velocity ω of PO and the normal force N on the particle at this instant.

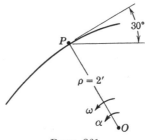

Ans. $\omega = 2.7$ rad./sec., $N = 0.413$ lb.

* 862. A particle of weight W is fastened to the rim of a circular hoop of radius r and negligible weight which is free to roll on a horizontal plane. If the hoop is released from rest with the particle initially on a horizontal line through the center of the hoop, determine the initial angular acceleration α of the hoop if

PROB. 861

the coefficient of friction between the hoop and the plane is (*a*) greater than unity and (*b*) less than unity. (*Hint:* The resultant of all forces acting on the hoop and particle taken together passes through the particle.)

Ans. (*a*) $\alpha = \dfrac{g}{2r}$, (*b*) $\alpha = \dfrac{g}{r}$

* 863. The flexible cable shown has a length of $\pi r/2$ and a uniform weight per unit length. If the cable is released from rest in the smooth circular tube with $\theta = 0$, find its velocity along the path when the center of the cable passes the bottom of the arc. (*Hint:* Analyze the forces on a differential element of the cable and integrate the differential relation between the free ends of the cable for a given position of the cable.)

Ans. $v = 2\sqrt{\dfrac{gr(\sqrt{2} - 1)}{\pi}}$

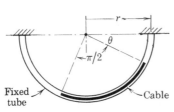

PROB. 863

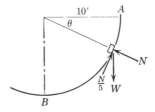

PROB. 864

* 864. A small object is released from rest at A and slides with friction down the circular path. If the coefficient of friction is $\frac{1}{5}$, determine the velocity of the object as it passes B. (*Hint:* Since the variables in the resulting differential relation are not separable, this problem may be solved by an approximate step-by-step numerical solution. Eliminate N between the equations of motion and combine with $v\,dv = a_t\,ds$, where $ds = 10\,d\theta$. Solve this relation for dv as a function of θ, v, and $d\theta$. Next divide the path into small intervals of, say, 10 deg. and replace dv by Δv and $d\theta$ by $\Delta\theta$. The change in velocity and the corresponding new velocity for each interval may be computed from the Δv

relation, where the first increment may be taken as the free-fall velocity with acceleration g.)   *Ans.* $v_B \approx 20$ ft./sec.

92. Polar Coordinates and Rotating Axes. There are a few special problems in curvilinear translation where the acceleration is more easily described in polar coordinates with respect to a fixed origin (Art. 73). For a particle of mass m Eqs. (60), then, require

$$\Sigma F_r = m\left[\frac{d^2r}{dt^2} - r\left(\frac{d\theta}{dt}\right)^2\right],$$

(78)

$$\Sigma F_\theta = m\left[r\frac{d^2\theta}{dt^2} + 2\frac{dr}{dt}\frac{d\theta}{dt}\right].$$

If the acceleration of the particle is described in terms of its motion relative to a rotating path (Art. 81), Eq. (70) may be used. Thus

$$\Sigma F = m(a_m \mathbin{+\mkern-8mu+} a_p \mathbin{+\mkern-8mu+} 2u\omega). \tag{79}$$

The term a_p is the acceleration of the particle P along the path considered as fixed, a_m is the acceleration of a point fixed to the rotating path and momentarily coincident with P, and $2u\omega$ is the Coriolis acceleration, where u is the velocity of P relative to the path and ω is the angular velocity of the path. The resultant force ΣF on the particle has the same direction as the resultant of the three acceleration terms.

If Eq. (79) is applied to the motion of a particle relative to the earth, it is more convenient to write the equation as

$$ma_p = \Sigma F \;\rightarrow\; ma_m \;\rightarrow\; 2mu\omega, \tag{80}$$

where a_p is the measured acceleration of the particle relative to the earth. The acceleration a_m for a reference point attached to the earth on its surface is $R\omega^2$, where R is the radius of the earth and ω is the angular velocity of the earth. This expression neglects the extremely small acceleration of the center of the earth. The term in $R\omega^2$ is itself usually neglected since the square of the small angular velocity $\omega = 0.729 \times 10^{-4}$ rad./sec. is even smaller. With the neglect of a_m the equation of motion for a particle falling in space (air friction neglected) becomes

$$a_p = g \;\rightarrow\; 2u\omega, \tag{81}$$

where ΣF has been replaced by the product of the mass m and the absolute acceleration of gravity g. Thus the measured acceleration a_p will be the vector difference between g and the Coriolis acceleration.

SAMPLE PROBLEM

865. The slider block of weight W starts from rest at time $t = 0$ with r essentially zero and slides down the rod under the action of its own weight. The rod has a constant clockwise angular velocity ω and passes the horizontal position when $t = 0$. Set up the equations of motion for the block neglecting friction.

Solution: The free-body diagram of the block discloses the two forces N and W. Application of Eqs. (78) gives

$$[\Sigma F_r = ma_r] \qquad\qquad W \sin \theta = \frac{W}{g}\left(\frac{d^2r}{dt^2} - r\omega^2\right),$$

$$[\Sigma F_\theta = ma_\theta] \qquad\qquad W \cos \theta - N = \frac{W}{g}\left(2\omega\frac{dr}{dt}\right).$$

Solution of the first of these equations for r is prerequisite to the determination of N from the second.

The identical formulation of the problem is made by using Eq. (79). The term a_m is the acceleration of a fixed point on the rod coincident with the block

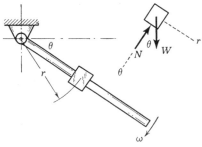

PROB. 865

at the instant considered, and is therefore $a_m = r\omega^2$ in the negative r-direction. The term a_p is the acceleration of the block relative to the straight rod and is $a_p = d^2r/dt^2$ in the positive r-direction. The Coriolis acceleration is $2u\omega = 2(dr/dt)\omega$ and, by the rule established in Art. 81, is in the direction of increasing θ. Thus the first two terms are $a_m \nrightarrow a_p = a_r$ and the third term is $2u\omega = a_\theta$.

PROBLEMS

* **866.** Solve the equations of motion of Sample Prob. 865 for r and N as functions of θ where the initial conditions of motion are defined in the problem statement.

Ans. $r = \dfrac{g}{2\omega^2}(\sinh \theta - \sin \theta)$, $N = W(2\cos \theta - \cosh \theta)$

* **867.** In the pump described in Prob. 688 an element of fluid is assumed to be a particle P which moves outward along the smooth radial vane. If the weight of the particle is W and if the impeller rotates about a vertical axis at

the constant angular velocity ω, find the force N exerted by the vane on P as a function of r.

$$Ans. \quad N = \frac{2W\omega^2}{g}\sqrt{r^2 - r_0^2}$$

* **868.** Derive the relation given in the footnote on p. 430 for the deflection from the vertical of a freely falling body. The result is based on Eq. (81), which neglects the acceleration of the center of the earth and the square of the angular velocity ω of the earth.

* **869.** The slotted arm in Prob. 683 rotates in a horizontal plane around the fixed cam with a constant counterclockwise velocity $K = 10$ rad./sec. The spring has a constant of 10 lb./in. and is uncompressed when $\theta = 0$. If $b = 4$ in., $c = 2$ in., and the small smooth roller A weighs 8 oz., find the force P exerted on A by the smooth sides of the slot when $\theta = 60$ deg.   *Ans.* $P = 6.07$ lb.

* **870.** Apply and integrate Eqs. (78) to obtain the equation of the path of a planet of mass m around its sun of mass m_0 considered as fixed. (*Hint:* Make use of the identity $\dfrac{1}{r}\dfrac{d}{dt}\left(r^2\dfrac{d\theta}{dt}\right) = r\dfrac{d^2\theta}{dt^2} + 2\dfrac{dr}{dt}\dfrac{d\theta}{dt}$ and the substitution $u = \dfrac{1}{r}$.

Also take r to be a minimum at $\theta = 0$.)

$$Ans. \quad \frac{1}{r} = A\cos\theta + \frac{\gamma m_0}{h^2} \text{ where } A = \text{constant}, \ h = r^2\frac{d\theta}{dt} = \text{constant}$$

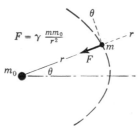

PROB. 870

93. Curvilinear Translation of a Rigid Body.

When a body which moves with curvilinear translation is acted upon by a system of forces whose lines of action are not concurrent, it becomes necessary to consider the locations of the forces on the body. In Art. 90 the equations of motion, Eqs. (76), for a translating rigid body were developed and are valid for both rectilinear translation and curvilinear translation. These equations are based on the fact that the resultant of all forces acting on a translating body (no rotational acceleration) passes through the center of mass and that there is no resultant moment about any axis through the center of mass.

The acceleration of curvilinear translation is most easily described in terms of its normal and tangential components which are common to all points in the body. The x- and y-directions used in Eqs. (76) may be replaced by the n- and t-directions, and, therefore, the equations of motion for a body moving with curvilinear translation, Fig. 114, are

$$\Sigma F_n = ma_n,$$

$$\Sigma F_t = ma_t, \tag{82}$$

$$\Sigma \overline{M} = 0,$$

where $a_n = v^2/\rho$ and $a_t = d|v|/dt$.

A zero summation of moments exists about any point on the line through G parallel to the direction of the resultant acceleration a, but it is not often convenient to use such a point. A moment equation similar to the third alternative of Eqs. (76) could also be used if desired.

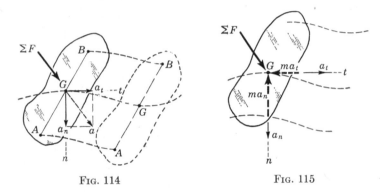

Fig. 114   Fig. 115

As in the case of rectilinear translation an alternative method utilizing D'Alembert's principle may be employed for solving the curvilinear translation problem. It is necessary only to apply a fictitious inertia force equal to ma through the center of gravity and in the direction opposite to a to produce equilibrium of forces. This hypothetical force is most conveniently applied in terms of its two components ma_n and ma_t through the center of mass in the directions *opposite* to the respective acceleration components as shown in Fig. 115. With these fictitious inertia forces added the body is in dynamic equilibrium, and the principles of statical equilibrium

$$\Sigma F_x = 0, \qquad \Sigma F_y = 0, \qquad \Sigma M = 0,$$

may be applied.

The essential advantage of the dynamic equilibrium method is that it enables a dynamics problem to be solved as a statics problem where the zero moment summation may be taken about any point. It must be remembered, though, that the inertia forces are *not* real forces, and hence they should be represented by dotted lines to emphasize this fact.

SAMPLE PROBLEM

871. Investigate the relations between the angle to which a curved road is banked and the tendency for a car rounding the curve to tip over or slide.

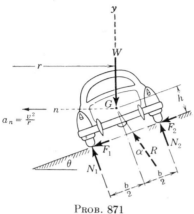

PROB. 871

Solution: The rear view of a car rounding an inwardly banked curve of mean radius r at a constant speed v is shown. The velocity of the car is normal to the plane of the figure, but the acceleration, $a_n = v^2/r$, is toward the center of the curve and is in the plane of the paper. The forces acting on the car may be represented by the weight W and the force R which is the resultant of the normal forces N_1 and N_2 and the lateral friction forces F_1 and F_2. The force R must pass through G since the car has linear acceleration of translation only.

The equations of motion are

$$[\Sigma F_n = ma_n] \qquad\qquad R\sin(\theta + \alpha) = \frac{W}{g}\frac{v^2}{r},$$

$$[\Sigma F_y = 0] \qquad\qquad R\cos(\theta + \alpha) = W.$$

Dividing gives

$$\tan(\theta + \alpha) = \frac{v^2}{gr} \qquad \text{or} \qquad v^2 = gr\frac{\tan\theta + \tan\alpha}{1 - \tan\theta\tan\alpha}.$$

The angle of bank which produces no tendency to tip or slip for a particular speed v is that angle for which there is no side friction. Thus $\alpha = 0$, $N_1 = N_2$, and

$$\tan\theta = \frac{v^2}{gr}.$$

This relation shows that a road can be properly banked for one speed only.

The speed at which the car overturns occurs when the reaction R acts entirely at the outside wheels. In this event $\tan\alpha = (b/2)/h$, and thus

$$v^2 = gr\frac{\tan\theta + (b/2h)}{1 - (b/2h)\tan\theta}.$$

This relation assumes sufficient friction to allow R to act at the outer wheels and is valid provided the coefficient of friction f is greater than $(b/2)/h$.

The car will slide before it will tip, on the other hand, if the coefficient of friction f is less than $(b/2)/h$. Thus $\tan\alpha = f$, and the speed at which sliding begins is given by

$$v^2 = gr\frac{\tan\theta + f}{1 - f\tan\theta}.$$

Solution by the method of dynamic equilibrium may also be effected. The reversed effective normal force $(W/g)(v^2/r)$ is added through G to the right in the direction opposite to the acceleration. The equilibrium triangle of forces quickly discloses the relation already developed.

PROBLEMS

872. At what speed can a car round a turn of 100 ft. radius on a flat unbanked road without slipping if the coefficient of friction between the tires and the road is 0.80 and if the center of gravity of the car is sufficiently low to prevent over-turning?

873. The center of gravity of a certain car is 2 ft. from the road, and the tread (transverse distance between wheels) is 6 ft. Also the coefficient of friction between the tires and the road is 0.80. What is the maximum speed v with which the car can enter a turn of 100 ft. radius banked inward at an angle of 15 deg. without tipping or sliding? Which would occur first?

Ans. $v = 45.1$ mi./hr. sliding

874. If the outer wheels of the car in Prob. 873 are running against a small shoulder on this same curve so that the car cannot slip sideways, at what speed will it tip over?

875. What is the minimum turning radius r which a bicycle can make on a horizontal road with a speed of 15 mi./hr. if the coefficient of friction between the tires and the road is 0.70? Find the corresponding angle θ with the vertical at which the cyclist must lean. Measure r to the center of gravity of rider and bicycle. *Ans.* $r = 21.5$ ft., $\theta = 35$ deg.

876. A car turns a curve of 50 ft. radius banked inward at a steep angle of 30 deg. with the horizontal. If the coefficient of friction between the tires and the road is 0.50, what is the slowest speed v which the car may have without slipping? *Ans.* $v = 6.70$ mi./hr.

877. The car described in Prob. 873 rounds a curve of 100 ft. radius banked outward instead of inward at an angle of 15 deg. with the horizontal. If the coefficient of friction between the tires and the road is 0.80, determine the maximum speed v at which the car can round the curve without tipping or sliding.

878. What are the minimum speed v and corresponding angle θ in order that the motorcycle may ride on the vertical wall of the cylindrical track? The coefficient of friction between the tires and the wall is 0.70.

Ans. $v = 25.3$ mi./hr., $\theta = 55$ deg.

879. If the motorcycle and rider of Prob. 878 travel at a speed of 45 mi./hr. around the cylindrical track, find the angle θ.

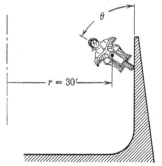

PROB. 878

880. The side rod on a small locomotive weighs 86 lb., and its center of gravity is located as shown. Find the maximum values of the forces on the crank pins A and B while the locomotive is traveling at the constant speed of 20 mi./hr.

Ans. $A = 210$ lb., $B = 259$ lb.

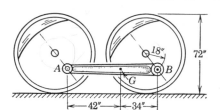

PROB. 880

881. The homogeneous 300 lb. log is supported by the two 10 ft. ropes. If the log is released from rest in the position shown, find the tension T_1 and T_2 in each rope as the log swings past the lowest position.

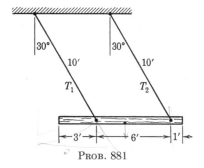

PROB. 881

882. The motorcycle rider of Prob. 878 is not satisfied with riding around the vertical wall and decides to go beyond the vertical by using a track with a spherical surface shown partially in the figure. If he is to ride in a horizontal circle at the angle $\alpha = 10$ deg. and if the coefficient of friction between his tires and the track is 0.70, find his necessary minimum velocity v. Assume that the effective radius of the horizontal circle is 30 cos 10° ft.

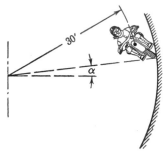

PROB. 882

* 883. The uniform square plate weighs 100 lb. and is supported in the horizontal position by the three light legs shown. Each leg is hinged at each end by a pin whose axis is parallel to the x-direction. The frame is prevented from collapsing by the two diagonal wires. If one wire breaks, find the force in each leg just before the plate hits the horizontal base.

Ans. $A = 100$ lb., $B = C = 50$ lb., all tension

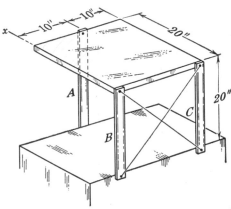

PROB. 883

* 884. The homogeneous triangular plate weighs 50 lb. and is attached to the two arms shown whose weights may be neglected. Determine the total force on pin A as the mechanism starts from rest in the position shown under a tension T of 100 lb. in the control cable. *Ans.* $A = 187.8$ lb.

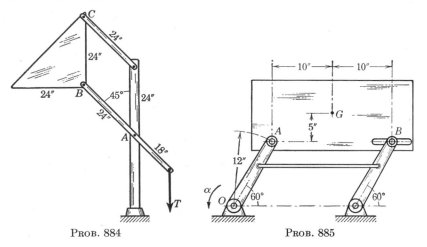

PROB. 884   PROB. 885

* 885. In the mechanism shown the light arms with connecting tie rod rotate in unison in a vertical plane with a constant counterclockwise angular acceleration $\alpha = 10$ rad./sec.^{2} The center of gravity of the 45 lb. rectangular member is at G.   If the angular velocity of the arms is 4 rad./sec. in the position shown, find the forces on pins A and B at this instant.   *Ans.* $A = 25.5$ lb., $B = 22.1$ lb.

* 886. If the mechanism described in Prob. 885 is started from rest in the position shown by means of a counterclockwise torque of 50 lb. ft. applied to the lever AO through its shaft at O, find the forces on pins A and B as the frame starts to move.   The weights of the levers and tie rod are negligible.

Ans. $A = 33.3$ lb., $B = 35.3$ lb.

PART *C*.   FIXED-AXIS ROTATION

94. Equations of Motion.   Consider any rigid body, Fig. 116, which rotates about a fixed axis.   Let O be the intersection of this axis with the plane of rotation.   Assume that the body has an angular velocity ω

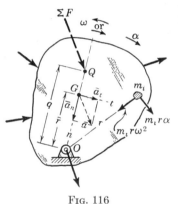

FIG. 116

and an angular acceleration α at the instant considered.   The forces external to the body in the plane of rotation are indicated schematically by the full arrows and include the reaction exerted by the bearing on the body at O.   If the plane of rotation is other than horizontal, the weight W of the body will appear on the free-body diagram.   The acceleration $\bar{a}$ of the center of gravity G has the components $\bar{a}_n = \bar{r}\omega^2$ and $\bar{a}_t = \bar{r}\alpha$.   Thus, from the principle of motion of the mass center, Art. 87, there are two relations which are known immediately.   First, the result-

ant ΣF of *all* forces (including the bearing reaction at O) acting on the body equals the mass m times $\bar{a}$.   Second, the direction of ΣF must coincide with that of $\bar{a}$.   These two relations are conveniently expressed by the components of the single vector equation and are $\Sigma F_n = m\bar{a}_n = m\bar{r}\omega^2$ and $\Sigma F_t = m\bar{a}_t = m\bar{r}\alpha$.   Contrary to the case of translation ΣF does *not* pass through G.   The proper position of the line of action of ΣF is found by evaluating the sum of the moments of all forces about the axis O.

The moment relation is obtained by considering the forces acting on a representative particle of mass m_i.   The resultant of these forces may be represented by the two effective forces equal to $m_i r\alpha$ and $m_i r\omega^2$ as shown.   Of the two effective forces only the tangential one exerts a moment about O, and the magnitude is $m_i r^2\alpha$.   If this moment is added to those for the remaining particles in the body, the sum

$$\Sigma M_O = \Sigma m_i r^2 \alpha = \alpha \Sigma m_i r^2$$

results. The acceleration α is common to all terms and may be factored outside the summation sign. The sum ΣM_O includes moments due to internal forces (actions and reactions between particles) and moments due to external forces. Since each internal action is accompanied by an equal and opposite internal reaction, it follows that the net contribution to ΣM_O by the internal forces is zero. Therefore the expression represents the algebraic sum of the moments about the axis of rotation of all external forces. The summation $\Sigma m_i r^2$ depends on the radial distribution of mass about the axis and is known as the *mass moment of inertia* I of the body about O.

The three equations of motion for a rigid body rotating about a fixed axis through O may now be written as

$$\Sigma F_n = m\bar{r}\omega^2,$$
$$\Sigma F_t = m\bar{r}\alpha, \tag{83}$$
$$\Sigma M_O = I_O\alpha.$$

The use of these equations of motion is straightforward when they are applied exactly and literally with the aid of a complete and correct free-body diagram.

In terms of the differential element of mass dm, the mass density ρ, and the volume element dV the defining expression for mass moment of inertia may be written as

$$I_O = \Sigma m_i r^2 = \int r^2 \, dm = \int \rho r^2 \, dV,$$

where the integral is evaluated over the entire volume of the body. The radius of gyration k of the body about the axis through O is defined by

$$k_O^2 = \frac{I_O}{m}.$$

Moments of inertia are involved in all problems of bodies which have rotational acceleration, and it is necessary to be familiar with their calculation in order to proceed further. A detailed discussion of mass moments of inertia is presented in Appendix A-II.

The line of action of the resultant force ΣF on a rotating rigid body, Fig. 116, may be found by locating point Q. By replacing ΣM_O by the moment about O of the resultant ΣF and using the second of Eqs. (83), the third of Eqs. (83) becomes

$$q\Sigma F_t = I_O\alpha \qquad \text{or} \qquad m\bar{r}\alpha q = k_O^2 m\alpha.$$

Thus

$$q = \frac{k_O^2}{\bar{r}}. \tag{84}$$

The point Q located by the distance q from O is known as the *center of percussion* about O. With Q located two alternative moment equations may be written, first, about Q and, second, about G. The moment sum about Q is clearly zero, and the moment sum about G is obtained by multiplying $\Sigma F_t = m\bar{r}\alpha$ by $q - \bar{r}$, which gives

$$m\bar{r}\alpha(q - \bar{r}) = m\alpha(k_O{}^2 - \bar{r}^2) = m\bar{k}^2\alpha = \bar{I}\alpha.$$

Thus the two alternative moment equations of motion for a rigid body rotating about a fixed point are

$$\Sigma M_Q = 0 \qquad \text{and} \qquad \Sigma\overline{M} = \bar{I}\alpha.$$

For the special case of rotation of a rigid body about a fixed centroidal axis $\bar{r} = 0$, M_O is replaced by $\overline{M}$ and I_O by $\bar{I}$. Thus for rotation about a fixed axis through the mass center Eqs. (83) become

$$\Sigma\overline{M} = \bar{I}\alpha,$$

$$\Sigma F_x = 0, \tag{85}$$

$$\Sigma F_y = 0,$$

where the x- and y-directions are arbitrary. Such a body may be said to be in translational equilibrium ($\bar{a} = 0$) but not in rotational equilibrium. For this case of centroidal rotation it may be observed, since the resultant force is zero, that the resultant of all forces acting on the body is a couple equal to $\bar{I}\alpha$. Hence $\Sigma\overline{M}$ is the same as a moment sum about any axis parallel to the centroidal axis.

An alternative method of solution for a rigid body rotating about a fixed axis consists of creating the artificial state of dynamic equilibrium. This state is produced by adding to the body the inertia force $\Sigma F = m\bar{a}$ equal and opposite to and collinear with the resultant ΣF. Thus the body may be visualized as being in equilibrium under the action of the two forces. It is usually simpler to add the two components of the fictitious inertia force, as shown in Fig. 117a by the dotted lines. For this free-body diagram the principles of equilibrium

$$\Sigma F_x = 0, \qquad \Sigma F_y = 0, \qquad \Sigma M = 0$$

must be used. The essential advantage of the dynamic equilibrium method is that a zero moment sum may be taken about any point. If preferred, the tangential inertia force may be added through the center of gravity as shown in Fig. 117b provided an *inertia couple*

$$m\bar{r}\alpha(q - \bar{r}) = \bar{I}\alpha$$

is applied in the sense opposite to that of α. It must be noted carefully

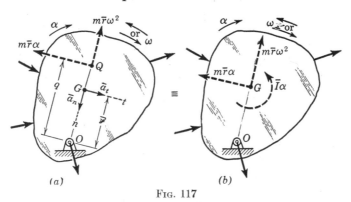

Fig. 117

that the inertia forces and the inertia couple are applied in the sense *opposite* to the corresponding linear acceleration components of the center of gravity and the angular acceleration of the body, respectively.

SAMPLE PROBLEMS

887. The radius of gyration about the axis of the uniform integral pulleys is 12 in., and their combined weight is 96.6 lb. If friction in the bearing is negligible, find the distance s through which the 32.2 lb. weight has moved 4 sec. after release from rest. The cables are wrapped securely around the pulleys. Also find the bearing reaction at O.

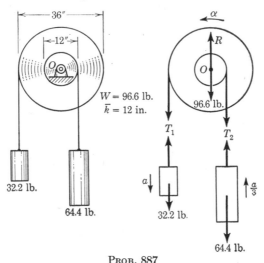

PROB. 887

Solution: Comparison of the static moments about O shows that the 32.2 lb. weight accelerates down. If the acceleration of this weight is a, the acceleration of the 64.4 lb. weight is $6a/18$ upward. Also the centroidal moment of inertia of the combined pulleys is

$[I = k^2m]$ $\qquad\qquad\qquad \bar{I} = \left(\dfrac{12}{12}\right)^2 \dfrac{96.6}{32.2} = 3$ lb. ft. sec.^{2}

The free-body diagram of each of the three members is shown. For the two weights

$[\Sigma F = ma]$ $\qquad 32.2 - T_1 = \dfrac{32.2}{32.2}\, a; \qquad T_2 - 64.4 = \dfrac{64.4}{32.2} \dfrac{a}{3}.$

For centroidal rotation of the pulleys

$[\Sigma \bar{M} = \bar{I}\alpha]$ $\qquad\qquad\qquad \dfrac{18}{12} T_1 - \dfrac{6}{12} T_2 = 3\,\dfrac{a}{\frac{18}{12}}.$

Solution of the three equations gives

$$a = 4.20 \text{ ft./sec.}^2, \qquad T_1 = 28.0 \text{ lb.}, \qquad T_2 = 67.2 \text{ lb.}$$

With the constant acceleration known the distance dropped by the 32.2 lb. weight in 4 sec. is

$[s = \frac{1}{2}at^2]$ $\qquad\qquad s = \frac{1}{2} \times 4.20 \times 4^2 = 33.6$ ft. $\qquad\qquad\qquad$ *Ans.*

The bearing reaction is obtained from the vertical equilibrium of forces on the drum and is

$[\Sigma F_y = 0]$ $\qquad R - 96.6 - 28.0 - 67.2 = 0, \qquad R = 191.8$ lb. $\qquad\qquad$ *Ans.*

888. The center of gravity of the 3.10 lb. connecting rod shown in the a-part of the figure is at G, and the radius of gyration of the rod about the pivot axis O is 9.14 in. If the rod is released from rest with $\theta = 0$, find the total force on the bearing O when the position $\theta = 45$ deg. is passed. Neglect any friction in the bearing.

Solution I: The free-body diagram of the rod in an intermediate position θ is shown in the b-part of the figure. The actual forces only are shown. The bearing reaction is represented by its t- and n-components where the proper sense of these components will become clear as the solution progresses. The normal component O_n depends on the angular velocity ω, which in turn is found from the angular acceleration α. The moment equation about O gives

$[\Sigma M_O = I_O\alpha]$ $\qquad\qquad 3.10 \times \dfrac{8}{12} \cos \theta = \left(\dfrac{9.14}{12}\right)^2 \dfrac{3.10}{32.2} \alpha,$

$$\alpha = 37.0 \cos \theta.$$

Then

$[\omega \, d\omega = \alpha \, d\theta]$ $\qquad\qquad \displaystyle\int_0^\omega \omega \, d\omega = \int_0^{\pi/4} 37.0 \cos \theta \, d\theta,$

$$\omega^2 = 52.3 \text{ (rad./sec.)}^2.$$

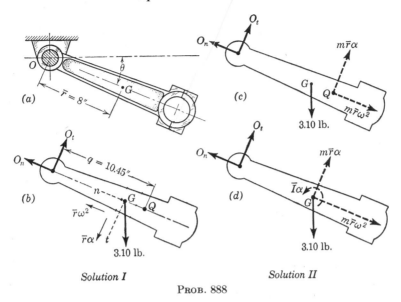

Solution I   *Solution II*

PROB. 888

The remaining two equations of motion applied to the 45 deg. position yield

$$[\Sigma F_n = m\bar{r}\omega^2] \quad O_n - 3.10 \times 0.707 = \frac{3.10}{32.2} \times \frac{2}{3} \times 52.3, \quad O_n = 5.55 \text{ lb.,}$$

$$[\Sigma F_t = m\bar{r}\alpha] \quad 3.10 \times 0.707 - O_t = \frac{3.10}{32.2} \times \frac{2}{3} \times 37.0 \times 0.707, \quad O_t = 0.51 \text{ lb.}$$

The total bearing force is

$$O = \sqrt{(5.55)^2 + (0.51)^2} = 5.57 \text{ lb.} \qquad Ans.$$

The proper sense for O_t may be observed at the outset by applying the alternate moment equation, $\Sigma \bar{M} = \bar{I}\alpha$. This relation eliminates all forces but O_t and requires a clockwise moment to agree with the known direction of α. Also, the component O_t may be found directly with the aid of the second alternative moment equation and the distance q, which is $k_O{}^2/\bar{r} = (9.14)^2/8 = 10.45$ in. Thus

$$[\Sigma M_Q = 0] \quad 10.45 O_t - 3.10 \times 0.707 \times (10.45 - 8) = 0, \quad O_t = 0.51 \text{ lb.}$$

Solution II: The rod may be put in dynamic equilibrium by the addition of the normal and tangential inertia forces through the center of percussion as shown in the c-part of the illustration. The principles of equilibrium may now be applied. Thus

$$[\Sigma M_O = 0] \quad \frac{3.10}{32.2} \times \frac{2}{3} \alpha \times \frac{10.45}{12} - 3.10 \times \frac{2}{3} \cos \theta = 0,$$

$$\alpha = 37.0 \cos \theta.$$

The angular velocity is obtained as shown in *Solution I*, and the components O_n and O_t come from

$$[\Sigma F_n = 0] \quad O_n - 3.10 \times 0.707 - \frac{3.10}{32.2} \times \frac{2}{3} \times 52.3 = 0, \qquad O_n = 5.55 \text{ lb.}$$

$$[\Sigma F_t = 0] \quad 3.10 \times 0.707 - O_t - \frac{3.10}{32.2} \times \frac{2}{3} \times 37.0 \times 0.707 = 0, \qquad O_t = 0.51 \text{ lb.}$$

These resulting expressions are the same as those arising from the equations of motion used in *Solution I*.

If desired, the inertia forces may be added through the center of gravity provided that the inertia couple $\bar{I}\alpha$ is applied in the sense opposite to α as shown in the d-part of the figure. The centroidal moment of inertia is found from the parallel-axis theorem and is

$$\bar{I} = \bar{k}^2 m = (k_O{}^2 - \bar{r}^2)m = \left[\left(\frac{9.14}{12}\right)^2 - \left(\frac{8}{12}\right)^2\right]\frac{3.10}{32.2} = 0.0130 \text{ lb. ft. sec.}^2$$

The three representations of the free-body diagram illustrated with this problem should be studied and their equivalence understood.

PROBLEMS

889. The solid cylindrical pulleys weigh 32.2 lb. each and are mounted in bearings with negligible friction. The 10 lb. force on pulley A is constant. Determine the angular acceleration α of each pulley.

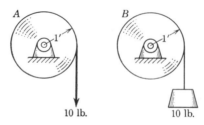

PROB. 889

890. If the connecting rod of Prob. 888 is given an initial swing which carries it over the top position ($\theta = 270$ deg.) with an angular velocity of 10 rad./sec., find the bearing reaction O at this position. *Ans.* $O = 3.31$ lb.

891. The radius of gyration of a 40 lb. flywheel about its vertical shaft is 6 in., and the center of gravity of the wheel is 0.003 in. from the axis of the shaft. If a constant moment of 10 lb. ft. is applied to the flywheel through its shaft, find the horizontal force F exerted on the bearing 5 sec. after the wheel starts from rest.

892. The 40 lb. circular disk is free to rotate on its central vertical shaft. An electric disk sander is placed on the large disk in any position as shown, and its switch is turned on with the large disk at rest. The sander rotates clockwise when viewed from above and requires a moment of 1.5 lb. ft. applied to the motor housing to prevent rotation about its own axis. Find the angular acceleration α of the large disk an instant after the sander starts if no lateral forces are applied to the sander.

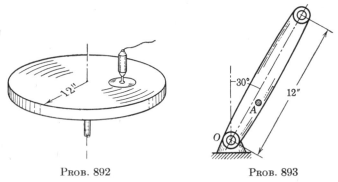

PROB. 892   PROB. 893

893. A flexible shaft (not shown) is attached to the arm at A and exerts a counterclockwise couple of 2 lb. ft. on the arm in the plane of the figure. Determine the angular acceleration α of the symmetrical 5 lb. arm in the position shown if it has a radius of gyration about O of 8 in. and the bearing friction is negligible.   *Ans.* $\alpha = 10.86$ rad./sec.^{2} counterclockwise

894. A 50 lb. horizontal component of the bearing reaction at O is recorded when the uniform slender rod is struck with a force F. Determine the magnitude of F at the instant that the 50 lb. reaction was measured.

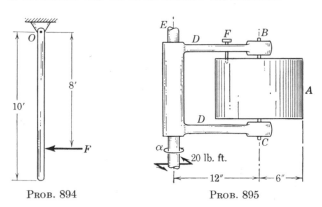

PROB. 894   PROB. 895

895. The 64.4 lb. cylindrical rotor A is mounted freely on the shaft BC. The arms D have negligible weight and are rigidly attached to the vertical shaft E with fixed axis. Through a motor drive the shaft E exerts a torque of 20 lb. ft. on the arm assembly. Determine the angular acceleration α of the arms (a) when the locking pin F is in place and (b) when the pin is removed.
                    Ans.   (a) $\alpha = 8.89$ rad./sec.^{2}, (b) $\alpha = 10$ rad./sec.

896. The rim of the flywheel shown in section is welded to the central web which in turn is welded to the hub. The weights of the web and hub are negligible compared with the 100 lb. rim. If the maximum safe shearing force which the rim weld and hub weld can each support is 4000 lb. per inch of weld length, find the maximum safe acceleration α which can be given to the flywheel by a torque suddenly applied to the shaft.

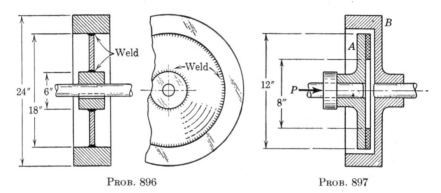

PROB. 896   PROB. 897

897. Part A of the single-plate clutch is driven at a constant speed of 600 rev./min. by a powerful motor. An engaging force of $P = 100$ lb. is applied, and slipping occurs for 2 sec. before the flywheel B reaches the operating speed. The coefficient of friction is 0.30, and it may be assumed that the friction force acts at the mean radius. Determine the moment of inertia I of the flywheel.

Ans. $I = 0.398$ lb. ft. sec.^{2}

898. The motor pinion A of the log hoist has a negligible moment of inertia and is subjected to a counterclockwise starting torque of 40 lb. ft. Determine the tension T in the cable if the coefficient of friction between the 500 lb. log and the incline is 0.80.

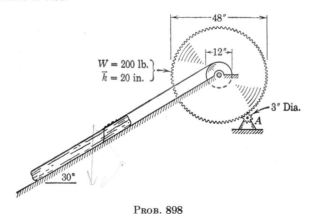

PROB. 898

899. A large pendulum consists of the 50 lb. circular metal disk A welded to the uniform shaft B, which weighs 40 lb. Determine the reaction on the bearing O an instant after release from rest in the horizontal position shown.

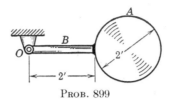

PROB. 899

900. The uniform 10 lb. link is subjected to a constant frictional moment of 5 lb. ft. in its tight bearing at O during rotation. Find the force on the bearing at O an instant after motion starts when the link is released from rest in the position shown. *Ans.* $O = 6.25$ lb.

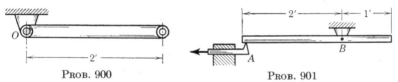

PROB. 900   PROB. 901

901. If the support at A is suddenly removed, find (*a*) the momentary reaction at B in the horizontal position and (*b*) the reaction at B as the bar swings through the vertical. The weight of the uniform slender bar is 16.1 lb.

902. The slender rod of weight W and length l is mounted freely in a ball bearing on the fixed shaft whose axis is inclined an angle θ with the vertical. If the rod is released from rest in the highest position shown, find its angular velocity ω when it swings through the lowest (dotted) position. Solve by the method of this article.

$$Ans. \quad \omega = \sqrt{\frac{6g \sin \theta}{l}}$$

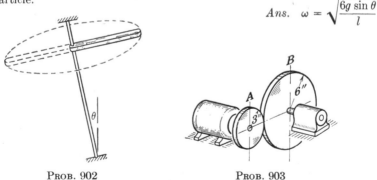

PROB. 902   PROB. 903

903. Gears A and B weigh 6 lb. and 30 lb., respectively, and may be treated as circular disks. If the motor accelerates gear B from rest to a speed of 920 rev./min. in 1.2 sec., find the torque M to which the motor shaft is subjected where it is attached to the pinion. *Ans.* $M = 5.61$ lb. ft.

904. Gear A is driven by a motor which supplies a constant clockwise torque of 20 lb. ft. on its shaft, and the output shaft of gear C drives a small machine. The moments of inertia of A, B, and C about their own axes are 0.05, 0.05, and 0.01 lb. ft. sec.^{2}, respectively. If gear C reaches a speed of 3000 rev./min. in 2 sec. from rest, find the constant torque M supplied to the machine by the shaft of gear C.

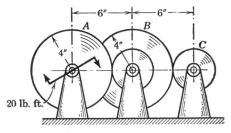

Prob. 904

905. The gear weighs 10 lb. and has a radius of gyration of 4 in. Each rack weighs 12 lb. and slides against the smooth vertical guide. Determine the torque M required on the shaft of the gear to give an angular acceleration of 8 rad./sec.^{2} *Ans.* $M = 1.77$ lb. ft.

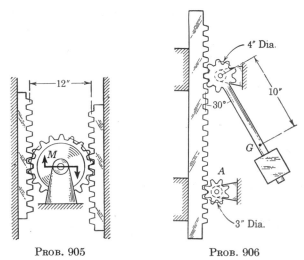

Prob. 905   Prob. 906

906. Determine the starting torque M which a motor must supply to the light pinion A in order to raise the weighted arm with an initial angular acceleration of 2 rad./sec.^{2} from the position shown. The radius of gyration of the 10 lb. arm assembly about its pivot is 12 in., and its center of gravity is at G. The 20 lb. rack moves with negligible friction in its guides.

907. Find the moment M required to rotate the drum at a constant speed ω if the diameter D of the rope is small compared with r and if there is negligible friction in the bearings.

$$Ans. \quad M = Lr\left(1 + \frac{D\omega^2}{2\pi g}\right)$$

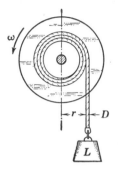

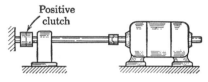

Positive clutch

PROB. 907   PROB. 908

908. The direction of rotation of an electric motor for a high-speed computing device may be reversed quickly with negligible energy loss by engaging the positive clutch in the connecting shaft when the power is shut off. The shaft twists in bringing the rotor to a stop and then untwists in returning the rotor to the same speed in the opposite direction, at which instant the clutch is disengaged. The moment acting on the shaft is proportional to the angle of twist of the shaft and equals 2 lb. ft. per each degree of twist. If the moment of inertia of the rotor is 0.008 lb. ft. sec.^{2} and that of the shaft is negligibly small, find the maximum moment M in the shaft due to reversing the direction of rotation from a speed of 1800 rev./min. $\qquad$ $Ans.$ $M = 180.4$ lb. ft.

909. Determine the force on the bearing O for the link described in Prob. 900 as it swings past the vertical position.

* **910.** Determine the force R and the moment M supported by the weld, joining parts A and B of the pendulum in Prob. 899, an instant after release from rest in the horizontal position. $\qquad$ $Ans.$ $R = 3.9$ lb., $M = 12.9$ lb. ft.

* **911.** A long heavy cable of length L and weight μ per unit length is wound around a light drum with negligible friction in the bearings of its horizontal shaft. One end of the cable hangs down a very small distance, and the resulting unbalance causes the drum to rotate and unwind the cable with increasing speed. Determine the velocity v of the cable as it leaves the drum completely. $\qquad$ $Ans.$ $v = \sqrt{gL}$

* **912.** The uniform slender bar of weight W and length l is released from rest in the vertical position and pivots on its square end about the corner O. (*a*) If the bar is observed to slip when $\theta = 30$ deg., find the coefficient of friction f. (*b*) If the end of the bar is notched so that it cannot slip, find the angle θ at which contact between the bar and the corner ceases.

$Ans.$ (*a*) $f = 0.188$, (*b*) $\theta = 53° 8'$

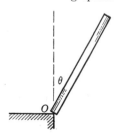

PROB. 912

* **913.** A uniform pole is hoisted into a vertical position with one end resting on a horizontal surface. The guy wires supporting the pole are accidentally released, and the pole falls to the ground. If the end of the pole is observed to

PROB. 913

slip when an angle $\theta = 30$ deg. is reached, find the coefficient of friction between the pole and the surface. *Ans.* $f = 0.351$.

95. Distributed Inertia Forces. The internal forces induced in a body by reason of high rotative speeds or large angular accelerations are usually important design considerations. The calculation of the internal forces which result from such motions is often very involved. However, when the body is essentially uni-dimensional, such as a slender rod or a thin ring, it is usually possible to calculate the internal inertia effects without undue difficulty. The general procedure is to isolate a differential element or a finite portion of the body with a free-body diagram and to write the motion equations for the forces acting on the part isolated. The addition of the fictitious inertia forces to produce dynamic equilibrium is an advantage in some instances.

SAMPLE PROBLEM

914. Determine the variation of the centrifugal tension in the slender rod of weight W and length $2l$ which rotates in a horizontal plane about an axis through O normal to the rod.

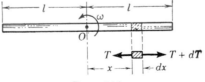

PROB. 914

Solution: The free-body diagram of an element of length dx shows a tension T acting on the left-hand section, where the coordinate is x, and a tension $T + dT$ on the right-hand section, where the coordinate is $x + dx$. The weight of the element is assumed small compared with the tension T. If μ stands for the weight of the bar per unit length, the equation of motion for this element gives

$$[\Sigma F_n = mr\omega^2] \qquad\qquad T - (T + dT) = \frac{\mu \, dx}{g} x\omega^2,$$

$$-dT = \frac{\mu\omega^2}{g} x \, dx.$$

At the center of the bar the tension will be designated by T_0, so that the integration limits give

$$\int_{T_0}^{T} -dT = \frac{\mu\omega^2}{g} \int_0^x x \, dx,$$

$$T = T_0 - \frac{\mu\omega^2 x^2}{2g}.$$

Since the tension is zero at $x = l$, the tension at the center becomes $T_0 = (\mu\omega^2 l^2)/(2g)$. This value for T_0 may also be obtained by considering the acceleration of the mass center of half the bar, which is $(l/2)\omega^2$. Thus the force T_0 is $\frac{1}{2}(W/g)(l/2)\omega^2 = (\mu\omega^2 l^2)/(2g)$. The tension at any value of x becomes

$$T = \frac{\mu\omega^2}{2g}(l^2 - x^2) = \frac{Wl\omega^2}{4g}\left(1 - \frac{x^2}{l^2}\right). \qquad\qquad Ans.$$

The stress at any position in the bar is the tension T divided by the cross-sectional area of the bar and is known as a *centrifugal stress*.

It is left for the student to show that the same results may be obtained by isolating a finite portion of the rod from x to l and writing the appropriate equation of motion.

PROBLEMS

915. Determine the centrifugal stress σ in the rim of a flywheel of weight density μ rotating with a constant rim speed v. Assume the radial thickness of the rim to be small compared with the radius of the wheel and neglect the effect of the web or spokes. Solve, first, by considering one half of the rim as a free body and, second, by considering the free body as an element of the rim subtending an angle $d\theta$.

$$Ans. \quad \sigma = \frac{\mu}{g} v^2$$

916. The ring of weight W and radius r rotates about a diametral axis with an angular velocity ω. Determine the tension T in the ring at A and B if the dimensions of its rim are small compared with r. Compare with Prob. 915.

PROB. 916

917. The centrifuge bucket shown is rotating in a horizontal plane about the vertical axis O with a speed of 10,000 rev./min. The density of the liquid in the bucket will be assumed essentially constant throughout at 0.040 lb./in.[3] Find the variation in pressure p in the liquid as a function of r expressed in inches.

$Ans.$ $p = 56.8(r^2 - 36)$ lb./in.^{2}

PROB. 917

PROB. 918

* **918.** The uniform slender rod of length l and weight W is welded at its end tangent to the rim of the circular disk of radius r which rotates at a constant high speed ω about O. Determine the bending moment M in the rod as a function of x and the tangential and normal force components T and N, respectively, exerted by the weld on the end of the rod because of rotational inertia.

$$Ans.\quad M = \frac{Wr\omega^2(l-x)^2}{2gl}, \quad T = \frac{Wl\omega^2}{2g}, \quad N = \frac{Wr\omega^2}{g}$$

* **919.** If the disk and attached rod of Prob. 918 are given an angular acceleration α in either direction, find the magnitude of the moment M exerted by the weld on the rod as it starts from rest.

$$Ans.\quad M = \frac{Wl^2\alpha}{3g}$$

* **920.** A slender rod of mass density ρ and variable cross-sectional area A is to be designed to support the rotation of body B at an angular velocity ω. The centrifugal force applied to the end of the rod by B divided by a desired design stress σ gives an area A_l for the end section of the rod. Determine the necessary variation of the cross-sectional area A as a function of x in order that the stress σ be constant over the length of the rod. (*Hint:* The free-body diagram of an element of the rod is shown.)

$$Ans.\quad A = A_l e^{\frac{\rho\omega^2}{2\sigma}(l^2-x^2)}$$

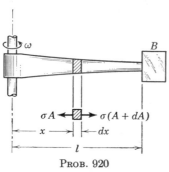

PROB. 920

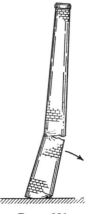

PROB. 921

* **921.** A falling chimney, such as the one shown, will usually crack, before it hits the ground, at a point where the bending moment is greatest. Show that this position of maximum moment always occurs at the center of percussion relative to the upper end for a slender chimney of constant cross section if the restraining moment at the bottom is neglected.

96. Fixed-Axis Rotation of a Body Having Axial Dimensions.   When a rotating body is not symmetrical with respect to a single plane of rotation, the dimensions in the direction of the axis of rotation must be considered.   Problems of this type are conveniently solved by the use of D'Alembert's principle, and the sample problems which follow will illustrate the method used.

SAMPLE PROBLEMS

922. The identical rotors each of weight W shown in cases (a) and (b) are mounted eccentrically on their shafts with their centers of gravity a distance e from the shaft axis.   Determine the bearing reactions due to the unbalance which exists at a constant rotational speed ω.

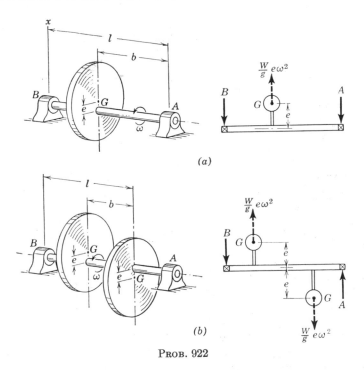

PROB. 922

Solution, Case (a)*:* The bearing reactions due to the rotational unbalance of the rotor may be computed independently of the reactions due to the static weight of the rotor.   In so far as the forces on the shaft are concerned the mass of the rotor may be assumed to be concentrated at the center of gravity as shown in the free-body diagram.   The addition of the inertia force produces dynamic equilibrium, and the principles of statics give

$[\Sigma M_A = 0]$ $Bl - \dfrac{W}{g} e\omega^2 b = 0, \qquad B = \dfrac{b}{l}\dfrac{W}{g} e\omega^2,$ *Ans.*

$[\Sigma F_x = 0]$ $A + B - \dfrac{W}{g} e\omega^2 = 0, \qquad A = \left(1 - \dfrac{b}{l}\right)\dfrac{W}{g} e\omega^2.$ *Ans.*

The addition of a weight W_0 on the opposite side of the shaft from W and at a distance e_0 from the axis will balance the rotor and produce zero bearing forces if $W_0 e_0 = We$. If the shaft with rotor and balancing weight is mounted in frictionless bearings, a static equilibrium of moments will exist about the shaft axis, and a condition of *static balance* is said to exist. Such a test for static balance will not be influenced by the location of the balancing weight with respect to its position along the shaft.

Solution, Case (b): The free-body diagram of the shaft is shown with the weights of the rotors concentrated at the centers of gravity and with the inertia forces added. Equilibrium of forces clearly requires

$$A = B = \frac{b}{l}\frac{W}{g} e\omega^2 \qquad\qquad Ans.$$

since the inertia forces in this problem constitute a couple. This couple is called a *rocking couple* and exists only when the shaft is rotating. The shaft is in static balance since a static test discloses that the sum of the moments of the eccentric weights about the shaft axis is zero. The shaft would be in *dynamic balance* if two eccentric weights were added such as to produce an equal and opposite inertia couple.

Static balance requires the equilibrium of inertia *forces*, whereas dynamic balance requires, in addition, the equilibrium of the inertia *couples*. Most balancing problems involve a combination of the two requirements and also involve inertia forces which do not all lie in a single plane containing the axis of rotation.

923. A flywheel is mounted so that its geometric axis makes an angle ϕ with the axis of rotation through its center as shown. Find the moment M (rocking couple) exerted on the shaft at a rotational speed ω. Neglect the effect of the hub and spokes and consider the flywheel to be a rotating hoop of weight W and radius r with a rim of small cross section.

Solution: The diagrams to the right of the flywheel show the edge view of the wheel and the orthogonal projection on either side. The center line only of the rim is shown. The wheel will be in dynamic equilibrium under the action of the inertia forces of all its elements and the moment M applied by the shaft. If ρ stands for the mass of the rim per unit length, the inertia force for an element $r\,d\theta$ of the rim is $\rho r\,d\theta\,r_0\omega^2$, where r_0 is the actual radius of rotation for this element. The inertia force for a symmetrically spaced element below the axis is also shown. From the edge view of the disk it is seen that only the vertical components of these inertia forces contribute to M. Each vertical component is

$$\rho r\,d\theta\,r_0\omega^2 \sin\beta = \rho r^2\omega^2 \cos\phi \sin\theta\,d\theta,$$

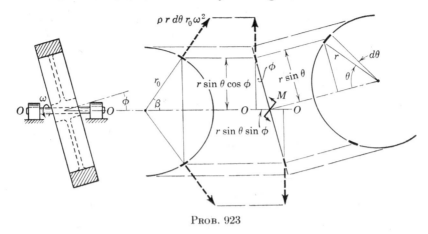

PROB. 923

and the couple produced by both of them is the force multiplied by $2r \sin \theta \sin \phi$ or

$$dM = 2\rho r^3 \omega^2 \sin \phi \cos \phi \sin^2 \theta \, d\theta.$$

Integration from $\theta = 0$ to $\theta = \pi$ includes the couples due to all pairs of elements. Thus

$$M = 2\rho r^3 \omega^2 \sin \phi \cos \phi \int_0^\pi \sin^2 \theta \, d\theta = \frac{W r^2 \omega^2 \sin 2\phi}{4g}, \qquad Ans.$$

where the weight of the rim is $W = 2\pi r \rho g$ and the integral equals $\pi/2$. If the angle ϕ is very small, the sine may be replaced by the angle, and the moment becomes

$$M = \frac{W r^2 \omega^2 \phi}{2g}.$$

PROBLEMS

924. Find the horizontal forces induced in the bearings of the vertical shaft by the unbalance of the 1 lb. knob on the wheel for a constant rotational speed of 600 rev./min.

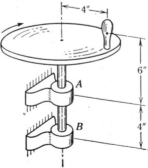

PROB. 924

925. The edge of the 322 lb. uniform steel plate is hinged about an axis inclined with the vertical as shown. The hinge A is capable of supporting force normal to AB only, whereas the hinge pin at B supports thrust as well as lateral force. If the plate is swinging with a constant angular velocity of 5 rad./sec. as its center of gravity passes through the lowest position, find the force normal to AB supported by each hinge.   *Ans.* $A = 338$ lb., $B = 198$ lb.

PROB. 925

926. The arm A of a large radial drilling machine weighs 4200 lb. and has a center of gravity at G_1. The drilling head B weighs 960 lb. with center of gravity at G_2 and is in its extreme outward position. Determine the horizontal forces exerted by the arm on the column, assuming contact at C and D with the entire weight supported at D, if the arm and head are being rotated about the vertical column at the constant rate of 2 rad./sec.

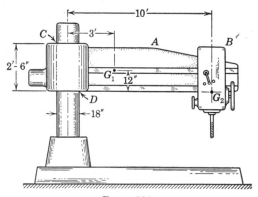

PROB. 926

927. Two circular steel disks 1 in. thick are mounted on the shaft shown A 1 in. diameter hole is drilled in each disk in the location indicated. Deter mine the magnitude of the bearing reactions due to the rotational unbalance of the system for a speed of 1000 rev./min.   *Ans.* $|A| = |B| = 14.12$ lb

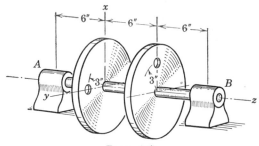

PROB. 927

928. At the instant represented the uniform 16.1 lb. arm OC has an angular velocity of 4 rad./sec. and an angular acceleration of 16 rad./sec.² about the shaft AB. Compute the total lateral forces on the bearings due to the inertia of the rod only. $Ans.$ $A = 9\sqrt{2}$ lb., $B = 3\sqrt{2}$ lb.

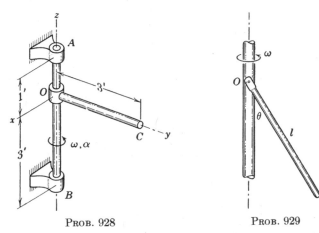

PROB. 928   PROB. 929

929. The slender rod of weight W and length l is hinged at O to the vertical shaft which rotates with a constant angular velocity ω.   Find the angle θ assumed by the bar.   (*Question:* Why does the resultant inertia force not act through the center of gravity of the bar?)

930. If the bar in Prob. 929 is welded to the shaft at O at an angle θ, find the bending moment M in the bar at O due to the angular velocity ω of the vertical shaft.

$$Ans.\quad M = \frac{Wl\sin\theta}{6}\left(\frac{2l\omega^2}{g}\cos\theta - 3\right)$$

* 931. Use the results of Sample Prob. 923 to determine the rocking couple M exerted on the shaft by the rotating circular disk of weight W and radius r whose plane makes an angle ϕ with the plane normal to the shaft through its center.

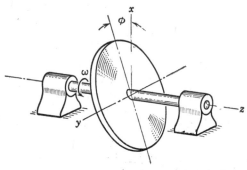

PROB. 931

* **932.** A square plate of weight W and length a on a side is mounted on a central shaft in the manner shown. Determine the rocking couple M which the plate exerts on its shaft at a rotational speed ω.   *Ans.* $M = \dfrac{Wa^2\omega^2 \sin 2\phi}{24g}$

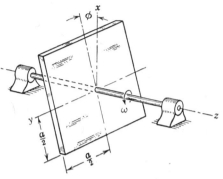

PROB. 932

* **933.** Determine the moment M exerted on the shaft by the flywheel of Sample Prob. 923 because of an angular acceleration α as the wheel starts from rest.

$$Ans. \quad M = \frac{Wr^2\alpha \sin 2\phi}{4g}$$

PART *D.*   PLANE MOTION

97. Equations of Motion. The kinematics of a body having plane motion was discussed in Part D of Chapter IX, and it was found that such motion may be considered a combination of translation and rotation. This same combination will be evident in the kinetics of plane motion.

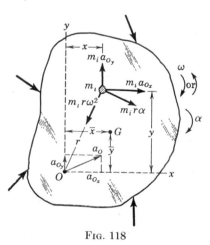

FIG. 118

Consider a body, Fig. 118, which has any general motion in the plane of the figure. This motion is determined entirely by the projections on this plane of all forces acting on the body. Let point O be any convenient reference point whose acceleration a_O is known. A set of x–y reference axes with origin at O is selected. The acceleration of any particle of mass m_i may be expressed by the principles of relative motion in terms of the acceleration components of O added vectorially to the normal and tangential acceleration components of m_i with respect to O. It follows that the resultant force on m_i may be expressed in terms of components each of which is the mass of the particle times the corresponding acceleration. These components of the resultant or effective force on m_i are shown in the free-body diagram of the particle in Fig. 118. A sum of the moments of these force components about O is now made, and the similar expressions for these moments for all particles are added together to give the sum

$$\Sigma M_O = \Sigma m_i r^2 \alpha + \Sigma m_i a_{O_x} y - \Sigma m_i a_{O_y} x.$$

When the expressions $I_O = \Sigma m_i r^2$, $m\bar{y} = \Sigma m_i y$, and $m\bar{x} = \Sigma m_i x$ are substituted, the moment sum is

$$\Sigma M_O = I_O \alpha + m\bar{y} a_{O_x} - m\bar{x} a_{O_y}. \tag{86}$$

The moment sum of the actual forces acting on the particles involves the internal forces of action and reaction between the particles and forces external to the body. The internal forces occur in pairs of equal and opposite forces, so their moment sum is zero. Thus ΣM_O is the sum of the moments about O of *all external forces* applied to the body.

Equation (86) is one of the three motion equations for plane motion. The principle of the motion of the mass center, expressed by Eqs. (74), provides the additional two equations of motion, $\Sigma F_x = m\bar{a}_x$ and $\Sigma F_y = m\bar{a}_y$, for this two-dimensional case.

In most problems of plane motion the mass center G is used as the reference point. In this case $\bar{x}$ and $\bar{y}$ in Eq. (86) are zero, I_O becomes $\bar{I}$, and the three equations of motion for a body having plane motion are

$$\Sigma F_x = m\bar{a}_x,$$

$$\Sigma F_y = m\bar{a}_y, \tag{87}$$

$$\Sigma \overline{M} = \bar{I}\alpha.$$

The first two of these equations are the scalar equivalents of the single vector equation which relates the resultant external force ΣF on a body to the mass m and translational acceleration $\bar{a}$ of the mass center. The third of Eqs. (87) represents the relation between the moment sum $\Sigma \overline{M}$ of all external forces about the center of gravity, the moment of inertia $\bar{I}$ with respect to the centroidal axis through G normal to the plane of motion, and the angular acceleration α which has the same sense as $\Sigma \overline{M}$. Thus the kinetics of plane motion is represented in terms of the *translation* of the mass center and the *rotation* about the mass center. The conclusions here are represented in Fig. 119, where the a-part of the figure represents the free-body diagram of any body having plane motion. The external forces acting may be replaced by a single resultant force ΣF through the mass center and the resulting couple $\Sigma \bar{M}$ as shown in Fig. 119b. The force and couple may be combined into the single force ΣF, Fig. 119c, which does not pass through G and is displaced a distance

$$\frac{\Sigma \bar{M}}{\Sigma F} = \frac{\bar{I}\alpha}{m\bar{a}} = \frac{\bar{k}^2\alpha}{\bar{a}}$$

from the position through G. It should be recalled that the position of the resultant force vector was not specified in the development of Eqs. (74) for the motion of the mass center but that it is now determined for plane motion.

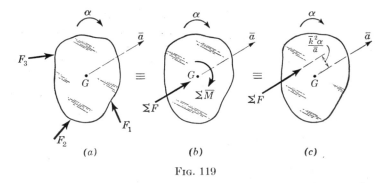

(a) (b) (c)

Fɪɢ. 119

Two important special cases arise in the interpretation of Eq. (86). The first case occurs when the reference point O has zero acceleration. The moment equation is, then, merely

$$\Sigma M_O = I_O\alpha,$$

which is the same as the third of Eqs. (83) for the rotation of a rigid body about a fixed axis through O. However, it is seen now that this moment equation derived for a fixed axis holds for a reference point which has zero acceleration but moves with constant velocity.

The second special case occurs when the acceleration of the reference point O is directed toward or away from the mass center as represented in Fig. 120a. With the x-axis oriented through G it is seen that $\bar{y} = 0$ and $a_{O_y} = 0$ in Eq. (86), and thus

$$\Sigma M_O = I_O\alpha.$$

This result may be applied to a rolling wheel, Fig. 120b, which does not slip and whose center of mass coincides with the geometric center of the wheel. Under these conditions point C, the instant center of zero velocity, has an acceleration a_C toward the center of the wheel through G, and, therefore,

$$\Sigma M_C = I_C\alpha. \tag{88}$$

In the case of an unbalanced wheel, such as shown in Fig. 120c, this moment equation about the instant center C may *not* be applied except in the two positions where G crosses the vertical center line.

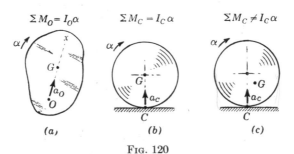

Fig. 120

D'Alembert's principle has been used as an alternative method of solution for problems in translation and rotation previously discussed. Likewise it may be used as an alternative method of representing the problem in plane motion. A glance at Fig. 119b, which shows the resultant of the external forces applied to a body moving with plane motion, shows that the fictitious state of dynamic equilibrium may be produced by adding the inertia force $m\bar{a}$ equal and opposite to ΣF and the inertia couple $\bar{I}\alpha$ equal and opposite to $\Sigma\bar{M}$. Thus the body of Fig. 121a which

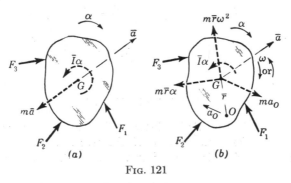

Fig. 121

has plane motion may be analyzed by the principles of statical equilibrium. It should be emphasized that the fictitious inertia force $m\bar{a}$ is added through the center of mass in the sense *opposite* to $\bar{a}$ and that the inertia couple $\bar{I}\alpha$ is added in the sense *opposite* to α. The inertia force and inertia couple may be combined into a single inertia force equal and opposite to ΣF in Fig. 119c if desired. The inertia force $m\bar{a}$ is usually best found by expressing it in terms of components. Thus, if the acceleration of a point O, Fig. 121b, is known or can be found easily, the equation

$$\bar{a} = a_O +\!\!\!+ \bar{r}\omega^2 +\!\!\!+ \bar{r}\alpha$$

may be written. The inertia force can then be expressed by its components ma_O, $m\bar{r}\omega^2$, and $m\bar{r}\alpha$ in the directions opposite to these components as shown in Fig. 121b.

As in the preceding treatments of dynamic equilibrium the fictitious inertia force and couple should be indicated by dotted lines to distinguish them from the real forces and couples applied. If the dynamic equilibrium method is employed, it is essential that the principles of equilibrium,

$$\Sigma F_x = 0, \qquad \Sigma F_y = 0, \qquad \Sigma M = 0,$$

be stated and not the principles of motion, Eqs. (87).

With either of the two methods it is equally important, as in the previous kinetics problems, to draw a careful and complete free-body diagram of the rigid body under consideration and to use literally the principles which are applicable. The directions of certain forces or accelerations may not be evident at the start of a problem, and it may be necessary to make initial assumptions whose validity will be proved or disproved when the solution is carried out. It is essential, however, that all assumptions made are consistent with the principle of action and reaction and with any kinematical requirements. Thus, if the unknown linear acceleration a of the center of a wheel rolling without slipping is assumed positive to the right, the unknown angular acceleration α must be positive in a clockwise sense in order that $a = +r\alpha$.

SAMPLE PROBLEMS

934. If the coefficient of friction between the 322 lb. wheel and the plane is 0.20, determine the acceleration a of the center G of the wheel if the force P in the cable which is wrapped around the central hub is (a) 60 lb. and (b) 100 lb.

Solution: The free-body diagram of the wheel is drawn as shown. If the wheel rolls without slipping, it must roll to the *right* because of the clockwise unbalance of moments about C. The friction force is, therefore, seen to act to the left in order that the moment equation for clockwise angular acceleration about G may be satisfied. If the wheel slips, the friction force will still be to the left to oppose this slipping. Irrespective of whether the wheel slips or not, the three equations of plane motion, Eqs. (87), hold. Thus

$[\Sigma \bar{M} = \bar{I}\alpha]$ $\qquad\qquad\qquad 4F - 2P = 3^2 \dfrac{322}{32.2} \alpha$

$[\Sigma F_x = m\bar{a}_x]$ $\qquad\qquad\qquad P - F = \dfrac{322}{32.2} a,$

$[\Sigma F_y = 0]$ $\qquad\qquad\qquad N = 322 \text{ lb.}$

PROB. 934

Case (a): Assume that the wheel does not slip with $P = 60$ lb. With this assumption $a = r\alpha$, where $r = 4$ ft., and, with these values, solution of the equations of motion just written yields

$$F = 40.8 \text{ lb.}, \qquad a = 1.92 \text{ ft./sec.}^2$$

The assumption of no slipping must now be checked. The maximum friction force which the surfaces can support is

$$F = fN = 0.20 \times 322 = 64.4 \text{ lb.},$$

which is greater than the 40.8 lb. needed to support the rolling of the wheel without slipping. Thus the assumption of no slipping was correct, and the answers are as calculated.

Since the wheel does not slip, the moment equation, Eq. (88), about the instant center C of zero velocity may be used. Thus

$[\Sigma M_C = I_C \alpha]$ $\qquad 60 \times 2 = \dfrac{322}{32.2} (3^2 + 4^2) \dfrac{a}{4}, \qquad a = 1.92 \text{ ft./sec.}^2 \qquad Ans.$

This equation may be used only if the acceleration of C is toward the mass center G, which occurs for a nonslipping wheel with center of gravity G at the geometrical center.

Case (b): Although it may be suspected now that the wheel will slip with $P = 100$ lb., for the sake of illustration let it be assumed again that the wheel rolls without slipping. With $a = 4\alpha$ and the new value of P solution of the equations of motion gives

$$F = 68.0 \text{ lb.}, \qquad a = 3.20 \text{ ft./sec.}^2$$

The assumption of no slipping is seen to be invalid since 68.0 lb. represents more friction force than can possibly be supported. Thus the wheel slips and $a \neq r\alpha$. With $P = 100$ lb. and the correct value of $F = 64.4$ lb. the equations of motion yield

$$\alpha = 0.640 \text{ rad./sec.}^2 \qquad \text{and} \qquad a = 3.56 \text{ ft./sec.}^2 \qquad Ans.$$

935. Determine the forces on the piston pin A and crank pin B of the connecting rod of the reciprocating engine for the crank position of 60 deg. and for a constant crank speed of 1500 rev./min. clockwise. The connecting rod weighs 6 lb. with center of gravity at G and has a centroidal radius of gyration of $\bar{k} = 4.20$ in. The pressure of the expanding gases on the 5 lb. piston at this position is 100 lb./in.^{2}

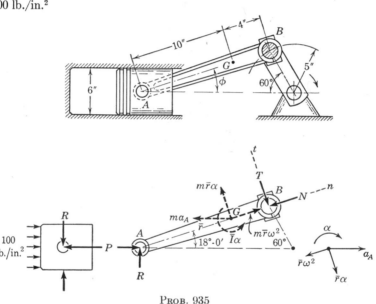

Prob. 935

Solution: The forces acting on the connecting rod will depend on its acceleration. In Sample Prob. 740 for the same position of this same connecting rod the acceleration of A was found to be $a_A = 3320$ ft./sec.^{2} to the right, and the angular acceleration of the rod was found to be $\alpha = 7750$ rad./sec.^{2} clockwise. The angular velocity of the connecting rod was determined in Prob. 708 and is $\omega = 29.5$ rad./sec. counterclockwise. In addition the angle ϕ may be scaled from the graphical solutions of these sample problems or calculated by the law of sines which gives

$$\phi = \sin^{-1}\left(\tfrac{5}{14}\sin 60°\right) = \sin^{-1} 0.309 = 18° \, 0'.$$

One of the forces acting on the rod is determined by the motion of the piston. From the free-body diagram of the piston the horizontal component of the piston-pin force is found from the equation

$$[\Sigma F = ma] \qquad 100 \times \frac{\pi \times 6^2}{4} - P = \frac{5}{32.2} \times 3320, \qquad P = 2310 \text{ lb.}$$

The free-body diagram of the connecting rod is drawn, and the forces at A and B are represented by their components. The weight of the rod is negligible in this problem compared with the remaining forces and is therefore omitted. Dynamic equilibrium is created by adding the inertia force $m\bar{a}$ through G opposite to $\bar{a}$ and the inertia couple $\bar{I}\alpha$ opposite to α. The acceleration $\bar{a}$ is most easily expressed in terms of the acceleration of A and is

$$\bar{a} = a_A \to\!\!\!\!\to \bar{r}\omega^2 \to\!\!\!\!\to \bar{r}\alpha.$$

These components are shown at the extreme right of the figure. The corresponding inertia force components are

$$ma_A = \frac{6}{32.2} \times 3320 = 619 \text{ lb.,}$$

$$m\bar{r}\omega^2 = \frac{6}{32.2}\frac{10}{12} \times (29.5)^2 = 135.2 \text{ lb.,}$$

$$m\bar{r}\alpha = \frac{6}{32.2}\frac{10}{12} \times 7750 = 1204 \text{ lb.,}$$

and are applied in the directions *opposite* to the respective accelerations. The inertia couple is

$$\bar{I}\alpha = \frac{6}{32.2}\left(\frac{4.20}{12}\right)^2 \times 7750 = 177 \text{ lb. ft.}$$

and is applied counterclockwise since the angular acceleration is clockwise.

The remaining three unknown forces on the rod are now found by applying the principles of equilibrium. Thus

$$[\Sigma M_B = 0] \quad R \times 14 \cos 18° - 2310 \times 5 \sin 60° + 619 \times 4 \sin 18° + 1204 \times 4$$
$$- 177 \times 12 = 0,$$

$$R = 492 \text{ lb.;}$$

$$[\Sigma F_n = 0] \quad N - 135.2 + 619 \cos 18° - 2310 \cos 18° - 492 \sin 18° = 0,$$

$$N = 1895 \text{ lb.;}$$

$$[\Sigma F_t = 0] \quad T - 1204 - 619 \sin 18° - 492 \cos 18° + 2310 \sin 18° = 0,$$

$$T = 1149 \text{ lb.}$$

The total forces on the two pins are therefore

$$A = \sqrt{(2310)^2 + (492)^2} = 2360 \text{ lb.,} \qquad \qquad Ans.$$

$$B = \sqrt{(1895)^2 + (1149)^2} = 2220 \text{ lb.} \qquad \qquad Ans.$$

Analysis by dynamic equilibrium has the distinct advantage in this problem of allowing a moment summation to be formed about any convenient moment center, thus avoiding a simultaneous solution of the equations. Analysis of the rod by direct use of the three equations of motion, Eqs. (87), will normally lead to a simultaneous solution.

PROBLEMS

936. Find the acceleration a of the center of the homogeneous cylinder if it rolls without slipping down the incline. Also find the minimum coefficient of friction f to prevent slipping.

$$Ans. \quad a = \frac{2}{3} g \sin \theta, f = \frac{\tan \theta}{3}$$

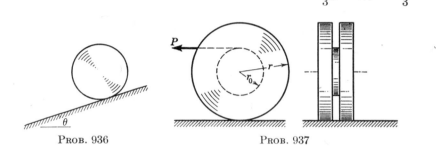

PROB. 936   PROB. 937

937. What should be the radius r_0 of the small circular groove in order that there be no friction force acting between the wheel and the surface irrespective of the magnitude of the horizontal force P applied to the cord? The centroidal radius of gyration of the wheel is $\bar{k}$.

938. The section of a large water main shown has a diameter of 6 ft. and a weight of 5200 lb. The tube material has a density of 150 lb./ft.^{3} and a breaking strength in tension of about 300 lb./in.^{2} A stick of wood which is used to prevent the tube from moving is inadvertently removed, and the tube begins to roll down a long 3 per cent grade on a straight paved road. Determine the distance s down the road at which the tube flies apart because of excessive centrifugal stress. (See Prob. 915 and base the calculation on the angular velocity of the tube.)   *Ans.* $s = 1.820$ mi.

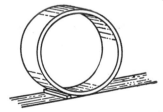

PROB. 938

939. Determine the acceleration a of the center of a solid homogeneous cylinder released on a plane inclined at an angle of 60 deg. with the horizontal if the coefficient of friction is 0.30. (From the results of Prob. 936 it may be concluded that the cylinder slips as it rolls.)

940. The circular cylinder with a cord wrapped around its periphery and fastened as shown is released on the incline. If the coefficient of friction f is less than $\frac{1}{2} \tan \theta$, find the acceleration a of the center of the cylinder.

$Ans.$ $a = \frac{2}{3}(\sin \theta - 2f \cos \theta)g$

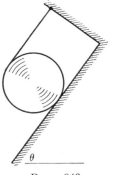

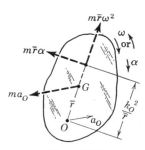

PROB. 940   PROB. 941

941. Show that a body having plane motion may be put in dynamic equilibrium by adding the three inertia forces shown, where a_O is the acceleration of some convenient point O in the body.

942. Determine the acceleration a of the center G of the attached wheels for the system shown. Each cable is wrapped securely around its respective wheel.

$Ans.$ $a = 3.39$ ft./sec.²

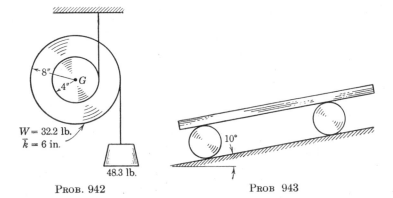

PROB. 942   PROB 943

943. The 40 lb. plank is placed on the two cylindrical rollers, each weighing 20 lb., and is then released from rest. Determine the acceleration a of the plank if no slipping occurs.

944. The solid cylinder weighs 16.1 lb. and rolls without slipping down the circular guide, starting from the rest position shown. Determine the normal reaction N under the cylinder as it passes the bottom position. (See Prob. 763.)

Ans. $N = 18.98$ lb.

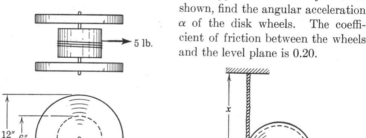

PROB. 944   PROB. 945

945. A 25 lb. roll of heavy wrapping paper in the form of a solid cylinder with a diameter of 12 in. is resting on a horizontal table top. If a horizontal force of 10 lb. is applied evenly to the paper as shown, determine the linear acceleration a of the center of the roll and the angular acceleration α of the roll. The coefficient of friction between the paper and the table is 0.20.

Ans. $a = 6.44$ ft./sec.^{2}, $\alpha = 25.8$ rad./sec.^{2}

946. Each of the solid circular disk wheels weighs 10 lb., and the inner solid cylinder weighs 15 lb. The disks and cylinder are mounted on the small central shaft independently of one another with negligible friction in their bearings. If a horizontal 5 lb. force is applied to a cord wrapped around the cylinder as shown, find the angular acceleration α of the disk wheels. The coefficient of friction between the wheels and the level plane is 0.20.

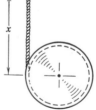

PROB. 946   PROB. 947

947. A long uniform cable of length L and weight W is wrapped at a constant radius around a spool of negligible weight. One end of the cable is fixed as shown, and the spool is released from rest with the distance x essentially zero. Show that the acceleration of the center of the spool is constant and find the velocity v of the center of the spool when all the cable has unwound.

Ans. $v = \sqrt{gL}$

948. A homogeneous solid sphere rolls without slipping down the trough shown. Find the acceleration a of the center of the sphere and the minimum coefficient of friction f which the surfaces could have before slipping would occur for given values of θ and β.

$$Ans. \quad a = \frac{g \sin \theta}{1 + \frac{2}{5} \sec^2 \beta}, \ f = \frac{\tan \theta}{\sec \beta + \frac{5}{2} \cos \beta}$$

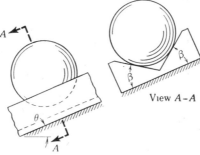

View A–A

PROB. 948

949. Determine the forces on the piston and crank pins for the connecting rod of Sample Prob. 935 when the piston is at the extreme right end of its stroke (bottom dead center). At this position the net gas pressure on the piston is small and may be neglected. A constant crank speed of 1500 rev./min. is assumed.

950. The uniform link weighs 20 lb. and is initially at rest in the vertical position before the 10 lb. force is applied as shown. Neglect friction in the bearing of the light guide roller and compute the linear acceleration a of the center of the roller and the angular acceleration α of the bar an instant after the 10 lb. force is applied.

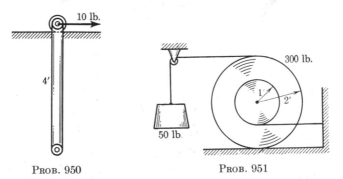

PROB. 950

PROB. 951

951. Determine the acceleration a of the 50 lb. weight if the coefficient of friction between the 300 lb. wheel and the plane is 0.20. The radius of gyration of the wheel about its center is 1.5 ft., and the cables are wrapped around the wheel and its integral hub. *Ans.* $a = 6.10$ ft./sec.^{2}

952. A large steel roller bearing has the dimensions shown. The outer race A is fixed and the inner race B is turned by the action of friction between it and the shaft on which it is fitted. Find the value of this frictional torque M applied to the inner race necessary to accelerate the bearing to an operating speed of 3000 rev./min. in 2 sec. Assume that the rollers do not slip.

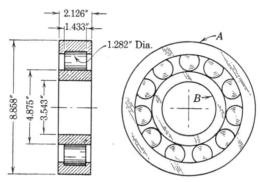

2.126″
1.433″
1.282″ Dia.
—A
B→
8.858″
4.875″
3.543″

PROB. 952

953. The truck, initially at rest with a solid cylindrical roll of paper in the position shown, moves forward with a uniform acceleration a. Find the distance s which the truck goes before the paper rolls off the edge of its horizontal bed. Friction is sufficient to prevent slipping.

$$Ans. \quad s = \frac{3d}{2}$$

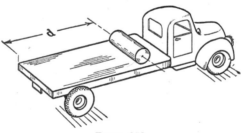

d

PROB. 953

954. Determine the forces on the piston and crank pins for the connecting rod of Sample Prob. 935 when the crank angle is 90 deg. instead of 60 deg. Take the gas pressure on the piston at this position to be 80 lb./in.²

955. The uniform 16.1 lb. link AB is released from rest in the position shown. Determine the reactions at A and B as the link begins to slide if friction in the guides is negligible.

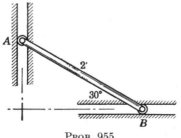

A
2′
30°
B

PROB. 955

Ans. $A = 5.2$ lb., $B = 7.1$ lb.

956. The circular disk has a net weight of 20 lb. after the 6 in. diameter hole is cut out of it. If the disk is released from rest on a horizontal surface in the position shown, find the momentary angular acceleration α of the disk. The coefficient of friction is 0.10.   *Ans.* $\alpha = 0.708$ rad./sec.²

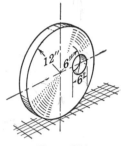

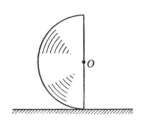

PROB. 956   PROB. 957

* **957.** A solid semicylinder is released from rest in the position shown. Determine the initial acceleration a of the geometrical center O and the minimum coefficient of friction f to prevent initial slipping.

Ans. $a = \dfrac{8g}{9\pi} = 9.11$ ft./sec.², $f = 0.321$

* **958.** It was proved in Prob. 511 of *Part I* that, if the common coefficient of friction between all surfaces is less than 0.268, the cylinders shown will collapse and slipping will occur initially under the upper cylinder and not under the lower cylinders. If the common coefficient of friction for all surfaces is 0.20, determine the linear acceleration a_1 of the upper cylinder and the linear acceleration a_2 of the centers of the lower cylinders when released from rest in the position shown.

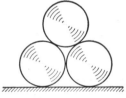

PROB. 958

Ans. $a_1 = 0.794$ ft./sec.², $a_2 = 1.375$ ft./sec.²

* **959.** If the axis of the roll of paper in Prob. 953 makes an angle θ with the rear axle of the truck, find the angular acceleration α of the roll if its radius is r and if the truck has an acceleration a. Assume no slipping.   *Ans.* $\alpha = \dfrac{2a \cos \theta}{3r}$

* **960.** Wheels A and B are identical 50 lb. solid circular disks with mass centers at G_1 and G_2. They are connected by the uniform 15 lb. rod G_1C whose end C is 2 in. off center. If wheel A is given a constant velocity of 6 ft./sec. to the left, find

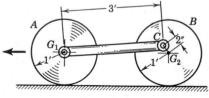

PROB. 960

the friction force F exerted by the plane on wheel B at the instant point C crosses the horizontal line $G_1 G_2$ between G_1 and G_2. The surfaces are sufficiently rough to prevent slipping. (*Hint:* The angular acceleration of CG_1, although very small, is not zero in the horizontal position.)   *Ans.* $F = 3.69$ lb.

CHAPTER XII

Work and Energy

98. General. The force-mass-acceleration equations of motion developed in the previous chapter are sufficient to solve most of the usual problems in dynamics. These equations are particularly useful when the instantaneous relationship between force and acceleration is desired. Additional kinematical equations are needed if the problem involves changes in motion due to the action of forces during an interval of time. For problems where forces act during intervals which are given in terms of linear or angular displacement the method of work and energy is particularly useful. This method effectively combines the equations of motion and the necessary kinematical relations.

99. Work. The concept of work was defined in Chapter VIII of *Part I* where virtual or assumed movements were considered in estab-

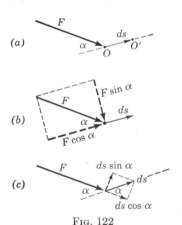

FIG. 122

lishing equilibrium configurations. In the present chapter real and finite displacements will be considered, but the definition of work remains unchanged. The *work* done by a force F during the movement ds of its point of application O, Fig. 122a, is

$$dU = F \, ds \cos \alpha.$$

This definition may be viewed either as the force component $F \cos \alpha$ in the direction of the displacement times the displacement, Fig. 122b, or as the force times the displacement component $ds \cos \alpha$ in the direction of the force, Fig. 122c.

With this definition it is seen that the component of the force at right angles to the displacement does no work. The work done by the force is positive when the working component $F \cos \alpha$ has the same sense as the displacement and negative when in the opposite sense. Work is a scalar quantity with the dimensions of [distance] × [force]. Work and moment are dimensionally the same, and in order to distinguish between them work may be expressed as

foot pounds (ft. lb.) and moment as pound feet (lb. ft.). The fundamental difference between work and moment is that work is a scalar
involving the product of force and distance both measured in the same
direction, whereas moment is a vector
and is the product of force and distance
measured at right angles to the force.

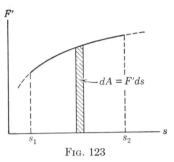

During a finite movement the work
done by the force is

$$U = \int F \cos \alpha \, ds.$$

This expression can be integrated if the
relation between F and s and between
$\cos \alpha$ and s is known.

FIG. 123

Experimental data often enable a graph to be constructed of the
working component $F' = F \cos \alpha$ and the displacement s of its point of
application as schematically represented in Fig. 123. The differential
area dA under the curve during the movement ds is the work done by
F' during that interval, and the net or total work done between any two
displacements s_1 and s_2 is the area under the curve between these limits.

In the case of an elastic spring of stiffness k and negligible weight the
force F supported by the spring at any deformation x, either compression or extension, is $F = kx$. Thus the work done on a spring during a
compression or extension from its undeformed position
or the work done by the spring during a relief of its
compression or extension is

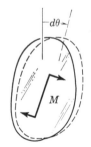

$$\int F \, dx = \int_0^x kx \, dx = \tfrac{1}{2}kx^2$$

which represents the triangular area * under the graph
of $F = kx$.

The work done by a couple M acting on a body,
Fig. 124, during a rotation $d\theta$ of the body in the plane
of the couple is $dU = M \, d\theta$. This expression is easily
obtained by representing the couple by two forces and evaluating the
work done by each force during the rotation $d\theta$. The total work
done by M during a finite angular displacement θ is

FIG. 124

$$U = \int M \, d\theta.$$

---

* This relation is represented in Fig. 79 on p. 282 of *Part I* for the case of compression.

The angle θ is expressed in radian measure, and work is positive when the rotation is in the sense of the couple and negative when in the sense opposite to the couple. A couple does no work during a movement which is entirely one of translation since the angular displacement is zero. In the event that the body rotates in a plane other than the plane of the couple the work done equals the magnitude of the couple vector times the magnitude of the rotation vector multiplied by the cosine of the angle between the vectors.

When a body slides on a fixed surface, the work done by the friction force acting on the body is negative since the friction force acts in the direction opposite to the displacement. In the case of a wheel which rolls on a fixed surface without slipping, a static friction force acts and does no work since the point of application does not slip. If the wheel slips as it rolls, kinetic friction is generated and negative work is done on the wheel.

The total work done by any system of forces and couples acting on a body during any movement is the algebraic sum of the works done by each force and couple considered separately.

100. Kinetic Energy of a Particle. Consider the motion of a particle of mass m, Fig. 125, subjected to the action of a system of forces whose resultant is F. The work done on m during a displacement ds is done by the tangential component only of F and is

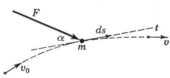

FIG. 125

$$dU = F \cos \alpha \, ds.$$

From the equation of motion in the tangential direction, $F \cos \alpha = ma_t$, the work may be expressed as

$$dU = ma_t \, ds.$$

But $a_t \, ds = v \, dv$, so that

$$dU = mv \, dv.$$

The net work done on m during an interval of its motion for which the velocity changes from v_0 to v is

$$\Delta U = \int dU = \int_{v_0}^{v} mv \, dv = \tfrac{1}{2}mv^2 - \tfrac{1}{2}mv_0{}^2.$$

The term $\tfrac{1}{2}mv^2$ is the work done in bringing the particle from rest to a velocity v and is known as the *kinetic energy* T of the particle. Hence the definition

$$T = \tfrac{1}{2}mv^2. \tag{89}$$

The net work done on m in changing its velocity from v_0 to v, therefore, equals the *change* $T - T_0$ in its kinetic energy, or

$$\Delta U = \Delta T. \tag{90}$$

Equation (90) is known as the *work-energy equation* and always involves the *change* in kinetic energy as a result of the net work done during the corresponding interval of motion.

If a particle moving with a velocity v is allowed to act on some body and is brought to rest during this action, the loss of its kinetic energy equals the work done on the other body by the contact force. Thus kinetic energy represents the capacity to do work by reason of acquired velocity.

Kinetic energy is a scalar quantity which depends only on the mass and the magnitude of the velocity. Since the velocity v is squared, kinetic energy is always a positive quantity. The units of kinetic energy are the same as those of work, as may be seen from the dimensional equation

$$[\tfrac{1}{2}mv^2] = [FL^{-1}T^2][LT^{-1}]^2 = [LF].$$

When a body is subjected to a system of forces the resultant of which acts through the center of mass, the body may be treated as a particle as was seen in Chapter XI. Thus the work-energy equation as developed for a particle may be applied to such a body.

When two or more particles (or translating bodies considered as particles) are joined together by connections which are frictionless and incapable of elastic deformation, the forces in the connections occur in pairs of equal and opposite forces, and the points of application of these forces necessarily have identical movements. Hence, the net work done by these internal forces is zero during any movement of the system. Thus Eq. (90) is applicable to the *entire system*, where ΔU is the total or net work done on the system by *external* forces and ΔT is the change in the total kinetic energy of the system. The total kinetic energy is the algebraic sum of the kinetic energies of all elements of the system.

In Chapter VIII on virtual work it was seen that the method of work has a basic advantage over the force and moment summation method for solving the equilibrium problem for a system of multi-connected bodies. The same advantage exists in the method of work and energy for the dynamics of interconnected bodies since again consideration of internal forces is not necessary.

Application of the work-energy method calls for an isolation of the body or system under consideration. For a single body a *free-body diagram* showing all externally applied forces should be drawn. For a system of connected bodies without springs an *active-force diagram* which shows only those external forces which do work (active forces) on the system may be drawn.

SAMPLE PROBLEMS

961. Determine the velocity v of the 100 lb. crate when it reaches the bottom of the chute if it is given an initial velocity of 15 ft./sec. down the chute at A. The coefficient of friction is 0.30.

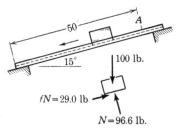

PROB. 961

Solution: The free-body diagram of the crate is drawn and includes the normal and friction forces calculated in the usual manner. The work done by the component of the weight down the plane is positive, whereas that done by the friction force is negative. The total or net work done during the interval is, then,

$$\Delta U = (100 \sin 15° - 29.0)50 = -155 \text{ ft. lb.}$$

The change in kinetic energy is

$$\Delta T = \frac{1}{2}\frac{100}{32.2}(v^2 - 225).$$

The work-energy equation gives

$$[\Delta U = \Delta T] \qquad\qquad -155 = \frac{1}{2}\frac{100}{32.2}(v^2 - 225),$$

$$v^2 = 125, \qquad v = 11.2 \text{ ft./sec.} \qquad\qquad Ans.$$

962. In the system shown the weights of the cable and pulleys and the friction in the pulley bearings are negligible. Determine the velocity v of the 2000 lb. weight after it has moved 10 ft. from the rest position from which the system was released.

Solution: The only external forces which do work on the entire system are the weights of the two bodies. With these two forces indicated the sketch may be used as the active-force diagram.

The 10 ft. displacement of the 2000 lb. weight is clearly up, whereas that of the 1500 lb. weight is 20 ft. down.   Also the velocity of the 1500 lb. weight is

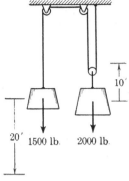

PROB. 962

twice that of the 2000 lb. weight.   The work-energy equation for the system is applied and gives

$$[\Delta U = \Delta T] \quad -2000 \times 10 + 1500 \times 20 = \frac{1}{2}\frac{2000}{32.2}(v^2 - 0) + \frac{1}{2}\frac{1500}{32.2}(4v^2 - 0),$$

$$v = 8.97 \text{ ft./sec.} \qquad Ans.$$

963. The 20 lb. slider starts from rest at A with no force in the attached spring and moves in the smooth horizontal slot under the action of a constant 50 lb. force in the cable.   If the modulus of the spring is 5 lb./ft., determine the velocity v of the block as it passes the position B.

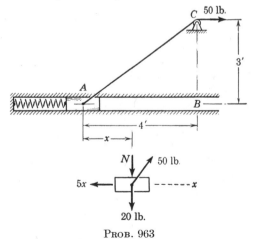

PROB. 963

Solution: It will be assumed that the stiffness of the spring is small enough to allow the block to reach position B.   The free-body diagram of the block is shown. The work done on the block by the spring force during the movement from A to B is negative and is

$$-\tfrac{1}{2}kx^2 = -\tfrac{1}{2} \times 5 \times 4^2 = -40 \text{ ft. lb.}$$

The work done by the variable horizontal component of the 50 lb. tension could be obtained by integration over the interval but is more simply computed from the fact that point C, at which the constant 50 lb. force is applied to the cable over the guide pulley, moves through a distance of $\sqrt{4^2 + 3^2} - 3 = 2$ ft. Thus the work done is $50 \times 2 = 100$ ft. lb., and the work-energy equation gives

$$[\Delta U = \Delta T] \qquad -40 + 100 = \frac{1}{2}\frac{20}{32.2}(v^2 - 0), \qquad v = 13.90 \text{ ft./sec.} \qquad Ans.$$

PROBLEMS

964. The pendulum is released from rest in the position shown. Determine its velocity as it passes the bottom position.

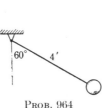

PROB. 964   PROB. 965

965. A small 2 oz. bead starts from rest at A and slides freely in the vertical plane along the fixed wire under the action of the constant 4 oz. horizontal force. Find the velocity v of the bead as it hits the stop at B. *Ans.* $v = 13.90$ ft./sec.

966. A car is traveling at 30 mi./hr. down a 5 per cent grade when the brakes on all four wheels lock. If the kinetic coefficient of friction between the tires and the road is 0.70, find the distance s which the car skids in coming to a stop.
Ans. $s = 46.3$ ft.

967. The skid marks left by all four wheels of a car on a level road are measured by a police officer to be 65 ft. in length. The driver of the car claims that he was not exceeding the speed limit of 50 mi./hr. before he applied the brakes. Furthermore the driver released the brakes before coming to a stop and was observed to continue at the speed of 20 mi./hr. after his skid. From experience with the road conditions prevailing the coefficient of kinetic friction is known to be at least 0.8. If the officer were familiar with the laws of mechanics, could he conclude that the driver was guilty of speeding?

968. Find the total energy E absorbed (negative work) by the brakes of a 1200 ton passenger train in bringing it to a stop from a velocity of 60 mi./hr. in a distance of 2 mi. down a 1 per cent grade. *Ans.* $E = 542 \times 10^6$ ft. lb.

969. The plunger weighs 40 lb. and is released from rest in the position shown. If the spring is deflected a maximum of ½ in. by the falling plunger, find the modulus k of the spring.

970. A 10 lb. block is released from rest on the incline with no force in the spring. Determine the maximum distance x which the block slides if the stiffness of the spring is 4 lb./ft. and the coefficient of friction is 0.20.

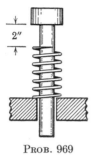

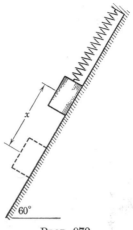

PROB. 969   PROB. 970

971. The light pulley around which the cable passes has negligible friction in its bearing. Determine the velocity v of the 50 lb. weight after it has moved 10 ft. from rest under the action of the constant 30 lb. tension.

Ans. $v = 16.82$ ft./sec.

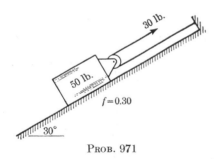

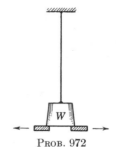

PROB. 971   PROB. 972

972. The weight W is attached to an elastic cable, and the lower supports are raised slightly until the cable tension and elongation are zero. If the supports are suddenly removed, find the maximum tension T in the cable.

973. The 10 lb. cylindrical plunger is accurately machined to give a slight force fit in the fixed horizontal tube shown in section. A constant force of 150 lb. is required to accelerate the plunger from rest to a velocity of 50 ft./sec. in a distance of 4 ft. If the coefficient of friction between the plunger and the tube is 0.30, find the average normal pressure p between the parts due to the press fit.

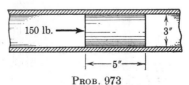

PROB. 973

974. Determine the velocity v of the 32.2 lb. freely sliding block of Prob. 788, shown again here, after it has moved 4 ft. from rest under the action of the constant force $P = 35$ lb.   The light cables are wrapped securely around the integral pulley of negligible weight whose diameters are in the ratio of 2:1.   Friction in the pulley bearing is negligible.   *Ans.* $v = 4.73$ ft./sec.

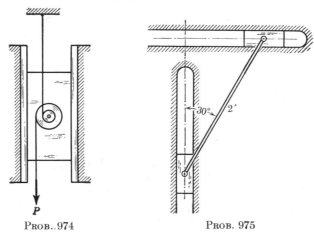

PROB. 974   PROB. 975

975. The two sliders weigh 8 lb. each, are connected by a light, rigid link, and move with negligible friction in their guides.   If the sliders are released from rest in the position shown, find the velocity v of the upper one as it crosses the center line of the vertical slot.

976. The 4 lb. collar slides freely on the fixed vertical shaft and is released from rest in the position at $x = 0$, for which the spring is compressed 2 in.   Determine the velocity v of the collar when $x = 12$ in.   *Ans.* $v = 4.77$ ft./sec.

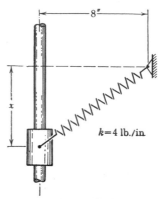

PROB. 976

977. Determine the net work done on the slider of Sample Prob. 963 by direct integration of ΣF_x over the 4 ft. displacement.

978. The 20 lb. slider is fitted in its horizontal guide with a small amount of clearance, and the coefficient of friction is 0.20. If the slider starts from rest in the position shown and moves under the action of the 50 lb. force, constant in magnitude and direction, find the maximum velocity v which is attained.

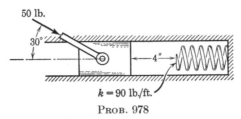

PROB. 978

979. The 10 lb. plunger is released from rest in the position shown, where the right-hand spring is compressed 3 in. Determine the maximum velocity v reached by the plunger. Friction in the guide is negligible.

Ans. $v = 9.22$ ft./sec.

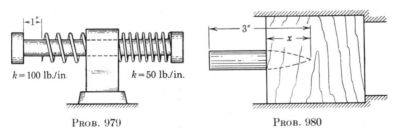

PROB. 979   PROB. 980

980. In tests on the resistance of a certain material to penetration the sharp-pointed 2 oz. projectile shown is fired at the specimen with a velocity of 500 ft./sec. Prediction of penetration depth x is based on the assumption that the resistance R offered by the material to the projectile depends directly on the projectile surface area embedded in the specimen. This area is proportional to x^2, so that $R = kx^2$ is written. If tests indicate an average penetration of 1.25 in., determine k.

981. If the pulley of Prob. 971 seizes so that it cannot turn and if the coefficient of friction between the cable and the seized pulley is 0.30, find the energy E lost by the work of friction between the cable and the pulley while the block moves 10 ft.

Ans. $E = 183$ ft. lb.

982. The system is released from rest with $x = 0$. Determine the velocity v of the center weight when $x = 3$ ft. and the maximum displacement x of the center weight.

Ans. $v = 5.14$ ft./sec., $x = 5.33$ ft.

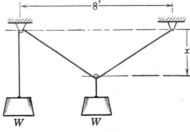

PROB. 982

983. Two identical beads are released from rest at A and slide on the fixed wires. (*a*) If friction is negligible, prove that the velocity of the beads at any elevation is independent of the path. (*b*) If friction is present and each bead has a coefficient of friction of $\frac{1}{5}$, would you expect the upper or lower path to result in the greater velocity at B? (*Hint:* Verify your intuitive answer to part (*b*) by a comparison of the results of Prob. 864 with those worked out for the straight wire, using the numerical values of Prob. 864.)

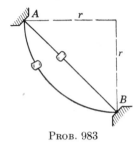

PROB. 983   PROB. 984

984. The chain of Prob. 800, shown again here, is released from rest on the smooth surface in the position shown. Find the velocity v of the chain as the last link leaves the edge. Compare the work-energy solution with solution by the method of the previous chapter.

$$Ans. \quad v = \sqrt{gL\left(1 - \frac{b^2}{L^2}\right)}$$

985. If the surface upon which the chain in Prob. 984 slides is not smooth and if it starts from rest with a sufficient number of links hanging over the edge to barely initiate motion, determine the velocity v of the chain as the last link leaves the edge. The coefficient of friction is f. Neglect friction at the edge.

* **986.** Find the velocity v of the slider in Sample Prob. 963 as it passes B if friction in the guide is not negligible and the coefficient of friction is 0.30.

$$Ans. \quad v = 10.55 \text{ ft./sec.}$$

* **987.** Determine the distance x from the position where the 10 lb. block of Prob. 970 is released from rest to the position where it finally stops. Assume both the static and kinetic coefficients of friction to be 0.20. *Ans.* $x = 2.00$ ft.

* **988.** The 100 lb. cylindrical plunger is accurately machined so that a thin film of light oil effects nearly perfect air seal and at the same time offers negligible frictional resistance to motion in the vertical tube with sealed lower end. If the plunger is released from rest in the position shown, where the air pressure inside the tube is equal to the atmospheric pressure of 14.7 lb./in.², find the maximum velocity v attained by the plunger. The absolute pressure in the tube varies inversely as the volume, and the pressure of the atmosphere on the top of the plunger is essentially constant. *Ans.* $v = 2.89$ ft./sec.

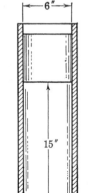

PROB. 988

* 989. The piston and ram of the steam hammer weigh 400 lb. The absolute pressure p acting on the piston is constant at 200 lb./in.^{2} for the first 4 in. of the stroke beginning at the top, for which $x = 2$ in. The pressure p then varies according to $pV = $ constant, where V is the total volume of the cylinder above the piston, for the remaining 10 in. of the 14 in. stroke. Determine the velocity v of impact of the ram with the work at the bottom of the stroke. The atmospheric pressure of 14.7 lb./in.^{2} acts on the lower side of the piston.

Ans. $v = 52.5$ ft./sec.

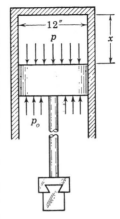

PROB. 989

101. Work-Energy in Plane Motion. It was shown in the previous article that the work-energy equation, $\Delta U = \Delta T$, may be applied to a system of joined particles whose internal connections are without friction and are incapable of absorbing energy (no internal springs). The term ΔU is the net work done on the system by all *external* active forces, and ΔT is the change in the total kinetic energy of the system. This principle holds for any rigid body or system of rigid bodies since a rigid body may be considered as a composite of joined particles whose connections meet the stated requirements. The principle $\Delta U = \Delta T$ does *not* hold for a deformable body since the particles of such a body are not rigidly connected, and some of the external work done will be absorbed in the internal "springs."

Before the principle of work and energy can be applied to rigid bodies it is necessary to know the expressions for the kinetic energy T of a rigid body having any one of the three types of plane motion. These expressions are derived as follows:

Translation: The translating body of mass m in Fig. 126a has a velocity v. The kinetic energy of any particle of mass m_i is $\frac{1}{2}m_i v^2$, and the kinetic energy of the entire body is

$$T = \Sigma \tfrac{1}{2}m_i v^2 = \tfrac{1}{2}v^2 \Sigma m_i,$$

or
$$T = \tfrac{1}{2}mv^2. \tag{91}$$

Rotation: The body in Fig. 126b is rotating about a fixed axis through O with an angular velocity ω. The linear velocity of any particle of mass m_i is $r\omega$, and the kinetic energy of this particle is $\frac{1}{2}m_i(r\omega)^2$. The kinetic energy of the entire rotating body is the sum of the kinetic energies of all its particles and is

$$T = \Sigma \tfrac{1}{2}m_i r^2 \omega^2 = \tfrac{1}{2}\omega^2 \Sigma m_i r^2,$$

or
$$T = \tfrac{1}{2}I_O \omega^2. \tag{92}$$

The term I_O is the moment of inertia about the fixed axis of rotation.
The similarity between the expressions for kinetic energy of rotation
and translation should be noted. Moment of inertia and angular velocity replace mass and linear velocity, respectively. The reader may
verify easily that the dimensions of both expressions are identical.

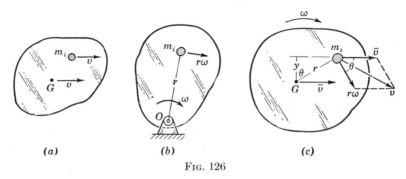

(a)   (b)   (c)

$$\text{F}_{\text{IG}}. \ 126$$

Plane Motion: The body in Fig. 126c has any plane motion, and, at
the instant considered, the velocity of its mass center G is $\bar{v}$ and the
angular velocity of the body is ω. The velocity v of any particle is conveniently expressed in terms of $\bar{v}$ and the velocity $r\omega$ of the particle relative to G as shown. The square of the particle velocity is obtained by
the law of cosines and is

$$v^2 = \bar{v}^2 + r^2\omega^2 + 2\bar{v}r\omega \cos \theta.$$

The kinetic energy of the representative particle of mass m_i is $\frac{1}{2}m_i v^2$,
and that for the entire body is

$$T = \Sigma\tfrac{1}{2}m_i\bar{v}^2 + \Sigma\tfrac{1}{2}m_i r^2\omega^2 + \Sigma(\tfrac{1}{2}m_i)(2\bar{v}r\omega \cos \theta),$$

$$= \tfrac{1}{2}\bar{v}^2\Sigma m_i + \tfrac{1}{2}\omega^2\Sigma m_i r^2 + \bar{v}\omega\Sigma m_i y.$$

The last summation is zero since the y-coordinate to the center of gravity
is zero, and the second summation is merely the moment of inertia $\bar{I}$
about the center of gravity G. Thus the kinetic energy for any rigid
body having plane motion is

$$T = \tfrac{1}{2}m\bar{v}^2 + \tfrac{1}{2}\bar{I}\omega^2. \tag{93}$$

This expression clearly shows the separate contribution to the total
kinetic energy due to the translational velocity of the mass center and
the rotational velocity about the mass center.

The kinetic energy of plane motion may be expressed also in terms
of the rotational velocity about the instant center C of zero velocity.

Since C momentarily has zero velocity, the proof for Eq. (92) holds equally well for this point. Thus the kinetic energy of plane motion may be expressed by

$$T = \tfrac{1}{2}I_C\omega^2 \tag{94}$$

in place of Eq. (93).

The total kinetic energy T of a system of bodies having plane motion is the sum of the kinetic energies of all its parts calculated by Eqs. (91), (92), and (93) or (94) for the particular kinds of motion involved. When the work-energy principle $\Delta U = \Delta T$ is applied to such a system, ΔT is the change in the *total* kinetic energy of the system and ΔU is the net work done by *all* active forces which are applied *externally* to the system during the interval involved.

SAMPLE PROBLEMS

990. Determine the velocity v of the center of the circular disk after it has rolled a distance s down the incline from rest. Friction is sufficient to prevent slipping.

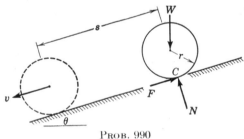

PROB. 990

Solution: Of the three forces shown on the free-body diagram of the disk only the weight does work. The friction force does no work if the wheel does not slip.

Thus
$$\Delta U = Ws \sin \theta,$$

$$\Delta T = \frac{1}{2}\frac{W}{g}v^2 + \frac{1}{2}\left(\frac{1}{2}\frac{W}{g}r^2\right)\omega^2 = \frac{3}{4}\frac{W}{g}v^2.$$

The work-energy equation is

$[\Delta U = \Delta T]$ $\qquad Ws \sin \theta = \dfrac{3}{4}\dfrac{W}{g}v^2, \qquad v = \sqrt{\dfrac{4gs \sin \theta}{3}}.$ $\qquad$ *Ans.*

The kinetic energy may also be expressed by

$$\frac{1}{2}I_C\omega^2 = \frac{1}{2}\left(\frac{1}{2}\frac{W}{g}r^2 + \frac{W}{g}r^2\right)\omega^2 = \frac{3}{4}\frac{W}{g}v^2.$$

991. The ends of the uniform slender link are confined to move in the smooth vertical and horizontal guides.   If the link falls from rest in the vertical position ($\theta = 0$), find its angular velocity ω and angular acceleration α for any position θ.

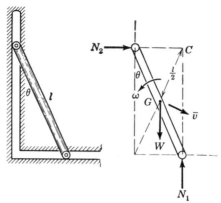

PROB. 991

Solution: From the free-body diagram of the link it is seen that W is the only force which does work.   The vertical drop of G is $(l/2)(1 - \cos \theta)$, and the work done is

$$\Delta U = \frac{Wl}{2}(1 - \cos \theta).$$

The kinetic energy at any position may be expressed as the energy of rotation about the instant center C.   Thus

$$\Delta T = T = \frac{1}{2}I_C\omega^2 = \frac{1}{2}\left[\frac{1}{12}\frac{W}{g}l^2 + \frac{W}{g}\left(\frac{l}{2}\right)^2\right]\omega^2 = \frac{1}{6}\frac{W}{g}l^2\omega^2.$$

This same result may be obtained by considering the energy due to the translational velocity of G and that due to rotational velocity about G.   Therefore the energy is

$$\frac{1}{2}\frac{W}{g}\bar{v}^2 + \frac{1}{2}\bar{I}\omega^2 = \frac{1}{2}\frac{W}{g}\left(\frac{l}{2}\omega\right)^2 + \frac{1}{2}\left(\frac{1}{12}\frac{W}{g}l^2\right)\omega^2 = \frac{1}{6}\frac{W}{g}l^2\omega^2.$$

The principle of work and energy is applied to give

$[\Delta U = \Delta T]$ $\qquad\qquad \dfrac{Wl}{2}(1 - \cos \theta) = \dfrac{1}{6}\dfrac{W}{g}l^2\omega^2,$

$$\omega = \sqrt{\frac{3g}{l}(1 - \cos \theta)}. \qquad\qquad Ans.$$

The angular acceleration of the bar may be obtained by differentiation. Thus

$$\frac{d(\omega^2)}{dt} = 2\omega\alpha = \frac{3g}{l}\frac{d}{dt}(1 - \cos\theta) = \frac{3g\omega}{l}\sin\theta,$$

$$\alpha = \frac{3g}{2l}\sin\theta. \qquad Ans.$$

The positive direction of α is counterclockwise, which is the same as that for θ.

992. Specify the necessary modulus k of the spring which will allow the gear sector to rotate a maximum of $\frac{1}{8}$ turn when released from rest in the position shown. Also find the velocity v of the 6 lb. plunger when the spring is compressed 1 in. during this motion. The gear sector weighs 10 lb. and may be treated as a semicircular disk. Also, friction in the parts is negligible.

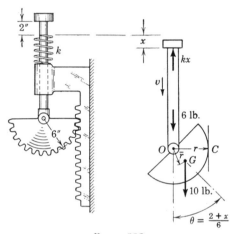

PROB. 992

Solution: The sector and attached plunger are taken as the system to be isolated, and the active-force diagram, showing all external forces which act on the system and do work, is drawn. The 10 lb. and 6 lb. weights and the spring force are the only such active forces.

For a rotation of $\frac{1}{8}$ of a turn $\theta = \pi/4$, and the compression of the spring is $x = (6\pi/4) - 2 = 2.71$ in. Also $\bar{r} = 4r/(3\pi) = 2.55$ in. The vertical movement of G for $\theta = \pi/4$ is

$$(2 + x) - (\bar{r} - \bar{r}\cos\theta) = 4.71 - 2.55(1 - 0.707) = 3.96 \text{ in.}$$

The work-energy principle for $\Delta T = 0$ is

$$[\Delta U = 0] \qquad 10 \times 3.96 + 6 \times 4.71 - \tfrac{1}{2}k(2.71)^2 = 0,$$

$$k = 18.48 \text{ lb./in.} \qquad Ans.$$

For a spring compression of 1 in. the angular movement of the sector is

$$\theta = \frac{2 + 1}{6} = 0.5 \text{ rad.} \quad \text{or} \quad \theta = 28° \, 39',$$

and the vertical movement of G is

$$(2 + 1) - 2.55(1 - 0.878) = 2.69 \text{ in.}$$

Thus the net work done during the 1 in. compression of the spring is

$$\Delta U = 10 \times 2.69 + 6 \times 3 - \tfrac{1}{2} \times 18.48 \times 1^2 = 35.7 \text{ in. lb.}$$

The kinetic energy of the disk may be computed from the expression $\tfrac{1}{2} I_C \omega^2$, where

$$I_C = \bar{I} + m\overline{GC}^2 = I_O - m\bar{r}^2 + m\overline{GC}^2 = I_O + m(\overline{GC}^2 - \bar{r}^2).$$

The law of cosines applied to the triangle OGC gives

$$\overline{GC}^2 - \bar{r}^2 = r^2 - 2r\bar{r} \cos\left(\frac{\pi}{2} - \theta\right) = 21.3 \text{ in.}^2,$$

and the moment of inertia about O is

$$I_O = \frac{1}{2}\left(\frac{1}{2} \times 2mr^2\right) = \frac{1}{2} mr^2 = \frac{10 \times 6^2}{2 \times 32.2 \times 12} = 0.466 \text{ lb. in. sec.}^2$$

Therefore the kinetic energy of the disk is

$$\frac{1}{2} I_C \omega^2 = \frac{1}{2}\left(0.466 + \frac{10}{32.2 \times 12} \times 21.3\right)\frac{v^2}{6^2} = 0.01414 v^2 \text{ in. lb.}$$

Finally, the kinetic energy of the plunger is accounted for, and the work-energy equation gives

$$[\Delta U = \Delta T] \qquad 35.7 = 0.01414 v^2 + \frac{1}{2}\frac{6}{32.2 \times 12} v^2,$$

$$v = 40.4 \text{ in./sec.} \qquad\qquad Ans.$$

The kinetic energy of the gear sector may be determined also from the relation $\tfrac{1}{2} m\bar{v}^2 + \tfrac{1}{2}\bar{I}\omega^2$. In this method it is necessary to relate $\bar{v}$ and ω to the velocity v of the plunger, and the labor is comparable to that of obtaining I_C as was done in the present solution. Unless strict adherence to principles is observed the casual reader may be tempted to evaluate the kinetic energy of a full rolling disk and take half of it for the given sector. Such calculation is erroneous since the kinetic energies of the particles of each half of the disk are not the same by reason of their different velocities.

PROBLEMS

993. The 40 lb. wheel has a radius of gyration about its center of 15 in. and rolls up the plane without slipping under the action of the constant 10 lb. force. Determine the angular velocity ω of the wheel when its center has moved 12 ft. from rest.

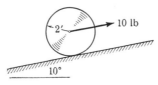

PROB. 993

994. A circular hoop of weight W rolls without slipping on a fixed surface. If the center of the hoop has a velocity v, find the kinetic energy T.

995. The suspended log shown is used as a battering ram. At what angle θ should the log be released from rest in order to strike the object to be smashed with a velocity of 20 ft./sec.? *Ans.* $\theta = 41°\ 16'$

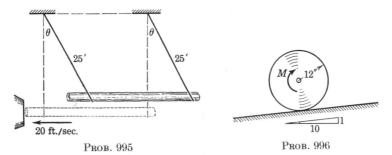

PROB. 995   PROB. 996

996. Find the torque M applied to the 40 lb. circular disk necessary to give its center a velocity of 4 ft./sec. in a distance of 10 ft. up the incline from rest. The wheel does not slip.

997. The locomotive drivers of Prob. 745 are shown again here. If the locomotive has a velocity of 60 mi./hr., determine the kinetic energy T of the 190 lb. connecting rod AB when it is in the position shown. *Ans.* $T = 6910$ ft. lb.

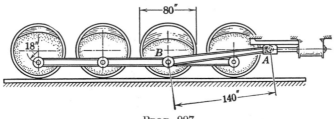

PROB. 997

998. The hoop of negligible wall thickness has a radius of 6 in. and rolls without slipping. If its center is given an initial velocity of 5 ft./sec. up the incline from point A, find its velocity v when point B is passed on the way down.

Ans. $v = 7.55$ ft./sec.

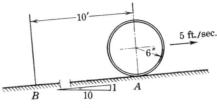

PROB. 998

999. The hoisting drum weighs 150 lb. and has a radius of gyration of 8 in. If the 100 lb. weight acquires a velocity of 10 ft./sec. after falling 20 ft. from rest, find the constant frictional moment M_f acting on the drum bearing. The small sheave has negligible weight and is perfectly free to rotate about its bearing.

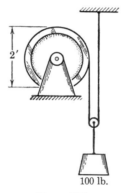

PROB. 999

1000. The wheel has a centroidal radius of gyration of 7 in. and weighs 45 lb. A constant 5 lb. force is applied to the light cable wrapped around the inner hub. Determine the velocity v of the center of the wheel after it has rolled 8 ft. to the right from rest without slipping.

Ans. $v = 4.62$ ft./sec.

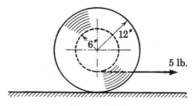

PROB. 1000

1001. The gear and attached drum have a combined weight of 150 lb. and a radius of gyration of 10.5 in.   The weight of the motor pinion is small and may be neglected.   The 400 lb. load acquires an upward velocity of 15 ft./sec. after rising 20 ft. from rest with constant acceleration.   Determine the torque M on the motor pinion.   *Ans.* $M = 52.5$ lb. ft.

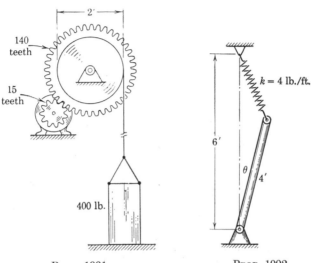

PROB. 1001   PROB. 1002

1002. What initial clockwise angular velocity ω must the uniform 10 lb. bar have as it crosses the vertical position ($\theta = 0$) in order that it just reach the horizontal ($\theta = 90$ deg.)?   The spring has a modulus of 4 lb./ft. and is unstretched when $\theta = 0$.

1003. If the frame F of the car must be jacked up to a height of $x = 14.5$ in. to release the compression in the springs, determine the least value of x resulting from a sudden removal of the jack if there are no shock absorbers.   The constant of each spring is 409 lb./in., and the line AC may be assumed to remain

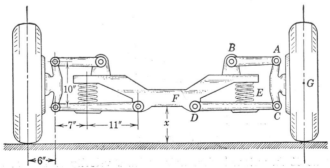

PROB. 1003

vertical throughout the movement. The weight of the frame F and that part of the attached body supported by F is 1500 lb. *Ans.* $x = 4.68$ in.

1004. The circular cylinder of weight W and radius r is released from rest in the position shown and rolls without slipping on the circular surface. Determine the reaction N between the surface and the cylinder when the bottom position is reached.

$$Ans. \quad N = \frac{W}{3}(7 - 4\cos\theta)$$

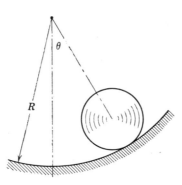

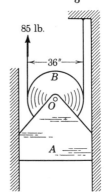

PROB. 1004 PROB. 1005

1005. The 100 lb. load A and the attached 50 lb. sheave B have an upward velocity of 10 ft./sec. after rising 15 ft. from rest under the action of the constant 85 lb. cable tension. Determine the frictional moment M_f in the bearing O if the radius of gyration of the sheave is 12 in. and the cable does not slip on the sheave. Friction along the vertical guides is negligible.

1006. A constant torque of 15 lb. ft. is applied by a motor to the 20 lb. drum A in the direction to cause the 200 lb. spool B to roll up the incline on its hubs without slipping. Determine the velocity v of the center of the spool after the drum A has turned 10 rev. from rest. The radius of gyration of B about its center O is 10 in., and that of A about its center is 4 in. *Ans.* $v = 5.68$ ft./sec.

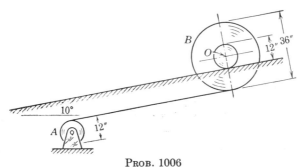

PROB. 1006

1007. The 60 lb. weight is descending with a velocity of 4 ft./sec. when a constant counterclockwise moment of 40 lb. ft. is applied to the solid cylindrical drum A, which weighs 20 lb. If the centroidal radius of gyration of the integral 40 lb. pulley B is 10 in., find the number of revolutions n through which A turns before the system comes to rest.

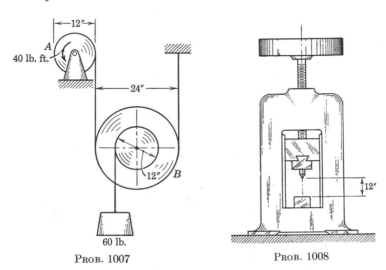

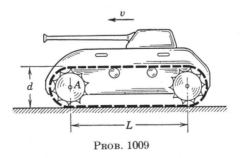

PROB. 1007   PROB. 1008

1008. A type of press frequently used in the hot working of nonferrous metals is shown in the figure. The flywheel and attached screw together weigh 600 lb. and have a radius of gyration about the vertical center line of 16 in. The screw has a double thread of 2 in. lead, and the forming head and die weigh 80 lb. If the flywheel has a speed of 100 rev./min. in the position shown, determine the rotational speed N just before the die strikes the work. Neglect friction.

Ans. $N = 117.1$ rev./min.

1009. Crawler-type tractors with endless treads are used mainly for low-velocity earth-moving machinery. In the case of the military tank, however,

PROB. 1009

appreciable velocities are attained. Determine that portion M of the constant total torque applied to the front driving sprocket A necessary to give the tread alone its motion corresponding to a velocity v of the tank in a distance s from rest. Neglect the thickness of the tread compared with the dimensions d and L. The tread has a weight μ per unit of its length.

$$Ans. \quad M = \frac{\mu v^2 d}{gs}\left(L + \frac{\pi d}{2}\right)$$

1010. The gear train is set in motion by releasing gear A and its attached weighted arm from rest in the position shown. The center of gravity of the 20 lb. weighted arm alone is 10 in. from O, and the radius of gyration of the arm about O is 12 in. The weight and radius of gyration of each of the gear units are given on the sketch. Determine the angular speed ω of gear C as the arm swings through the vertical position if friction is negligible. The gear ratio for each stage is 2:1.

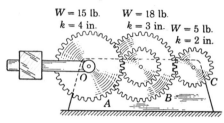

PROB. 1010

1011. The railway work car has a total weight of 3600 lb. and is driven by an electric motor A which takes its power from a trolley not shown. The front wheels and axle together weigh 600 lb. and have a radius of gyration of 8 in., and the rear wheels and axle are identical. The motor armature, shaft, and pinion together weigh 200 lb. and have a radius of gyration of 3 in. Determine the torque M on the armature due to the electrical field necessary to give the car an acceleration of 6 ft./sec.^{2} (*Comment:* Compare the work-energy method of solution for this problem with a solution based on the equations of motion developed in the previous chapter.) $Ans.$ $M = 390$ lb. ft.

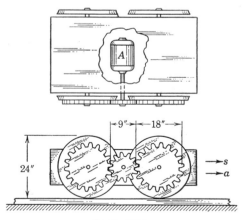

PROB. 1011

1012. The elliptical cylinder is released from rest in the position shown, where $a > b$, and rolls without slipping on the horizontal surface. Determine the maximum angular velocity ω of the cylinder.

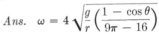

$$Ans. \quad \omega = 2\sqrt{\frac{2g(a-b)}{a^2 + 5b^2}}$$

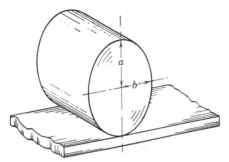

PROB. 1012

1013. The half-cylinder is released from rest in the position shown and rocks on the horizontal surface without slipping. Determine the angular velocity ω of the cylinder as it passes the equilibrium position $\theta = 0$.

$$Ans. \quad \omega = 4\sqrt{\frac{g}{r}\left(\frac{1 - \cos\theta}{9\pi - 16}\right)}$$

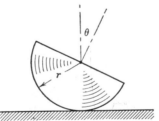

PROB. 1013

1014. The disk of Prob. 956 is repeated here. If the disk is released from rest in the position shown and rolls without slipping, find its angular velocity ω as the hole passes the top position.

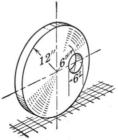

PROB. 1014

* 1015. In the planetary gearing of Prob. 760, shown again here, the spider A rotates about O independently of the central gear B, and the ring gear D is

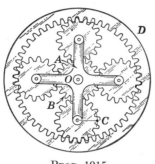

stationary. Gear B and the four planet gears are identical, and each has a pitch diameter of 6 in., a centroidal radius of gyration of 2 in., and a weight of 3 lb. The spider weighs 4 lb. and has a radius of gyration of 4 in. about O. If a constant moment of 10 lb. in. is applied to gear B through its shaft at O, find the number of revolutions n through which the spider must turn from rest before B reaches a velocity of 1200 rev./min. *Ans.* $n = 4.47$ rev.

* 1016. The unbalanced gear oscillates on the inclined rack because of the action of the spring.

PROB. 1015

Determine the modulus k of the spring which will allow the gear to rotate a maximum of ½ turn from the position shown, where it is released from rest with no force in the spring. Also find the angular velocity ω of the gear when it has revolved ¼ turn. The gear weighs 40 lb. with center of gravity at G and has a radius of gyration about O of 4.10 in.

Ans. $k = 2.36$ lb./in., $\omega = 4.22$ rad./sec.

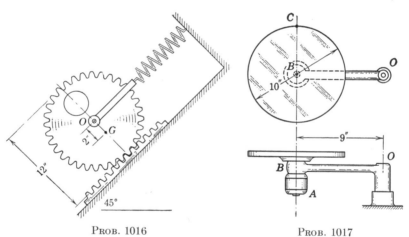

PROB. 1016   PROB. 1017

* 1017. The mechanism of Prob. 759 is repeated here. The combined weight of the circular disk and attached shaft and armature of motor A is 15 lb., and this unit has a radius of gyration of 6 in. about its own axis. The arm BO and attached motor housing weigh 10 lb. and have a radius of gyration of 7 in. about the axis at O. There is negligible friction in the bearings so that the disk and armature unit rotates independently of the arm BO. If the motor is coasting at the constant speed of 1800 rev./min. and a constant torque of 0.5 lb. ft. is applied to the arm through the shaft at O, find the angular velocity ω of BO after it has revolved through 4 turns from rest. *Ans.* $\omega = 8.27$ rad./sec.

* **1018.** The ring of mass m and radius r is mounted on light spokes (not shown) and rotates about its shaft (y-axis) with an angular velocity ω. Simultaneously its shaft, which is hinged at O, rotates about the x-axis with an angular velocity Ω. Determine the kinetic energy T of the ring by integrating the energy for an element over the entire periphery and show that this expression equals the sum of the energies $\frac{1}{2}I_y\omega^2 + \frac{1}{2}I_x\Omega^2$. Can this result be generalized for any type of rotor symmetrical about either axis of rotation? Does the result hold for an incomplete hoop?

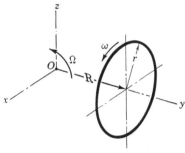

PROB. 1018

> *Ans.* Holds for symmetrical but not for unsymmetrical rotor

* **1019.** In the differential gears the shaft and gear A are fixed and do not rotate. If a constant torque of 2 lb. in. is applied to gear B through its shaft, determine the angular speed N of B after it has turned through 4 rev. from rest.

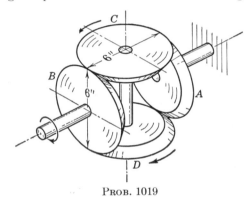

PROB. 1019

Each of the four identical bevel gears has a weight of 5 lb. and a centroidal radius of gyration of 2 in. (*Hint:* Use the results cited in the statement of Prob. 1018 and neglect the thickness of each gear in the direction of its axis compared with its diameter.)

> *Ans.* $N = 248$ rev./min.

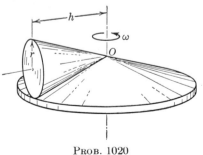

PROB. 1020

* **1020.** Derive the expression for the kinetic energy T of a solid right circular cone of mass m rolling on a fixed conical surface such that the axis of the rolling cone remains in a horizontal plane and rotates about the vertical axis through the vertex O with an angular velocity ω.

> *Ans.* $T = \dfrac{9}{20} mh^2\omega^2 \left(1 + \dfrac{r^2}{6h^2}\right)$

102. Energy Equation and Conservation of Energy. The *energy* of a body may be defined as the capacity of the body to do work by reason of its motion or configuration. Mechanical energy includes kinetic and potential energies, and nonmechanical energy includes thermal, chemical, electrical, and atomic energies.

Kinetic energy T is energy due to motion (velocity) and has been described in the preceding two articles.

Potential energy V (see Art. 65 of Part I) is conveniently expressed in terms of the potential energy of position V_g of a body in a field of force and the potential energy V_e of a body due to its elastic state of deformation.

Potential energy of position V_g is the work done against the field of force in changing the position of the body in that field. The most common force field is the gravitational field of the earth which may be considered of constant intensity near the surface of the earth. Thus the potential energy V_g of a body of weight W which is elevated a distance h above an arbitrary datum plane is $+Wh$ relative to this datum plane. Conversely, if the body is a distance h below the plane, the potential energy of position is $-Wh$. The expression for V_g, then, accounts for the work done by the force of gravity. When V_g depends only on the position of a body in the field of force and not upon the path followed in reaching that position, the force field is said to be *conservative*. In a conservative field the net work done on a body during any movement which returns the body to its original position and state of motion is zero.

Elastic potential energy V_e, also known as *strain energy*, is energy stored in a body during an elastic deformation. For a simple spring of stiffness k which is compressed or extended an amount x the elastic energy is $V_e = \frac{1}{2}kx^2$ and equals the work done on the spring in producing the deformation. Elastic energy represents work done by a *conservative* force as long as the force equals kx and therefore does not exceed the elastic limitation of the material. All the energy stored is potentially available since the spring or body will do work equal to V_e on any body against which it is allowed to act during the relief of its extension or compression.

The total mechanical potential energy of a system is $V = V_e + V_g$, and the total mechanical energy is $E = T + V$. The work-energy principle, expressed by Eq. (90), may now be modified to read

$$\Delta U = \Delta T + \Delta V_e + \Delta V_g = \Delta E. \tag{95}$$

If this alternate form of the work-energy principle is used, it must be clearly understood that ΔU is the work done on the system by all external active forces *except* the weights of the members. The work done by these gravitational forces is included in the term V_g. Also with this formulation of the energy principle a spring with its strain energy V_e may be considered a part of the system.

A body or system of bodies subjected to forces either external or internal which depend only on the position and configuration of the system and its particles is said to be a *conservative system*. If, during any interval, no work is done on such a conservative system by external forces (other than gravity or other potential forces), then no part of the energy of the system is lost. Therefore, the principle of conservation of energy requires that the total mechanical energy of a conservative system remain unchanged. Hence, $T + V =$ constant or

$$\Delta T + \Delta V = 0. \tag{96}$$

Equation (96) is known as the *law of conservation of dynamical energy* and is one of the basic principles of mechanics. This law is a limiting principle and holds only in the ideal case of no kinetic friction. A kinetic friction force always does negative work which is dissipated from the system in the form of heat loss.

A kinetic friction force is *nonconservative* since its value does not depend on the position of the body upon which it acts but on relative movement of the contacting surfaces and the direction of the movement. A system subjected to kinetic friction forces is *nonconservative*, and the sum of its potential and kinetic energies decreases with continued motion of the system. Although all mechanical systems are actually nonconservative, still, for those where the kinetic friction forces are small, analysis based on a conservative system is justified.

Many systems which involve mechanical energy also involve non-mechanical energy.

Thermal energy Q is energy due to the heat content of a body. This energy is indicated by the temperature of a body, which is actually a measure of the kinetic energy of the molecules. The common engineering unit of heat energy is the British thermal unit (B.t.u.), which is equivalent to 778 ft. lb. of mechanical energy.

Chemical energy C is energy due to atomic arrangement and may be considered a form of potential energy. The combustion of fuel, for instance, is accompanied by atomic rearrangement and liberation of thermal energy. Chemical energy is usually expressed in B.t.u.'s of equivalent heat energy.

Electrical energy E_e is the energy associated with electrical charges. Electrical energy is related to mechanical energy by the work done by electrical forces which accompany the flow of electric charges.

Atomic energy A is energy released because of the rearrangement of the structure of the atom and is the most recent form of energy to be used by man. Atomic energy may be considered also a form of potential energy.

When a change in energy and a transfer of energy between mechanical and nonmechanical forms take place in a system during any interval, it is convenient to account for the total energy E of the system and changes in energy by the equation

$$E_1 + E_{in} - E_{out} = E_2.$$

This simple balance states that the total energy E_1 of the system at the beginning of the interval plus any energy put into the system (includes positive work done on the system) minus any energy taken out of the system (includes negative work done on the system) must equal the final energy E_2 of the system at the end of the interval.

It is important to recognize that energy is a relative quantity. Thus the potential energy V_g depends on the arbitrary selection of a datum plane for zero potential energy. Also kinetic energy T is arbitrarily (but conveniently) expressed relative to the condition at zero velocity. Hence any physical measurement of energy describes in reality a change in energy. Since the energy equation may be written in terms of the energy change $E_2 - E_1$, it follows that all reference to any arbitrary datum used for the expression of energy will cancel.

SAMPLE PROBLEM

1021. The two-wheeled skip A has a total weight of 600 lb. and is pulled up the incline by the action of the descending 350 lb. counterweight B. Each of the two wheels of the skip weighs 100 lb. and has a radius of gyration of 12 in. The drum C upon which the cable is wound weighs 100 lb., and its radius of gyration is 10 in. The counterweight slide is greased and gives a coefficient of friction of 0.20. If the skip has a velocity of 3 ft./sec. up the incline in the position shown, find the maximum compression x of the spring bumper. Assume that tipping of the cart as it strikes the spring is negligible and that the wheels do not slip on the track.

Solution: The skip, cables, drum, counterweight, and spring will be considered together as the isolated system. Other than the weights of the members (potential forces) the only external active force on the system as a whole is the friction force acting up the plane on the counterweight, and its magnitude is $F = 0.2 \times 350 \times 0.5 = 35$ lb. Thus the net work done on the system during the downward movement of $2(6 + x)$ ft. of the counterweight is

$$\Delta U = -35 \times 2(6 + x) = -70(6 + x) \text{ ft. lb.}$$

The change in potential energy of position of the system is the weight of the skip times its vertical rise minus the weight of the counterweight times its vertical drop or

$$\Delta V_g = 600(6 + x) \frac{\sqrt{3}}{2} - 350 \times 2(6 + x) \frac{\sqrt{3}}{2} = -50\sqrt{3}(6 + x) \text{ ft. lb.}$$

The change in elastic potential energy is the strain energy of the spring

$$\Delta V_e = \tfrac{1}{2}kx^2 = 50x^2 \text{ ft. lb.}$$

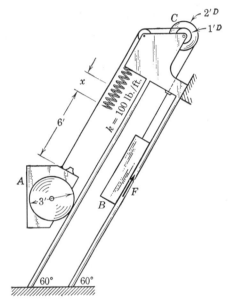

PROB. 1021

The change in kinetic energy of the system is the zero kinetic energy at the final position of maximum spring compression minus the initial kinetic energy or $\Delta T = -T$. The initial kinetic energy of each part is

$$T_{\text{skip}} = \frac{1}{2}\frac{600}{32.2} \times 3^2 + 2 \times \frac{1}{2}\frac{100}{32.2} \times 1^2 \times \left(\frac{3}{1.5}\right)^2 = 96.3 \text{ ft. lb.,}$$

$$T_{\text{drum}} = \frac{1}{2}\frac{100}{32.2} \times \left(\frac{10}{12}\right)^2 \times \left(\frac{3}{0.5}\right)^2 = 38.8 \text{ ft. lb.,}$$

$$T_{\text{ctwt.}} = \frac{1}{2}\frac{350}{32.2} \times (2 \times 3)^2 = 195.6 \text{ ft. lb.}$$

Thus

$$\Delta T = -96.3 - 38.8 - 195.6 = -331 \text{ ft. lb.}$$

The work-energy principle, Eq. (95), gives

$$[\Delta U = \Delta T + \Delta V_e + \Delta V_g] \quad -70(6 + x) = -331 + 50x^2 - 50\sqrt{3}\,(6 + x).$$

Solution of the quadratic gives

$$x = 3.11 \text{ ft.} \qquad\qquad Ans.$$

The second root of the equation is $x = -2.77$ ft., which is of no interest since the skip must move 6 ft. before it strikes the spring, and x is, therefore, positive.

The difference between the solution given here and that which would follow the method of the previous article is that the work done by the weights of the members is included in the ΔV_g term instead of the ΔU term.

If friction were absent, the net work done on the system as a whole would be zero. The total energy would remain constant, and $\Delta T + \Delta V_e + \Delta V_g = \Delta E = 0$.

PROBLEMS

In the following problems account for the work done by the weights of the various bodies in the potential energy term ΔV_g and not in the work term ΔU.

1022. The 5 lb. plunger is released from rest in the position shown, where the light spring is compressed to one half of its free length of 6 in. Determine the maximum height h above the starting position which is reached by the plunger.

$Ans.$ $h = 2.40$ in.

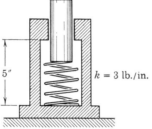

5″

$k = 3$ lb./in.

PROB. 1022

1023. Problem 784 illustrates a man who hoists himself vertically up for a short distance on a bosun's chair. The man starts from rest and acquires a small upward velocity after a short movement. Discuss the application of the work-energy equation to the system during this movement.

1024. The small 3 lb. weight A is released from rest in the position shown and slides without friction along the smooth fixed rod. If the free length of the spring is 20 in., find the velocity v with which the weight strikes the support at B.

1025. A large 6-cylinder internal-combustion engine is cranked at 100 rev./min. by a small auxiliary starting engine before the ignition is turned on. During the suction stroke each of the 6 cylinders admits 0.420×10^{-3} lb. of fuel which has an energy content of 20,000 B.t.u./lb. When the engine

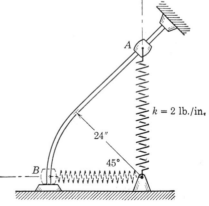

A

$k = 2$ lb./in.

24″

45°

B

PROB. 1024

fires and its speed increases, the overriding starter clutch is automatically disengaged. The kinetic energy of the 450 lb. flywheel with radius of gyration of 16 in. is large compared with the kinetic energy of the other moving parts. Determine the speed N of the engine 2 rev. after the ignition is turned on, assuming that each of the 6 cylinders fires once during the 2 rev. (4-cycle engine). Because of the heat loss only 25 per cent of the fuel energy is converted into mechanical energy. *Ans.* $N = 286$ rev./min.

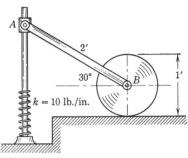

PROB. 1026

1026. The link AB has a weight of 10 lb. and may be treated as a uniform slender rod. The 15 lb. wheel is a circular disk with sufficient friction on the horizontal surface to prevent slipping. The link is released from rest in the position shown, and end A slides down the smooth rod. Neglect friction in the moving parts and determine (a) the angular velocity ω of the link as A strikes the spring with AB in the horizontal position and (b) the maximum deflection x of the spring.

1027. The system is released from rest in the position shown. The 10 lb. weight passes through the hole in the bracket but the 8 lb. rider does not. Determine the maximum distance s which the 10 lb. weight descends from the starting position. (What happens to the kinetic energy of the rider?)

Ans. $s = 6.53$ ft.

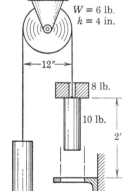

PROB. 1027

1028. At the surface of the earth a body is subject to a gravitational force W. Determine the potential energy V_g relative to the earth's surface when this body is elevated to an altitude h which is not negligible compared with the radius R of the earth. If the earth had no atmosphere, with what velocity v would an object strike the earth if released at a distance from the earth many times greater than the radius of the earth?

1029. The gravitational potential V in the vicinity of a fixed mass m_0 is the work which must be done on a unit mass in changing its position in the gravitational field of m_0. It is often convenient to consider, arbitrarily, that the potential is zero when the unit mass is at an infinite distance from m_0. Determine the potential V at a distance r from m_0. The gravitational constant is γ, and the mass m_0 may be considered concentrated at a point.

$$Ans. \quad V = -\frac{\gamma m_0}{r}$$

1030. The heavy cable A weighs 3 lb./ft., and the weight of the second cable is negligible. If the system is released from rest in the position shown, find the maximum distance s from the starting position which the 24 lb. weight moves. Assume that the actual shape of the belt may be approximated by two vertical sections and a semicircular section as shown.   *Ans.* $s = 10.50$ ft. down

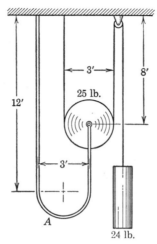

PROB. 1030

1031. The pulley has a weight of 40 lb. and a radius of gyration of 10 in., and the chain weighs 4 lb./ft.   If the pulley is released from rest in the position shown, determine its angular velocity ω when the lower end of the chain has dropped 3 ft.

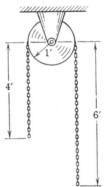

PROB. 1031

1032. Determine the maximum velocity v reached by the plunger in Prob. 1022.   *Ans.* $v = 20.3$ in./sec.

1033. Each of the springs has an unstretched length of 8 in. and a constant of 0.5 lb./in.   The small metal ball weighs 1 lb. and is shown in the equilibrium position which is the origin of coordinates with the y-axis vertically up.   If the ball is displaced and released from rest at a point whose coordinates are $x = -2$ in., $y = -2$ in., determine the velocity v of the ball as it passes through the point whose coordinates are $x = \frac{3}{2}$ in., $y = \frac{1}{2}$ in. during the course of its somewhat complex motion.

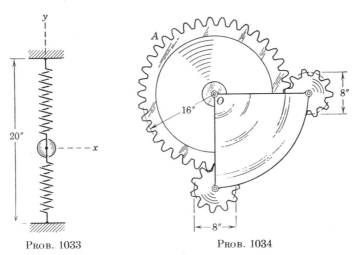

PROB. 1033   PROB. 1034

* **1034.** Gear A is fixed and does not rotate. Each of the smaller gears has a weight of 6 lb. and a radius of gyration of 3 in., and is freely mounted in a bearing on the sector. The sector is a uniform quarter-circular plate which weighs 10 lb. and is freely pivoted about O. Determine the maximum angular velocity ω reached by the small gears if the assembly is released from rest in the position shown. *Ans.* $\omega = 13.13$ rad./sec.

* **1035.** Determine the constant force P required to give the center of the pulley a velocity of 4 ft./sec. in an upward movement of the center of 3 ft. from the rest position shown. The pulley weighs 30 lb. with a radius of gyration of 10 in., and the cable has a total length of 15 ft. with a weight of 2 lb./ft. *Ans.* $P = 38.6$ lb.

* **1036.** Read Prob. 1029 and use the results to show that the gravitational potential V at any point inside a uniform spherical shell of mass m_0 and radius a is $V = -\gamma m_0/a$.

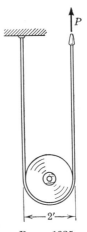

PROB. 1035

103. Power and Efficiency. The capacity of a machine is measured by the time rate at which it can do work or deliver energy. The total work or energy output is not a measure of this capacity since a motor, no matter how small, can deliver any amount of energy if given sufficient time. On the other hand a large and powerful machine is required to deliver a large amount of energy in a short period of time. Thus the capacity of a machine is rated by its *power*, which is defined as the *time rate of doing work*.

The work done by a force F, Fig. 127a, during a displacement ds of its point of application in the direction of the force is $dU = F\,ds$, and the time rate at which the force does work is the power

$$P = \frac{dU}{dt} = Fv, \tag{97}$$

where v is the velocity of the point of application of the force. Likewise, the work done by a couple M, Fig. 127b, during an angular displacement

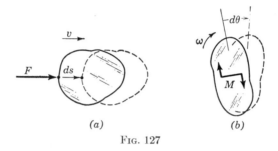

(a)   (b)

Fig. 127

$d\theta$ in the direction of the couple is $dU = M\,d\theta$, and the time rate at which the couple does work is the power

$$P = \frac{dU}{dt} = M\omega, \tag{98}$$

where ω is the angular velocity of the body. If the force F is not in the direction of the displacement ds, the power developed will be equal to the component of F in the direction of the velocity times the velocity. Likewise, if the couple and angular displacement vectors are not in the same direction, the cosine of the angle between them will be a factor.

The unit of mechanical power in common use is the *horsepower* (h.p.), and the common electrical unit of power is the *watt* or *kilowatt* (1000 watts). The definitions of these units and their equivalences are

$$1 \text{ h.p.} = 550 \text{ ft. lb./sec.} = 33{,}000 \text{ ft. lb./min.,}$$

$$1 \text{ watt} = 10^7 \text{ ergs/sec.} = 0.737 \text{ ft. lb./sec.,}$$

$$1 \text{ h.p.} = 746 \text{ watts} = 0.746 \text{ k.w.}$$

The work done in one hour at the rate of one horsepower is one *horse-power-hour* (h.p. hr.), and, similarly, the electrical energy used in one hour at the rate of one kilowatt is one *kilowatt-hour* (k.w. hr.). Thus

$$1 \text{ h.p. hr.} = 1,980,000 \text{ ft. lb.,}$$

$$1 \text{ k.w. hr.} = 2,654,000 \text{ ft. lb.}$$

The *efficiency* e of a machine is the ratio of the energy output of the machine during a certain interval to the energy supplied to the machine during the same interval. This definition assumes that the machine operates uniformly so that there is no accumulation or depletion of energy within it. Efficiency is always less than unity since every device operates with some loss of energy and since energy cannot be created within the machine. In mechanical devices which involve moving parts there will always be a loss of energy due to the negative work of kinetic friction forces. This work is converted to heat energy which in turn is dissipated to the surroundings. Frictional losses may be minimized by lubrication but may never be eliminated entirely. The ratio of the work done *by* a machine to the work done *on* the machine during equal intervals of time is the *mechanical efficiency* e_m. The mechanical efficiency at any instant of time may be expressed in terms of mechanical power P by

$$e_m = \frac{P_{\text{output}}}{P_{\text{input}}}.$$

The mechanical efficiencies of accurately made and properly lubricated machines are often 90 per cent or more.

In addition to energy loss by mechanical friction there may also be electrical and thermal energy loss in which case the *electrical efficiency* e_e and *thermal efficiency* e_t are also involved. The *overall efficiency* e of a machine is the product of its several efficiencies. Thus

$$e = e_m e_e e_t.$$

A device used for measuring the power output of a machine is called a dynamometer. A dynamometer may be either of the *absorption* type, where the energy developed by the machine is absorbed and usually converted into heat, or of the *transmission* type, where the energy is passed on unchanged. In Fig. 128 is shown a simple brake dynamometer of the absorption type for measuring the power output of an electric motor. The power of the motor is absorbed in the work of friction between the brake blocks and the pulley. From the statical equilibrium of the brake, the total frictional moment acting on the pulley is seen to be $M_f = Rb$, if the moment due to the weight of the brake is neglected. The reaction R is easily measured by a weighing scale, and the power at any constant angular speed ω is $P = M_f \omega = Rb\omega$. If a measurement

is taken during an acceleration α of the motor, part of the power will
be used in increasing the rotational kinetic energy. If the moment of

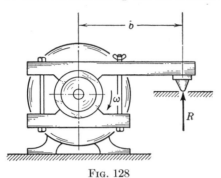

inertia of the rotating elements
is I, the equation of rotation
is

$$M = M_f + I\alpha,$$

where M is the driving torque
applied by the electrical field.
The capacity or power developed by the motor under these
circumstances is, then,

FIG. 128

$$P = M\omega = M_f\omega + I\alpha\omega.$$

Measurements of power output are generally made at various operating speeds, and a plot of the results will disclose the optimum speed
for maximum power.

SAMPLE PROBLEMS

1037. A car of weight W has an acceleration a up an incline θ. Determine
the power P delivered by the engine to the rear wheels when the car reaches a
velocity v. The horizontal force required to tow the car on a level road at a
constant speed with engine disengaged is R.

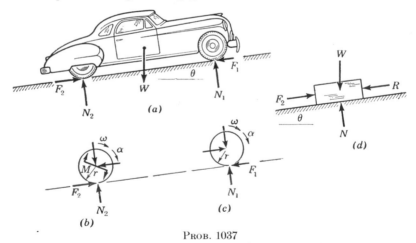

PROB. 1037

Solution: The free-body diagram of the car is shown in the a-part of the illustration. The normal forces N_1 and N_2 act on each respective pair of wheels
as do the friction forces F_1 and F_2. From the free-body diagram of the front
wheels in the c-part of the figure the direction of the friction force is such as to

provide the necessary clockwise moment about the bearing. From the free-body diagram of the rear wheels in the b-part of the illustration the friction force is in the direction to prevent the wheel from slipping under the applied torque M of the drive shaft.

The negative work done on the car by friction forces in the wheel bearings and by windage is accounted for by considering a retarding force R to act on the car which does negative work equal to that done by friction in the wheel bearings and windage. This force is equal to the experimentally determined "road resistance."

The power delivered to the rear wheels by the engine is $P = M\omega$. The torque M may be expressed in terms of known quantities from the equations of motion for the wheels separately and the car as a whole. Thus for the front and rear pair of wheels

$$[\Sigma \bar{M} = \bar{I}\alpha] \qquad\qquad F_1 r = I_1 \alpha; \qquad M - F_2 r = I_2 \alpha,$$

where I_1 and I_2 are the centroidal moments of inertia for the front and rear pair of wheels, respectively. For the complete car

$$[\Sigma F = ma] \qquad\qquad F_2 - F_1 - W \sin \theta - R = \frac{W}{g} a.$$

From these expressions the rear-axle driving torque M is

$$M = \left(W \sin \theta + R + \frac{W}{g} a \right) r + (I_1 + I_2)\alpha,$$

and, therefore, the power supplied to the rear wheels by the engine is

$$P = M\omega = \left(W \sin \theta + R + \frac{W}{g} a \right) v + (I_1 + I_2)\alpha\omega. \qquad Ans.$$

The term $Wv \sin \theta$ is the power required to increase the potential energy of the car at the given rate, Rv is the power used in overcoming friction and windage, and Wav/g is the power required to increase the translational kinetic energy at the given rate. This third term is merely

$$\frac{d}{dt} \left(\frac{1}{2} mv^2 \right) = mv \frac{dv}{dt} = \frac{W}{g} av.$$

The last terms $(I_1 + I_2)\alpha\omega$ represent the power used in increasing the rotational energy of the wheels and may be obtained from

$$\frac{d}{dt} \left(\frac{1}{2} I_1 \omega^2 + \frac{1}{2} I_2 \omega^2 \right) = (I_1 + I_2)\omega \frac{d\omega}{dt} = (I_1 + I_2)\alpha\omega.$$

Inasmuch as the rotational energy of the wheels is a small fraction of the total kinetic energy of the car, these last two terms may be neglected. This approximation amounts to neglecting F_1 in the case of the front wheels and the difference between M and $F_2 r$ for the rear wheels.

With neglect of the rotational energy of the wheels, the car may be simulated by a block, shown in the d-part of the figure, sliding up the incline under the action of F_2, W, and R. The power is then computed from the rate at which F_2 would do work and is

$$P = F_2v = \left(W \sin \theta + R + \frac{W}{g} a \right) v.$$

It should be noted that, in the actual car, neither one of the frictional forces F_1 and F_2 does work if slipping of the wheels does not occur.

1038. A test of power and efficiency for a gasoline engine is made by connecting the engine to an electrical dynamometer which operates as a generator. The frame or stator A of the dynamometer is mounted independently of its rotor in bearings which are coaxial with those of the rotor. In this way a direct measurement of the torque on the rotor developed by the generation of electric current may be made. The electrical energy generated is converted into heat by passing the current through electrical resistors. In the particular test involved the speed ratio shown is 3:1, and the engine is run at 2250 rev./min. The force R measured during the test is 22 lb. and that due to the unbalanced weight of the stator alone with the motor disconnected is 4 lb. A gasoline consumption of 17.5 lb./hr. is also measured.   If the gasoline liberates 20,000 B.t.u. of heat energy per pound when burned, determine the power output P of the engine and its overall efficiency e.

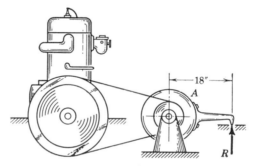

PROB. 1038

Solution: The power developed is obtained from the rate at which the moment on the generator shaft does work.   This moment is

$$M = \tfrac{3}{2}\Delta R = \tfrac{3}{2}(22 - 4) = 27 \text{ lb. ft.}$$

The power output is, then,

$[P = M\omega]$ $P = 27 \times 3 \times 2250 \times 2\pi = 1,145,000 \text{ ft. lb./min.}$

or

$$P = \frac{1,145,000}{33,000} = 34.7 \text{ h.p.}$$ *Ans.*

The overall efficiency e is

$$\left[e = \frac{P_{\text{output}}}{P_{\text{input}}} \right]$$ $$e = \frac{1,145,000 \times 60}{17.5 \times 20,000 \times 778} = 0.252.$$ *Ans.*

PROBLEMS

1039. A 150 lb. man walks at the constant rate of 2 mi./hr. up a uniform 10 per cent grade. What power P does he develop in overcoming the grade?

Ans. $P = 0.08$ h.p.

1040. Derive a formula for the horsepower transmitted by a shaft which revolves at a constant speed of N rev./min. under a torque of M lb. ft.

1041. Compute the power P developed by the electric motor of the railway work car described in Prob. 1011 when the car reaches a velocity of 20 mi./hr. with the acceleration of 6 ft./sec.^{2} Use the answer for motor torque M cited for this problem and neglect mechanical losses.

1042. The dump truck carries 6 yd.^{3} of earth with a density of 110 lb./ft.^{3}, and the elevating mechanism rotates the dump about the pivot A at the constant rate of 4 deg./sec. The center of gravity of the load is at G, and the weight of the empty dump is negligible compared with its load. Find the greatest power P required during the tilting of the load. *Ans.* $P = 11.30$ h.p.

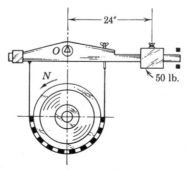

PROB. 1042

1043. The dynamometer shown is balanced on the knife edge at O. The brake band is tightened while the engine is running until the arm balances with the 50 lb. weight in the position shown corresponding to a measured speed N of 1640 rev./min. Determine the power output at this speed for the engine which drives the flywheel. With the 50 lb. weight removed and the brake band loose the arm is in static balance about O.

PROB. 1043

1044. In a test of a centrifugal sump pump a power input to the motor of 4.65 k.w. was measured at a speed of 1720 rev./min. The pump discharged fresh water at the rate of 72 ft.^{3}/min. with a total lift of 30 ft. Determine the overall efficiency e of the pump.   *Ans.* $e = 0.655$

1045. The 500 lb. load is hoisted with an upward acceleration of 2 ft./sec.^{2} by the tension T in the cable which passes over the fixed support. If the coefficient of friction between the cable and the support is 0.30, find the power P developed by T when the load acquires an upward velocity of 6 ft./sec. What is the mechanical efficiency e_m?

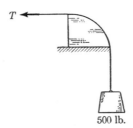

PROB. 1045

1046. A jet-propelled airplane weighs 12,500 lb. empty and is fueled with 10,000 lb. of kerosene with a heat energy content of 19,800 B.t.u./lb. The turbojet engine develops a constant forward thrust of 4000 lb., and fuel is consumed at the rate of 1.03 lb./hr. for each pound of thrust. If the maximum velocity in level flight is 650 mi./hr., determine the useful power P developed by the engine in driving the airplane against air resistance. Also find the overall efficiency e of conversion of heat energy to useful work in propelling the airplane at this speed.   *Ans.* $P = 6940$ h.p., $e = 0.217$

1047. The *propulsive coefficient* C for a ship is the ratio of the power required to overcome the resistance to motion through the water at a certain speed to the corresponding total power delivered by the engines to the propellers. The resistance to motion through the water is very nearly proportional to the square of the speed. For a certain ship a force of 40,000 lb. is required in a horizontal cable to tow the ship at 3 knots (1 knot = 1.689 ft./sec.), and, when the ship is under its own power at 10 knots, the engines deliver 28,000 h.p. to the propellers through the shaft (*shaft horsepower*). Determine C for the speed of 10 knots.

1048. A Diesel locomotive burns oil with an energy content of 19,000 B.t.u./lb. and pulls a 1000 ton train of cars up a 2 per cent grade with a constant velocity of 30 mi./hr. The frictional resistance to motion is 12 lb./ton. If the locomotive burns fuel at the rate of 2200 lb./hr., determine the power P developed by the locomotive at the drawbar and the overall efficiency e of conversion of heat energy to useful work in moving the entire train, including the 500,000 lb. locomotive.   *Ans.* $P = 4160$ h.p., $e = 0.317$

1049. A 3000 lb. car enters a 4 per cent grade at a speed of 60 mi./hr. and slows down at a uniform rate to 30 mi./hr. in a distance of ½ mi. Resistance to motion of the car due to friction is constant at 100 lb. Determine the power P delivered by the engine to the wheels when the speed of the car is 40 mi./hr. Neglect the rotational energy of the wheels. *Ans.* $P = 12.5$ h.p.

1050. The conveyor belt travels at the lineal speed of 3 ft./sec. and delivers boxes which weigh 80 lb. each to the upper level at the rate of one every 2 sec. On the average there are 5 boxes on the belt at any one time. With the belt empty and the motor disconnected a moment of 84 lb. ft. applied to the lower driving pulley A is required to turn it against friction in all the parts. Specify the necessary power capacity of the motor sufficient to allow for a 50 per cent overload factor.

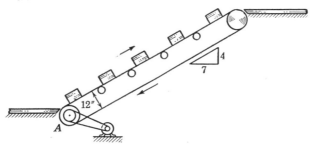

PROB. 1050

1051. The figure shows a typical "indicator diagram" for a 1-cylinder, 2-cycle reciprocating engine. The card is a graphical record taken directly on the engine of the pressure on the piston versus the piston travel during one complete cycle (one revolution of the crank). For the actual diagram 1 in. on the vertical scale corresponds to 200 lb./in.^{2} gage pressure, and 1 in. on the horizontal scale corresponds to 4 in. of actual piston travel. The area A within the loop on the card is measured with a planimeter and is found to be 0.910 in.^{2} Determine the power input P to the engine (*indicated power*) if the piston diameter is 6 in., the stroke is also 6 in., and the engine turns at 1750 rev./min. *Ans.* $P = 91.0$ h.p.

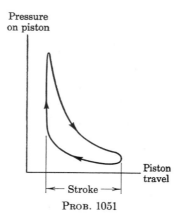

PROB. 1051

1052. A 13 ton airplane is propelled in level flight at 250 mi./hr. by two engines, each of which develops 1500 h.p. If the throttles are advanced so that each engine develops 2000 h.p., find the maximum rate of climb which the air-

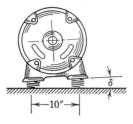

plane can have and still maintain an airspeed of 250 mi./hr. What is the total air resistance R to the motion of the airplane at this speed?

1053. The electric motor shown is delivering 4 h.p. at 1725 rev./min. Determine the angle δ through which the motor deflects under load if the constant of each of the four spring mounts is 40 lb./in. What direction is the motor running?

Ans. $\delta = 2° 5'$, clockwise rotation

|←—10″—→|

PROB. 1053

1054. At the bottom of a grade a 4000 lb. car has a velocity of 30 mi./hr. The engine produces a constant torque on the wheels so that the friction force between the wheels and the road is 900 lb. Frictional resistance to motion is constant at 100 lb. The grade becomes steeper according to $\sin \theta = s/1000$, where θ is the angle of the grade with the horizontal and s is the distance traveled in feet measured from the bottom of the grade. Determine the maximum power P developed by the engine and the distance s to the position where the car stalls. Neglect the rotational energy of the wheels.

* 1055. The drawbar pull F exerted by a steam turbine locomotive on a 1500 ton train of cars running on level track decreases uniformly with the velocity v as shown. Construct a curve showing the power delivered by the locomotive to the train versus the velocity and find the maximum power P developed and the velocity v at which this occurs.

Ans. $P = 6000$ h.p., $v = 75$ mi./hr.

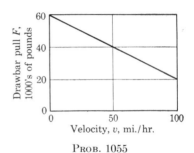

PROB. 1055

* 1056. In the speed range between 30 and 60 mi./hr. the diesel engine of a 15 ton truck develops a constant power output of 200 h.p. Resistance to motion is constant at 400 lb. Determine the time t required for the truck to change its speed from 30 to 60 mi./hr. Neglect the rotational kinetic energy of the wheels.

Ans. $t = 32.7$ sec.

CHAPTER XIII

Impulse and Momentum

104. Linear Impulse and Momentum. In Chapter XI the relationships between force, mass, and acceleration were used to describe the motion of rigid bodies. This approach to the kinetics problem is implied when acceleration is involved directly. In Chapter XII the principles of work and energy were used to advantage for intervals of motion where changes in velocity occur as a result of forces acting through distances. A third approach to the kinetics problem by the method of impulse and momentum is extremely useful when the action of forces expressed as a function of *time* is involved.

The equation of motion of a particle of mass m in the x-direction is

$$\Sigma F_x = ma_x = m \frac{dv_x}{dt},$$

where ΣF_x is the sum of the x-components of all forces acting on m, and a_x and v_x are the x-components of the acceleration and velocity, respectively. Since the mass m of the single particle is a constant, this equation may be written in either of the two forms

$$\Sigma F_x = \frac{d}{dt}(mv_x) \qquad \text{or} \qquad \Sigma F_x \, dt = d(mv_x). \tag{99}$$

The product of mass and linear velocity is defined as *linear momentum*, and, thus, the first of Eqs. (99) states that the resultant force in any one direction on a particle of mass m equals the time rate of change of its linear momentum in that direction. This formulation is an alternate way of stating Newton's second law of motion. The product of force and time is defined as *linear impulse*, and, thus, the second of Eqs. (99) states that the linear impulse of ΣF_x on m during time dt equals the change in linear momentum. The dimensions of both linear impulse and linear momentum are [force] × [time], (lb. sec.). The relations expressed by Eqs. (99) may also be written for the y- and z-directions,

551

and these equations are, then, the scalar components of a single vector relation which may be stated as

$$\Sigma F = \frac{d}{dt}(mv) \qquad \text{or} \qquad \Sigma F \, dt = d(mv).$$

In the vector formulation ΣF is the resultant of all forces on m, and mv is the resultant linear momentum of m. Linear impulse and linear momentum are both vector quantities which have the directions of ΣF and v, respectively. Thus the direction of ΣF coincides with the direction of the *change* in linear momentum which is also the direction of the acceleration.

The action of ΣF_x during a finite interval of time t is given by integration of the second of Eqs. (99). The integral is

$$\int_0^t \Sigma F_x \, dt = mv_x - mv_{0_x}, \qquad (100)$$

where v_x is the velocity in the positive x-direction at time t and v_{0_x} is the velocity in the positive x-direction at time $t = 0$. The integral on the left side of the equation is the linear impulse of ΣF_x during the time t, and the right side of the equation is the corresponding change in the linear momentum. When the functional relation between ΣF_x and t is unknown but experimental data for the variation of ΣF_x with t are available, the total impulse may be found by approximating the area under the curve of ΣF_x versus t. If ΣF_x is constant, the expression becomes

$$\Sigma F_x t = mv_x - mv_{0_x}.$$

It was shown in Chapter XI that the resultant of all forces acting on a translating rigid body passes through the center of mass and that such motion may be analyzed as though the body were a particle. Thus the foregoing principles of impulse and momentum developed for the motion of a particle may be applied equally well to a translating rigid body.

Consider now any general system of particles. These particles need not be joined but may be considered to have any motions whatsoever. If $F_{1_x}, F_{2_x}, F_{3_x} \cdots$ represent the x-components of all forces applied to a representative particle of mass m_i from sources *external* to the system, and if $f_{1_x}, f_{2_x}, f_{3_x}, \cdots$ represent the x-components of all internally applied forces on m_i, the first of Eqs. (99) may be written

$$F_{1_x} + F_{2_x} + F_{3_x} + \cdots + f_{1_x} + f_{2_x} + f_{3_x} + \cdots = \frac{d}{dt}(m_{i_x} v_{i_x}),$$

where v_{i_x} is the x-component of the velocity of m_i. Similar expressions

may be written for each particle of the system. By adding all these
equations and remembering that the sum of the internal actions and
reactions is zero, the sum of external forces in the x-direction becomes

$$\Sigma F_x = \Sigma \frac{d}{dt} (m_i v_{i_x}) = \frac{d}{dt} \Sigma (m_i v_{i_x}).$$

The expression $\Sigma(m_i v_{i_x})$ is the sum of the linear momenta of all particles
in the x-direction and is defined as the linear momentum G_x of the system in the x-direction. This momentum may be expressed in terms of
the motion of the mass center. The principle of moments is

$$m\bar{x} = \Sigma(m_i x_i),$$

where x_i is the x-coordinate of m_i, m is the total mass of the system, and
$\bar{x}$ is the x-coordinate to the mass center. Differentiation with respect
to the time gives

$$m\bar{v}_x = \Sigma(m_i v_{i_x}) = G_x.$$

Thus the linear momentum of any system equals the total mass of the
system multiplied by the velocity of the center of mass.

The symbol G_x and its interpretation may now be used in the equation for ΣF_x. With similar expressions for the y- and z-directions there
result

$$\Sigma F_x = \frac{dG_x}{dt},$$

$$\Sigma F_y = \frac{dG_y}{dt}, \tag{101}$$

$$\Sigma F_z = \frac{dG_z}{dt}.$$

Equations (101) are the scalar components of the single vector equation

$$\Sigma F = \frac{dG}{dt}, \tag{102}$$

where $G = m\bar{v}$. Equation (102) states that the resultant of the external
forces acting on any system of particles equals the magnitude and direction of the time rate of change of the linear momentum of the system.
This formulation is an extremely important concept in mechanics, and
is an alternate way of expressing the equation of motion of the mass
center of any system as stated previously in Chapter X by Eq. (75).

A rigid body is a special case of the more general system of particles,
and the principles developed here may be used to describe the relation

between the resultant force on the body and the time rate of change of linear momentum $m\bar{v}$ of the mass center of the body regardless of its motion. The linear momentum vector $G = m\bar{v}$ has the direction of $\bar{v}$ but does not pass through the mass center except in the special case of a translating rigid body.

Application of the principles of impulse and momentum requires the use of a free-body diagram where *all external forces* acting on the body or system are accounted for. In the method of work and energy it is necessary to consider only those forces which do work, whereas with the method of impulse and momentum *all* forces with components in the direction of motion exert impulses whether they do work or not.

The generality of Eq. (102), derived for any system of particles, is not needed when dealing with a translating rigid body whose mass does not change. This generality will be helpful in certain problems discussed in articles which follow.

SAMPLE PROBLEM

1057. The 100 lb. weight is pulled up the incline from rest by the action of the force P, which varies with the time according to the accompanying graph. Determine the velocity v of the weight 8 sec. after P begins to act. The coefficient of friction is 0.30.

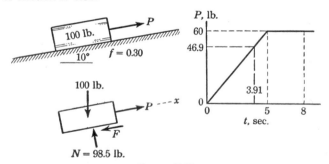

PROB. 1057

Solution: The free-body diagram of the block is drawn and discloses three forces which have components in the direction of motion. There is zero resultant force on the 100 lb. weight until P overcomes the limiting frictional force of $0.30 \times 100 \cos 10° = 29.5$ lb. and reaches the value of

$$P = 29.5 + 100 \sin 10° = 46.9 \text{ lb.}$$

when $t = (46.9/60)5 = 3.91$ sec. For the remaining 4.09 sec. the net force in the direction of motion is

$$\Sigma F_x = P - 46.9.$$

The impulse during the 4.09 sec. is

$$\int_{3.91}^{8} P\,dt - 46.9 \times 4.09 = 46.4 \text{ lb. sec.,}$$

where the integral is discontinuous and may be obtained from the area under the curve to the right of $t = 3.91$ sec. The impulse-momentum principle gives

$$\left[\int \Sigma F_x\,dt = \Delta(mv_x) \right] \qquad\qquad 46.4 = \frac{100}{32.2}(v - 0),$$

$$v = 14.94 \text{ ft./sec.} \qquad\qquad Ans.$$

PROBLEMS

1058. The driver of a car traveling at 60 mi./hr. down a 3 per cent grade jams on his brakes and skids all four wheels for 3 sec. before releasing the brakes. If the coefficient of kinetic friction between the tires and the road is 0.75, find the velocity v of the car at the end of the 3 sec. interval. *Ans.* $v = 12.61$ mi./hr.

1059. Determine the constant drawbar pull P required to increase the velocity of a 1500 ton train of freight cars from 30 mi./hr. to 50 mi./hr. up a 1 per cent grade in 3 min. Train resistance is 10 lb./ton.

1060. A 2 lb. body which has a velocity of 10 ft./sec. to the left is struck with an impact force F acting to the right on the body as represented in the graph. Approximate the loading by the dotted triangle and determine the final velocity v of the object. *Ans.* $v = 38.3$ ft./sec. to the right

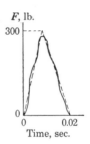

PROB. 1060

1061. In the pulley arrangement of Sample Prob. 962 find the time t required for the 1500 lb. block to reach a velocity of 10 ft./sec. after release from rest.

1062. A jet-propelled airplane weighing 8 tons is flying at a constant speed of 500 mi./hr. when the pilot ignites two rocket assist units, each of which develops a forward thrust of 1000 lb. for 12 sec. If the velocity of the airplane is 530 mi./hr. at the end of the 12 sec., find the time average ΔR of the increase in air resistance. The weight of the rocket fuel is negligible compared with the weight of the airplane. *Ans.* $\Delta R = 178$ lb.

1063. The resultant force F_x acting on a small 4 lb. object which slides with negligible friction along the horizontal x-direction pulsates with the time as shown in the graph. If the object has an initial velocity of 10 ft./sec. in the negative x-direction when $t = 0$, find its velocity v when $t = 6$ sec.

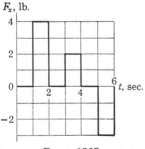

PROB. 1063

1064. The 400 lb. skip is rolling with negligible friction down the inclined track and unwinds the attached cable from the drum. When the skip reaches a speed of 10 ft./sec. down the plane, a constant clockwise moment of 30 lb. ft. is applied to the drum through a fluid coupling by its motor. Determine the velocity v of the skip 10 sec. later. Neglect friction in all bearings and the weights of the wheels, pulley, and drum. *Ans.* $v = 3.27$ ft./sec. up incline

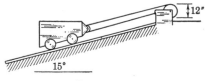

PROB. 1064

1065. A 3.22 lb. body is moving in a horizontal straight line with a velocity of 15 ft./sec. when a horizontal force F is applied to it at right angles to the initial direction of motion. If F varies according to the given relation, remains constant in direction, and is the only force acting on the body in its plane of motion, find the velocity of the body when $t = 2$ sec.

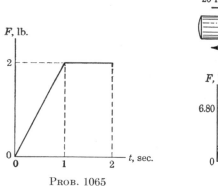

PROB. 1065

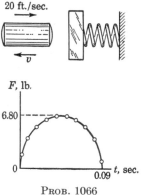

PROB. 1066

1066. Careful measurements made during the impact of the metal cylinder against the spring-supported plate disclose a semielliptical relation between the contact force F and the time t as shown. Determine the rebound velocity v of the cylinder if it weighs 8 oz. and strikes the plate with an initial velocity of 20 ft./sec.

1067. A small object weighing 4 oz. slides with negligible friction on the surface inclined to the horizontal plane as shown. In addition to the weight of

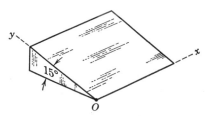

PROB. 1067

the object two forces, F_x in the x-direction and F_y in the y-direction, act on the object and vary with the time according to the following schedule:

t, sec.	F_x, oz.	F_y, oz.
0	0	0
0.1	0.27	1.15
0.2	0.78	1.83
0.3	1.45	2.35
0.4	2.33	2.80
0.5	3.33	3.16
0.6	4.52	3.50

Plot these data and determine the magnitude of the velocity v of the object 0.6 sec. after starting from O with an initial velocity of 2 ft./sec. in the y-direction.   *Ans.* $v = 11.3$ ft./sec.

1068. The drawbar pull exerted by a locomotive on a 1000 ton train of cars going up a 1 per cent grade is increased uniformly with the time from 40,000 lb. to 50,000 lb. in 30 sec. If the velocity of the train was 30 mi./hr. at the beginning of the interval, find the velocity v after 30 sec. Train resistance is constant at 10 lb./ton.   *Ans.* $v = 34.9$ mi./hr.

1069. An 8 oz. body vibrates along the x-axis under the action of an alternating force in the x-direction whose amplitude decreases with the time as shown in the accompanying graph and as given by

$$F_x = 2e^{-t} \cos 2\pi t,$$

where F_x is in pounds and t is in seconds. If the body is moving with a velocity of 4 ft./sec. in the negative x-direction at time $t = 0$, find its velocity v at time $t = 2\frac{1}{2}$ sec.

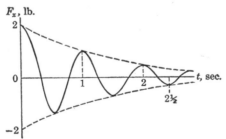

PROB. 1069

* 1070. If the resistance R to the motion of a train of weight W increases with velocity according to $R = R_0 + Kv$, where R_0 is the initial resistance to be overcome in starting the train and K is a constant, find the time t required for the train to reach a velocity v from rest on a horizontal track under the action of a constant tractive force F.

Ans. $t = \dfrac{W}{Kg} \log \dfrac{F - R_0}{F - R_0 - Kv}$

* **1071.** Prove that the displacement s of a particle of mass m subjected to the resultant force ΣF in the direction of its straight line motion during time t is given by $s = v_0 t + A\bar{t}/m$, where v_0 is the initial velocity at $t = 0$, A is the impulse (area under the curve of ΣF and t), and $\bar{t}$ is the time coordinate to the centroid of A measured from time t as shown.

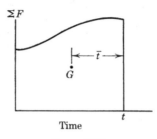

PROB. 1071

105. Diversion of Steady Fluid Streams. The principle of impulse and momentum finds important application in the analysis of the dynamics of fluids. In particular consider the diversion of a stream or jet of fluid by a curved vane, as represented in Fig. 129. The force exerted on the fluid by the vane may be determined with the aid of the general principle of linear impulse and momentum as expressed by

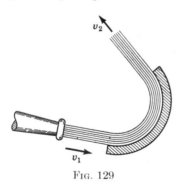

FIG. 129

Eq. (102). When applied to a portion of the fluid stream between the entrance and exit sections of the curved vane, this equation states that the resultant of all forces acting on this portion of the fluid equals the time rate of change of its linear momentum. If m' stands for the constant time rate of mass flow, then the time rate of change of momentum is the final momentum rate minus (vectorially) the initial momentum rate. Thus, if the vector difference between the final and initial velocities of the stream is $\Delta v = v_2 \rightarrow v_1$, the resultant force acting on the stream is

$$\Sigma F = m'\Delta v. \tag{103}$$

In problems involving the open flow of fluid streams the pressure in the fluid stream remains essentially constant, and the only force on the stream which need be considered is that exerted on it by the vane. Also, for relatively short vane lengths the loss of speed of the stream due to surface friction may be neglected so that the velocity along the vane remains essentially constant.

In the flow of streams where the static pressure change is appreciable this pressure distributed over the stream section must be considered an external force on the fluid in question.

SAMPLE PROBLEM

1072. The smooth vane shown diverts the stream of fluid of cross-sectional area A, mass density ρ, and velocity v into two equal parts. (*a*) Determine the force F required to hold the vane in a fixed position. (*b*) Find the force F when the vane is given a constant velocity u less than v and in the direction of v. (*c*) Determine the optimum speed u for the generation of maximum power by the action of the fluid on the moving vane.

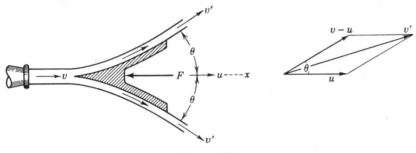

PROB. 1072

Solution: Part (a): The given sketch may be used as the free-body diagram of the fluid portion undergoing the momentum change. By symmetry there is no resultant change in momentum in the y-direction, and, consequently, there is no resultant force in this direction. With the vane stationary the magnitude of the exit velocity v' equals that of the entering velocity v with fluid friction neglected. The vector difference in velocity is

$$\Delta v_x = v' \cos \theta - v = -v(1 - \cos \theta),$$

and the mass rate of flow is

$$m' = \rho A v.$$

Substitution into the impulse-momentum equation for steady flow gives

$$[\Sigma F_x = m'\Delta v_x] \qquad\qquad -F = \rho A v[-v(1 - \cos \theta)],$$

$$F = \rho A v^2(1 - \cos \theta). \qquad\qquad Ans.$$

Part (b): In the case of the moving vane the final velocity of the fluid upon exit is the vector sum of the velocity u of the vane plus the velocity of the fluid relative to the vane. This combination is shown in the velocity diagram to the right of the figure for the exit conditions of the upper branch of the stream. The relative velocity is that which would be measured by an observer moving with the vane. This observer would measure $v - u$ feet of fluid passing over the vane per second, and the direction of this relative velocity is tangent to the vane at exit. The combination of these two velocity components gives the final absolute fluid velocity v' as shown. The x-component of v' is the sum of the components of its two parts, so $v_x' = (v - u) \cos \theta + u$. The vector change in x-velocity of the stream is

$$\Delta v_x = (v - u) \cos \theta + (u - v) = -(v - u)(1 - \cos \theta).$$

The mass rate of flow m' is the mass undergoing momentum change per unit of time. This rate is the mass flowing over the vane per unit time and not the rate of issuance from the nozzle. Thus

$$m' = \rho A (v - u).$$

The impulse-momentum principle applied to the positive x-direction gives

$$[\Sigma F_x = m' \Delta v_x] \qquad -F = \rho A (v - u)[-(v - u)(1 - \cos \theta)],$$

$$F = \rho A (v - u)^2 (1 - \cos \vartheta). \qquad Ans.$$

Part (c): The power developed by the force (equal and opposite to F) exerted by the fluid on the moving vane is

$$[P = Fu] \qquad P = \rho A (v - u)^2 u (1 - \cos \theta).$$

The velocity of the vane for maximum power for the one blade in the stream is specified by

$$\left[\frac{dP}{du} = 0 \right] \qquad \rho A (1 - \cos \theta)(v^2 - 4uv + 3u^2) = 0,$$

$$(v - 3u)(v - u) = 0, \qquad u = \frac{v}{3}. \qquad Ans.$$

The second solution $u = v$ gives a minimum condition of zero power. An angle $\theta = 180$ deg. completely reverses the direction of the fluid and clearly produces both maximum force and maximum power for any value of u.

PROBLEMS

1073. A fire hose with a 1.25 in. inside diameter nozzle has a discharge rate of 350 gal./min. under a gage pressure at the base of the nozzle of 60 lb./in.^{2} Determine the force F of this stream against a fixed surface normal to the stream and close to the nozzle.

1074. When the air only of a sand-blasting gun is turned on, the force of the air on a flat surface normal to the stream and 6 in. from the nozzle is 2 lb. With the nozzle in the same position the force increases to 5 lb. when the sand is admitted to the stream. If sand is used at the rate of 10 lb./min., find the velocity v of the particles of sand as they strike the surface.

Ans. $v = 580$ ft./sec.

1075. If the entire stream in Sample Prob. 1072 is deflected by the upper leg of the vane, find the vertical force F_y which must support the vane as it moves to the right with the constant velocity u.

1076. The tank is filled to a height h with a liquid of weight density μ. If the liquid emerges with negligible friction through the nozzle of exit area A, find the friction force F exerted by the horizontal surface on the bottom of the tank.

$$Ans. \quad F = \frac{\mu}{g} Av^2 = 2\mu Ah$$

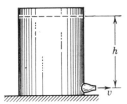

PROB. 1076

1077. The tender of a locomotive traveling at the constant speed of 60 mi./hr. replenishes its supply of water by scooping it up from a trough between the rails at the rate of 6 ft.³/sec. Find the added resistance R to motion due to the action of the scoop.

1078. A stream of water flowing at the rate of 500 gal./min. from a 2 in. diameter nozzle is diverted by the fixed vane. The vane is positioned so that ⅔ of the stream is diverted up and the remainder is deflected down and back as shown. Determine the total force F required to hold the vane in place. $Ans.$ $F = 144$ lb.

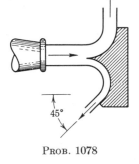

45°

PROB. 1078

1079. In the case of multiple vanes where each vane which enters the jet is followed immediately by another, as in a turbine or water wheel, determine the maximum power P which can be developed for a given blade angle and the corresponding optimum peripheral speed u of the vanes in terms of the jet velocity v for maximum power. Assume an infinite number of vanes so that the rate at which fluid leaves the nozzle equals the rate at which fluid passes over the vanes. $Ans.$ $P = \frac{1}{4}\rho Av^3(1 - \cos\theta), u = \frac{v}{2}$

1080. Find the force F required to give the vane of Sample Prob. 1072 a velocity of 10 ft./sec. to the left against the fluid stream which has a velocity of 90 ft./sec. The vane angle is $\theta = 30$ deg., the diameter of the circular jet is 1 in., and the fluid is water.

1081. The pipe bend shown has a cross-sectional area A and is supported in its plane by the tension T applied to its flanges by the adjacent connecting pipes (not shown). If the velocity of the liquid is v, its mass density ρ, and its static pressure p, determine T and show that it is independent of the bend angle θ. $Ans.$ $T = A(p + \rho v^2)$

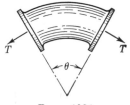

T T

θ

PROB. 1081

1082. A jet of fluid with velocity v, cross-sectional area A, and mass density ρ impinges on a fixed slanted trough shown in section. Some of the fluid is diverted in each of the two directions. If the trough is smooth, the velocity of both diverted streams remains v, and the only force which can be exerted on the fluid is normal to the surface of the trough. By writing the impulse-momentum equations for the directions along and normal to the trough determine the force F required to support the trough and the rate of flow Q (volume per unit time) in each of the two directions.

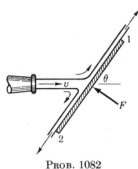

$Ans.$ $F = \rho A v^2 \sin \theta;$

$$Q_1 = \frac{Q}{2}(1 + \cos\theta),\ Q_2 = \frac{Q}{2}(1 - \cos\theta)$$

1083. The helicopter shown has a weight W and hovers in midair by imparting downward momentum to a column of air defined by the slip-stream boundary shown. Find the downward velocity v given to the air by the rotor at a section in the stream below the rotor where the pressure is atmospheric and the stream radius is r.

PROB. 1082

Also find the power P required by the engine. Neglect the rotational energy of the air, any temperature rise due to air friction, and any change in air density ρ.

$$Ans.\quad v = \frac{1}{r}\sqrt{\frac{W}{\pi\rho}},\ P = \frac{W}{2r}\sqrt{\frac{W}{\pi\rho}}$$

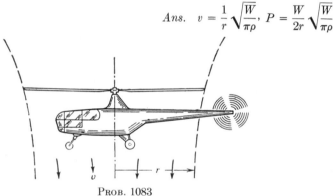

PROB. 1083

1084. An air stream with a velocity of 50 ft./sec. is pumped through the stationary duct A and exhausted through an experimental nozzle section. The average static pressure across the section B is 150 lb./in.^{2} gage, and the density of the air at this pressure and at the temperature prevailing is 0.820 lb./ft.^{3}

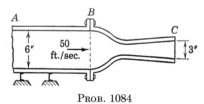

PROB. 1084

The average static pressure across the exit section C is measured to be 2 lb./in.^{2} gage, and the corresponding air density is 0.0760 lb./ft.^{3} Determine the total tension T in the bolts which secure the nozzle to the fixed duct section. (*Hint:* Analyze the nozzle and air within it between sections B and C at a given instant as the free body.)

1085. In a wind-tunnel test of a 4-bladed propeller the air approaches the test stand with a velocity of 200 mi./hr. and leaves the test stand with a velocity of 230 mi./hr. The density of the approaching air is 0.0760 lb./ft.³, and the inside diameter of the tunnel is 10 ft. Compute the thrust T on the propeller and the power output P of the motor. Neglect rotational energy of the air, any temperature rise due to air friction, and any difference in static pressure between the approach and exit sections. *Ans.* $T = 2390$ lb., $P = 1372$ h.p.

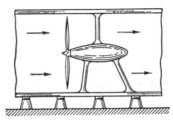

PROB. 1085

* 1086. The cross valve shown transfers water from the vertical pipe under a static pressure of 100 lb./in.² gage to the horizontal pipe at 25 lb./in.² gage. The constant flow rate through the vertical pipe is 260 gal./min. Determine the compression C in the valve stem if it has a vertical lift of ⅛ in. above the closed position. The 25 lb./in.² pressure may be assumed to act over the upper exposed area of the valve. (*Hint:* Analyze a free body consisting of the valve and stem, and a section of water in the vertical pipe.) *Ans.* $C = 475$ lb.

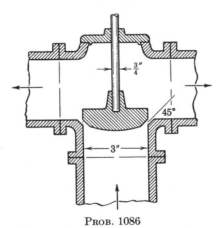

PROB. 1086

* 1087. In the figure is shown an impulse turbine wheel for a hydroelectric power plant which is to operate with a static head of water of 1000 ft. at each of its 6 nozzles and is to rotate at the speed of 270 rev./min. Each wheel and generator unit is to develop an output power of 22,000 k.w. The efficiency of the generator may be taken to be 0.90, and an efficiency of 0.85 for the conversion of the kinetic energy of the water jets to energy delivered by the turbine[¹]

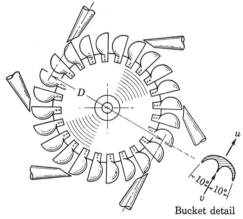

Bucket detail

PROB. 1087

may be expected. The mean peripheral speed of such a wheel for greatest efficiency will be about 0.47 times the jet velocity. If each of the buckets is to have the shape shown, determine the necessary jet diameter d and wheel diameter D. Assume that the water acts on the bucket which is at the tangent point of each jet stream.   *Ans.* $d = 6.42$ in., $D = 8.45$ ft.

* **1088.** In the figure is shown a detail of the stationary nozzle diaphragm A

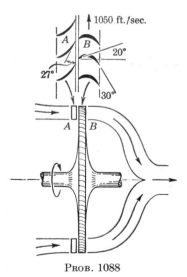

PROB. 1088

and the rotating blades B of a gas turbine. The products of combustion pass through the fixed diaphragm blades at the 27 deg. angle and impinge on the moving rotor blades. The angles shown are selected so that the velocity of the gas relative to the moving blade at entrance is at the 20 deg. angle for minimum turbulence, corresponding to a mean blade velocity of 1050 ft./sec. at a radius of 15 in. If gas flows past the blades at the rate of 30 lb./sec., determine the theoretical power output P of the turbine. Neglect fluid and mechanical friction with the resulting heat energy loss, and assume that all the gases are deflected along the surfaces of the blades with a velocity relative to the blade of constant magnitude.

Ans. $P = 1500$ h.p.

106. Motion with Variable Mass; Jet Propulsion. Consider a body, Fig. 130, which gains mass by virtue of its overtaking and swallowing a stream of matter. The mass of the body and its velocity at any instant are m and v, respectively. The stream of matter is assumed to be moving in the same direction with a constant velocity v_0 less than v and moving without disturbance except after it enters m. The force exerted by m on the particles of the stream to accelerate them from a

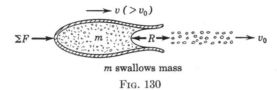

m swallows mass

FIG. 130

velocity v_0 to a greater velocity v is designated by R and is accompanied by an equal and opposite reaction on m. In addition to R all other forces which are applied externally to m are designated by ΣF, taken as positive in the direction of motion. The principle of motion of the mass center, Eq. (75), states that at any *instant* the resultant of all external forces on any mass system equals the mass at that instant times the acceleration of the center of mass. Thus the motion equation for m at the instant represented is

$$\Sigma F - R = m \frac{dv}{dt}.$$

If the time rate of accumulation of mass in m is designated by m' and the relative velocity between the moving stream and m is $\Delta v = v - v_0 = u$, then by Eq. (103) the force R equals $m'u$. Hence

$$\Sigma F = m \frac{dv}{dt} + m'u. \tag{104}$$

Equation (104) may be considered the equation of motion of m, where ΣF is the resultant of all forces on m in the direction of v exclusive of the force R exerted on m by the overtaken stream of matter.

The more important problem of a body which loses mass during motion is represented in Fig. 131. Mass within the body is ejected to

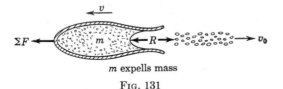

m expells mass

FIG. 131

the rear with an absolute velocity v_0 by the force R internally generated. Again, if ΣF represents all other forces externally applied to m in the direction of its velocity, the motion equation is

$$\Sigma F + R = m\frac{dv}{dt}.$$

If m_0' represents the time rate at which mass is ejected, and the relative escape velocity of the ejected mass is $\Delta v = v_0 - (-v) = u$, then again by Eq. (103) the force R is $m_0'u$. Hence

$$\Sigma F = m\frac{dv}{dt} - m_0'u. \tag{105}$$

Equation (105) may be considered the equation of motion of m, where ΣF is the resultant of all forces on m exclusive of the reaction R of the ejected stream. This reaction $R = m_0'u$ is known as the *jet reaction* or *momentum thrust* and forms the basis of jet propulsion.

Equations (104) and (105) were obtained by writing the force-mass-acceleration relation for the instantaneous motion of m alone. The equations may be obtained also by direct use of the impulse-momentum principle, Eq. (102), applied to the system composed of m and a portion m_0 of the mass stream, as represented in Fig. 132 for the case of ejected

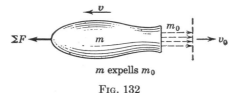

m expells m_0

Fig. 132

mass. In this formulation the jet reaction R is a force *internal* to the system considered. The dotted section which defines the extremity of m_0 is arbitrary as long as it is slightly removed from m so that the velocity of the stream m_0 at this section is constant. Thus the system is considered as having two parts at any instant, m moving with a velocity v and an arbitrary portion m_0 of ejected mass moving undisturbed away from m with a constant velocity v_0. Applying Eq. (102) to the entire system in the v-direction gives

$$\Sigma F = \frac{d}{dt}(mv - m_0v_0) = m\frac{dv}{dt} + v\frac{dm}{dt} - m_0\frac{dv_0}{dt} - v_0\frac{dm_0}{dt}.$$

The term dv_0/dt is zero since m_0 moves undisturbed once free of m. Also the rate at which m_0 increases must equal the rate at which m decreases, so that $dm_0/dt = -dm/dt$. Thus

$$\Sigma F = m\frac{dv}{dt} + (v + v_0)\frac{dm}{dt}.$$

Introducing the relative velocity between m and m_0 gives

$$\Sigma F = m\frac{dv}{dt} + u\frac{dm}{dt}. \qquad (106)$$

Equations (104) and (105) are both contained in Eq. (106) as may be seen when the rate of decrease of mass $m_0' = -dm/dt$ or the rate of increase of mass $m' = dm/dt$ is substituted.

Rocket Propulsion: A rocket is a vehicle in which is stored all the matter to be ejected during its motion. The matter is ejected at high velocity by the expansion of gases from the combustion process, and both ingredients for combustion, fuel and oxidizer, are contained within the rocket. The forces acting on a rocket in vertical flight, Fig. 133, are the momentum thrust T, the gravitational attraction W, and the atmospheric resistance R. In addition when the exhaust pressure is greater (or less) than the pressure in the surrounding medium, a positive (or negative) thrust acting over the cross-sectional area of the exhaust stream as a result of this pressure difference will be present.

FIG. 133

In most rockets the relative escape velocity u and mass rate m_0' of the expelled gas are essentially constant, and, thus, the momentum thrust will remain equally constant.

A rocket is the only known vehicle which will operate without a surrounding medium and, theoretically, is the only known means of achieving interplanetary travel.

Duct Propulsion: A device in which the surrounding fluid, liquid or gas, is ducted through it and expelled at higher velocity by thermal or mechanical means is said to operate by duct propulsion. This system involves the motion of a vehicle which both swallows and expels mass. The forces acting on such a vehicle are shown in Fig. 134 for the case of a *thermal jet* airplane. If the pressures across the entering and exhaust sections are nearly atmospheric, the net thrust T is the difference between the exhaust momentum rate and the intake momentum rate. If m_a' and m_g' represent the mass rates of entering air and exhaust gas, respectively, and R represents the resistance of the exterior surface of the airplane to motion through the surrounding atmosphere, the equation for accelerated flight is

$$m_g'u - m_a'v - R - W \sin \theta = m \frac{dv}{dt}.$$

The entering air is assumed to be at rest initially so that v is its velocity relative to the airplane, and the velocity of the exhaust gas relative to the airplane is u.

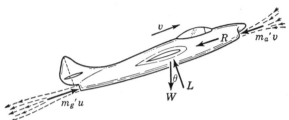

F<small>IG</small>. 134

If thermal power is used to accelerate the ducted fluid, as in the gas turbine of a turbojet engine, fuel at the mass rate m_f' will be burned. The total exhaust mass rate is, then, $m_g' = m_a' + m_f'$. In most such engines, however, m_f' is less than 2 per cent of m_a', so that the net thrust is approximately

$$T = m_g'(u - v).$$

SAMPLE PROBLEMS

1089. The end of a chain of length l and weight μ per unit length which is piled on a platform is lifted vertically with a constant velocity v by a variable force P.   Find P as a function of the height x of the end above the platform.

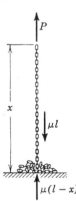

Solution: The principle of impulse and momentum for a system of particles expressed by Eq. (102) will be applied to the entire chain considered as the system.   The free-body diagram of the system shows the unknown force P, the total weight of all links μl, and the force $\mu(l - x)$ exerted by the platform on those links which are at rest upon it.   The momentum of the system at any position is

$$G_x = \frac{\mu x}{g} v,$$

and the momentum equation gives

$$\left[\Sigma F_x = \frac{dG_x}{dt} \right] \quad P + \mu(l - x) - \mu l = \frac{d}{dt} \left(\frac{\mu x}{g} v \right),$$

$$P = \mu \left(x + \frac{v^2}{g} \right). \qquad Ans.$$

P<small>ROB</small>. 1089

Motion with Variable Mass; Jet Propulsion

The force P is seen to be equal to the weight of the portion of the chain w. is off the platform plus the added term which accounts for the time rate of crease of momentum of the chain.

Solution by Eq. (104) may also be made by considering the moving part of the chain as a body which gains mass. The force ΣF is the resultant of al forces on the moving mass $\mu x/g$ of the chain except that exerted by the particles which are accumulated and is $\Sigma F = P - \mu x$. The velocity is constant so $dv/dt = 0$. The rate of adding mass is $m' = \mu v/g$. The relative velocity u of the attaching particles is v. Thus

$$\left[\Sigma F = m\frac{dv}{dt} + m'u \right] \qquad P - \mu x = 0 + \frac{\mu v}{g} v,$$

$$P = \mu\left(x + \frac{v^2}{g} \right).$$

1090. A jet-propelled airplane, similar to the one shown in Fig. 134, has a constant speed of 600 mi./hr. in horizontal flight. The turbojet engine consumes air through the intake scoop at the rate of 140 lb./sec. at this speed and uses fuel at the rate of 1.30 lb./sec. The gases are exhausted at a relative nozzle velocity of 1800 ft./sec. at atmospheric pressure. Determine the total drag D (air resistance) on the exterior surface of the airplane and the useful power P (thrust horsepower) of the engine at this speed.

Solution: The total thrust equals the drag for zero acceleration. Thus

$$[T = m_g'u - m_a'v] \qquad T = \frac{141.3}{32.2} \times 1800 - \frac{140}{32.2} \times 880,$$

$$D = T = 7900 - 3830 = 4070 \text{ lb.} \qquad\qquad Ans.$$

The useful power is

$$[P = Tv] \qquad P = \frac{4070 \times 880}{550} = 6510 \text{ h.p.} \qquad\qquad Ans.$$

PROBLEMS

1091. The net thrust for the airplane of Sample Prob. 1090 was shown to be 4070 lb., where the jet exhausts at atmospheric pressure (14.7 lb./in.²). If the exhaust pressure is decreased to 10 lb./in.² absolute, and the mass rate of flow remains the same, compute the new thrust T. The exhaust nozzle has a diameter of 20 in.

1092. A V-2 rocket with an empty weight of 8800 lb. is fired vertically up with a fuel load of 18,400 lb. The exit velocity of the exhaust gases relative to the nozzle is constant at 6500 ft./sec., and an initial acceleration of 32.0 ft./sec.² vertically up is measured. Determine the initial weight rate W' of exhausted gas if the static pressure across the jet equals that of the atmosphere. *Ans.* $W' = 269$ lb./sec.

1093. A cart of sand is being propelled on a horizontal surface by a force of 30 lb. as shown. If the sand drops out of a hole in the bottom at the rate of 10 lb./sec., find the acceleration a of the cart at the time when its total weight is 400 lb. and its forward velocity is 4 ft./sec. Frictional resistance to the motion of the cart is 17 lb. *Ans.* $a = 1.046$ ft./sec.^{2}

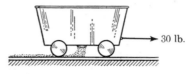

30 lb.

PROB. 1093

1094. A tank which weighs 100 lb. empty is propelled to the right by a force F as shown and scoops up water from a stream flowing in the opposite direction at the velocity of 4 ft./sec. The entrance area of the scoop is 3 in.^{2}, and water enters the scoop at a rate equal to the velocity of the scoop relative to the stream. Find the weight W of water in the tank at a certain instant for which $F = 25$ lb., $v = 5$ ft./sec., $a = 2$ ft./sec.^{2} Neglect the small impact pressure at the scoop entrance necessary to elevate the water into the tank.

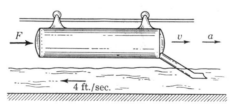

F v a

4 ft./sec.

PROB. 1094

1095. Is it possible for the absolute velocity v_0 of the exhaust gases of a rocket to be in the same direction as the velocity v of the rocket? Answer the same question for ducted jet propulsion.

1096. The ram-jet unit shown is a thermal jet engine in which the air is forced through the convergent section AB and compressed because of the large

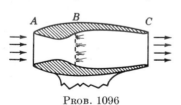

A B C

PROB. 1096

velocity of the unit. Fuel is injected and burned at section B, and the expanded gases leave the nozzle C with high velocity. Consider two such units, one on each tip of the two rotor blades of a helicopter which requires 100 thrust h.p. to hover at sea level. The 30 ft. diameter rotor revolves at the speed of 280 rev./min. because of the tangential thrust of the two ram jets. Determine the weight rate of air w_a through each jet if the relative exhaust velocity u of the gases is 1450 ft./sec. at atmospheric pressure. Neglect the weight of the fuel burned.

1097. A boat is propelled at a constant speed of 12 knots (1 knot equals 1.152 mi./hr.) by hydraulic jet propulsion.   Salt water enters the intake scoops amidships as shown and is piped to the pump which exhausts it astern at the rate of

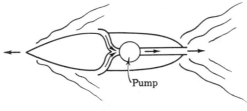

PROB. 1097

3550 gal./min. through a single pipe of 3.35 in. inside diameter.   Also, the gasoline engine power plant delivers 260 h.p. to the pump.   Determine the resistance R to the motion of the ship through the water and find the percentage e of the total output power of the engine which goes into driving the ship.

*Ans. $R = 1711$ lb., $e = 24.3$ per cent

1098. A chain of length l and weight μ per unit length is held vertically above the platform scale shown and released from rest with the lower end just touching the scale.   Determine the force F read on the scale as a function of the distance x through which the upper end has fallen.   *(Comment: The chain acquires a free-fall velocity of $\sqrt{2gx}$ since the links on the scale exert no force on those above which are still falling.   Work the problem in two ways, first, by evaluating the time rate of change of momentum for the entire system and, second, by considering the force F to be composed of the weight of links at rest on the scale and the force necessary to divert an equivalent stream of fluid.)*

PROB. 1098

1099. A small rocket of initial mass m_0 is fired vertically up near the surface of the earth (g constant).   If the air resistance is neglected, determine the manner in which the mass m of the rocket must vary as a function of the time t after launching in order that the rocket may have a constant vertical acceleration a with a constant relative escape velocity u of the gases.

* 1100. A small rocket of initial mass m_0 is fired vertically up near the surface of the earth (g constant), and the mass rate of exhaust m' and the relative escape velocity u are constant.   Determine the velocity v as a function of the time t if the resistance of the air could be neglected and if the weight of the rocket case and machinery is negligible compared with the weight of fuel carried.

Ans. $v = u \log \left(\dfrac{m_0}{m_0 - m't} \right) - gt$

* **1101.** The *propulsive efficiency* e for jet propulsion is defined as the ratio of the *thrust power* Tv to the *propulsion power*. The propulsion power is the rate at which kinetic energy is developed by the engine and includes the thrust power and the rate at which kinetic energy is lost in the exhaust jet. Determine and plot the propulsive efficiency e_r for a rocket and e_j for a ducted jet in terms of the velocity ratio $\nu = v/u$. For the ducted jet neglect the fuel rate m_f' compared with the total exhaust mass rate m_g'.

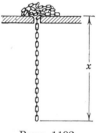

$$Ans. \quad e_r = \frac{2\nu}{1 + \nu^2}, \ e_j = \frac{2\nu}{1 + \nu}$$

* **1102.** One end of a pile of chain falls through a hole in its support as shown and pulls the remaining links after it in a steady flow. If the links which are initially at rest acquire the velocity of the chain without frictional resistance or interference from the support or from adjacent links, find the velocity v of the chain as a function of x if $v = 0$ when $x = 0$. [*Hint:* Apply Eq. (104) and treat the product xv as the variable when solving the differential equation. Also note at the appropriate step that $dx = v \, dt$.]

PROB. 1102

$$Ans. \quad v = \sqrt{\frac{2gx}{3}}$$

107. Angular Impulse and Momentum. A particle of mass m moving with velocity v, Fig. 135a, has a linear momentum mv. The *moment* of this linear momentum vector about the point O is mvr and is defined as the *angular momentum* H of the particle about the point. The angular momentum is a vector which may be represented by the conventional

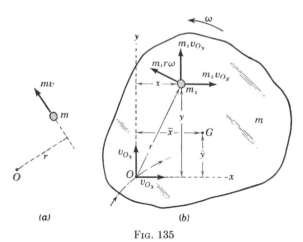

FIG. 135

right-hand rule for moments. The angular momentum of a rigid body, Fig. 135b, about an axis perpendicular to the plane of motion and passing through a point O fixed in the moving body is the sum of the moments of the linear momenta of all its particles about the axis. Since the velocity of a representative particle of mass m_i may be expressed in terms of the velocity components of O plus the velocity of m_i with respect to O, the linear momentum of m_i will be the vector sum of the components shown in the figure. Thus the angular momentum of the particle about O will be the sum of the moments of these linear momentum components about O. Summing up these terms for all particles gives for the total angular momentum of the body about point O fixed in the body

$$H_O = \Sigma m_i r^2 \omega + \Sigma m_i v_{O_y} x - \Sigma m_i v_{O_x} y,$$

where the counterclockwise direction is arbitrarily taken as positive. Introducing the definition of the moment of inertia about O and the coordinates to the mass center gives

$$H_O = I_O \omega + \bar{x} m v_{O_y} - \bar{y} m v_{O_x}. \tag{107}$$

It should be observed that for clockwise rotation the signs of the last two terms in this equation would be reversed if H_O is measured positive clockwise. Equation (107) finds its greatest use when the axis through O is fixed (pure rotation), which gives

$$H_O = I_O \omega,$$

and also when the mass center G is used as the reference point, in which case

$$\bar{H} = \bar{I} \omega.$$

The linear momentum of a body is the vector $G = m\bar{v}$ which has the direction of the velocity of the center of mass. Since angular momentum equals the moment of linear momentum, the position of the vector $m\bar{v}$ may be located for each of the three types of plane motion shown in Fig. 136. In the a-part of the figure for translation the momentum vector $m\bar{v}$ passes through G. This condition is easily seen since the resultant moment of the linear momenta of all particles about G is

$$\Sigma m_i \bar{v} y = \bar{v} \Sigma m_i y = 0,$$

where m_i is the mass of a representative particle. It follows that the angular momentum of a translating body about an axis through a moving or fixed point such as A is $H_A = m\bar{v}b$.

For pure rotation about O in Fig. 136b the moment of the linear momentum is

$$m\bar{v}q = I_O \omega, \qquad \text{and} \qquad q = \frac{I_O \omega}{m\bar{v}} = \frac{k_O^2}{\bar{r}}.$$

Thus the linear momentum vector passes through the center of percussion relative to O. If the body rotates about a fixed axis through G, the linear momentum is zero, and the angular momentum vector $\bar{I}\omega$ has all the properties of a free vector. In this event the angular momentum is the same about all parallel axes, fixed or moving.

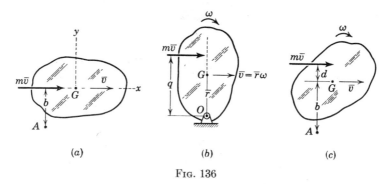

$$\text{(a)} \qquad\qquad \text{(b)} \qquad\qquad \text{(c)}$$

FIG. 136

In the case of plane motion, Fig. 136c, the distance d of the linear momentum vector from the center of mass is obtained from

$$m\bar{v}d = \bar{I}\omega, \qquad \text{so} \qquad d = \frac{\bar{I}\omega}{m\bar{v}} = \frac{\bar{k}^2\omega}{\bar{v}}.$$

If the linear momentum vector is shown acting through the mass center G, a couple (angular momentum) equal to $m\bar{v}d = \bar{I}\omega$ must be shown. This representation is useful when the angular momentum of a body having plane motion is desired about some point, fixed or moving, such as A. Thus the angular momentum about A at a particular instant is $H_A = m\bar{v}(b + d) = m\bar{v}b + \bar{I}\omega$.

The relation between the angular momentum of a body and the applied moments is obtained from the rotational equation of motion. For rotation about the fixed axis through O, Fig. 136b, the sum of the moments of all forces about O is $\Sigma M_O = I_O\alpha = I_O(d\omega/dt)$. Since the moment of inertia I_O of the rigid body is constant, the motion equation may be written

$$\Sigma M_O = \frac{d}{dt}(I_O\omega). \tag{108}$$

In precisely the same manner the moment equation about the mass center for the case of any plane motion may be written

$$\Sigma \bar{M} = \frac{d}{dt}(\bar{I}\omega). \tag{109}$$

In words Eqs. (108) and (109) state that the resultant moment about
the fixed axis of pure rotation or about an axis through the mass center
in any plane motion equals the time rate of change of angular momentum about the respective axis.

Equations (108) and (109) hold during the entire time of motion, and
each may be integrated to give

$$\int_0^t \Sigma M_O \, dt = I_O \omega - I_O \omega_0 \qquad (110)$$

for rotation about the fixed axis through O and

$$\int_0^t \Sigma \overline{M} \, dt = \overline{I} \omega - \overline{I} \omega_0 \qquad (111)$$

for a reference axis through the mass center in plane motion.   In each
case the angular velocity changes from ω_0 at time $t = 0$ to ω at time t.
These equations state that the total *angular impulse* equals the corresponding net change in angular momentum.

The angular impulse-momentum equations are analogous to the
linear impulse-momentum equations developed in Art. 104.   Comparison shows that the dimensions of angular impulse and momentum
are [moment] $\times$ [time], (lb. ft. sec.), whereas those for linear impulse
and momentum are [force] $\times$ [time], (lb. sec.).
Thus these quantities *cannot be added.*

The rolling wheel, Fig. 137, is an important
special case of plane motion which deserves
separate comment.   It was shown in Art. 97 of
Chapter XI that the equation $\Sigma M_C = I_C \alpha$ holds
with respect to the instant center C of zero
velocity at all times during the motion provided

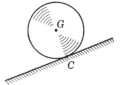

Fig. 137

the wheel does not slip and provided the geometric center of the wheel
is also the mass center.   This motion equation may be written

$$\Sigma M_C = \frac{d}{dt} (I_C \omega)$$

or integrated to give

$$\int_0^t \Sigma M_C \, dt = I_C \omega - I_C \omega_0. \qquad (112)$$

Integration is permitted since the same differential relation holds
throughout rolling under the conditions stated.   In this case the moment
axis is not attached to the wheel but moves with it and always coincides

with the instantaneous center C. The advantage of Eq. (112) for a rolling wheel is that the contact forces at C are eliminated from the equation. Considerable caution is warranted, however, since Eq. (112) must *not* be used except for a symmetrical wheel which does not slip.

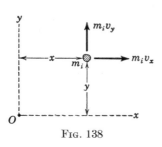

Fig. 138

Equations (108) and (109) were both developed for the motion of a rigid body, but it is important to recognize more general applicability to any system of particles. In Fig. 138 let m_i be the mass of a representative particle of any system, and consider the components of its motion in the x–y plane. From the principle of linear impulse and momentum the resultant force on m_i in the x-direction and that in the y-direction are

$$F_x + f_x = \frac{d}{dt}(m_i v_x), \qquad F_y + f_y = \frac{d}{dt}(m_i v_y),$$

where F_x and F_y stand for forces applied from sources external to the system and f_x and f_y represent internally applied forces. The resultant moment in a counterclockwise sense about a fixed point O is

$$M_i = (F_y + f_y)x - (F_x + f_x)y = x\frac{d}{dt}(m_i v_y) - y\frac{d}{dt}(m_i v_x).$$

Differentiation will show that this expression is the same as

$$M_i = \frac{d}{dt}(x m_i v_y) - \frac{d}{dt}(y m_i v_x),$$

or

$$M_i = \frac{d}{dt}(x m_i v_y - y m_i v_x) = \frac{dH_i}{dt}.$$

Thus the resultant moment M_i about O of all forces on m_i equals the time rate of change of angular momentum about O. By adding all such equations written for every particle of the system there results

$$\Sigma M_i = \Sigma \frac{dH_i}{dt} = \frac{d}{dt}\Sigma H_i.$$

The contribution to ΣM_i by the internal forces is zero since they occur in pairs of equal and opposite forces and their moments cancel. If the resultant moment of external forces about O is denoted by ΣM_O and the sum ΣH_i of the angular momenta of all particles about O by H_O the impulse-momentum equation becomes

$$\Sigma M_O = \frac{dH_O}{dt}. \tag{113}$$

Similar analyses in the two other coordinate planes will disclose similar equations, and thus Eq. (113) may be considered the vector combination of these three relations. Consequently, it may be stated that the resultant vector moment about any fixed *point* for a system of particles equals the time rate of change of angular momentum of the system about an axis through the point parallel with the vector moment axis. Although the proof will not be given here, Eq. (113) also holds with respect to a moving axis through the center of mass of any system.

SAMPLE PROBLEM

1103. The force P which is applied to the cable wrapped around the central hub of the symmetrical wheel is increased slowly according to $P = 1.50t$, where P is in pounds and t is in seconds. Determine the angular velocity ω of the wheel 10 sec. after P is applied if the wheel is rolling to the left with a linear velocity of its center of 3 ft./sec. at time $t = 0$. The wheel weighs 120 lb. with a centroidal radius of gyration of 10 in. and rolls without slipping.

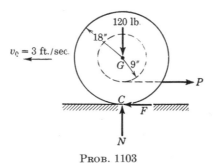

PROB. 1103

Solution I: The free-body diagram of the wheel is shown. The correct direction of the friction force is established by the necessity for a positive clockwise moment of forces about G to produce the resulting clockwise angular acceleration. Direct application of the angular impulse-momentum equation with respect to the mass center, Eq. (111), gives

$$\left[\int_0^t \Sigma \bar{M}\, dt = \Delta(\bar{I}\omega) \right]$$

$$\int_0^{10} \left(\frac{18}{12} F - \frac{9}{12} \times 1.50t \right) dt = \frac{120}{32.2} \left(\frac{10}{12} \right)^2 \left[\omega - \left(-\frac{3}{\frac{18}{12}} \right) \right],$$

where the positive direction is taken as clockwise. The force F is a variable and so must be left under the integral sign. The second equation needed to eliminate F is that of linear impulse and momentum which applies to the motion of the center of mass of any system. Thus

$$\left[\int_0^t \Sigma F \, dt = \Delta(m\bar{v}) \right] \qquad \int_0^{10} (1.50t - F) \, dt = \frac{120}{32.2} \left[\frac{18}{12} \omega - (-3) \right].$$

The integral involving F is easily eliminated between the two equations, and the result is

$$\omega = 3.13 \text{ rad./sec. clockwise.} \qquad \qquad Ans.$$

Solution II: Since the wheel is symmetrical, an axis moving with the instant center C may be used. The necessity of a simultaneous solution is eliminated since F does not appear in the equation. Hence

$$\left[\int_0^t \Sigma M_C \, dt = \Delta(I_C \omega) \right]$$

$$\int_0^{10} \frac{9}{12} \times 1.50t \, dt = \frac{120}{32.2} \left[\left(\frac{10}{12} \right)^2 + \left(\frac{18}{12} \right)^2 \right] \left[\omega - \left(-\frac{3}{\frac{18}{12}} \right) \right],$$

which gives $\omega = 3.13$ rad./sec.

Solution by use of the instant center is not permitted if any slipping occurs or if the geometric center and center of gravity do not coincide.

1104. Determine the velocity v of the 10 lb. weight 4 sec. after it is released from rest. The drum weighs 32.2 lb. with a radius of gyration of 8 in. and has negligible friction in its bearing at O.

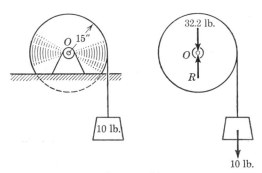

PROB. 1104

Solution: The drum and the weight may be isolated separately with the angular impulse-momentum equation applied to the drum and the linear impulse-momentum equation applied to the weight. The tension T in the cable may be eliminated and the resulting equation solved for v. A simpler method involves the application of Eq. (113) in integral form to a fixed axis for both parts considered a single system. The fixed axis will be taken at O to eliminate the 32.2 lb. weight and the bearing reaction R from the equation. From the free-body diagram of the entire system the resultant moment about O of all external forces is that due to the weight only. Also the angular momentum of the weight about O is the moment of its linear momentum. Thus

$$[\Sigma M_O t = \Delta H_O] \qquad 10 \times \frac{15}{12} \times 4 = \frac{32.2}{32.2} \left(\frac{8}{12}\right)^2 \frac{v}{\frac{15}{12}} + \left(\frac{10}{32.2} v\right) \times \frac{15}{12},$$

$$v = 67.2 \text{ ft./sec.} \qquad\qquad Ans.$$

PROBLEMS

1105. The rotor of a steam turbine weighs 80 lb. with a radius of gyration of 12 in. and requires 6 min. to come to rest from a speed of 10,000 rev./min. after the steam is shut off. Determine the average value of the resisting moment M_f due to internal friction.

1106. The center of the homogeneous solid cylinder is given an initial velocity of 2 ft./sec. up the incline. Determine the time t required for it to reach a velocity of 4 ft./sec. down the incline if it rolls without slipping. *Ans.* $t = 2.81$ sec.

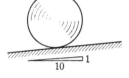

PROB. 1106

1107. In the single-plate clutch of Prob. 897 part A is driven by a powerful motor at a speed of 600 rev./min. The flywheel B has a moment of inertia of 0.371 lb. ft. sec.^{2} about its axis and is rotating initially in the opposite direction with a speed of 400 rev./min. If the coefficient of friction is 0.30 and an engaging force $P = 50$ lb. is applied for $\frac{3}{4}$ sec. and then removed, find the reduced speed N of the flywheel. Assume the frictional action to occur at a mean radius of 5 in.

1108. In Prob. 892 the disk weighs 40 lb. and turns with negligible friction in its bearing. The electric sander, when running and in contact with the disk, requires a clockwise moment (viewed from above) of 1.5 lb. ft. applied to it to prevent its housing from turning. If the 40 lb. disk is initially at rest and the sander is brought into contact with it for intermittent intervals of 1, 3, 2, and 3 sec and at various positions on the disk surface and without lateral forces applied to the sander, find the angular velocity ω of the disk after the last interval.

Ans. $\omega = 21.7$ rad./sec.

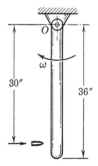

PROB. 1109

1109. A 3 oz. bullet is traveling at a speed of 2000 ft./sec. in the plane of rotation of the uniform 10 lb. bar. If the bar is swinging and the bullet strikes it when in the vertical position, determine the angular velocity ω of the bar just before collision so that the angular momentum of the system about O is zero at this instant.

1110. Each identical bevel gear and attached shaft has a moment of inertia about its own axis of 0.200 lb. ft. sec.² and rotates in fixed bearings at a speed of 1000 rev./min. while in mesh. Determine the magnitude of the total angular momentum H of the system.   *Ans.* $H = 10.84$ lb. ft. sec.

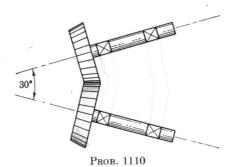

PROB. 1110

1111. A 50 lb. flywheel with radius of gyration of 15 in. is revolving freely in a clockwise direction at a speed of 300 rev./min. when a counterclockwise moment M is applied to its shaft. If M is applied for 4 sec. and decreases with the time in a manner which can be approximated by the parabolic variation shown, find the speed N of the flywheel after 4 sec. The slope dM/dt is zero at $t = 0$.   *Ans.* $N = 216$ rev./min. clockwise

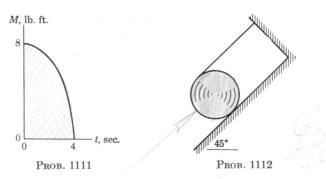

PROB. 1111   PROB. 1112

1112. Determine the time t required for the center of the homogeneous cylinder to reach a velocity of 6 ft./sec. when released from rest on the incline. The coefficient of friction is 0.40, and a sufficient length of cord is wrapped around the cylinder.

1113. Determine the time t required for the center of a solid homogeneous cylinder of 9 in. radius to acquire a velocity of 20 ft./sec. after it is released from rest on a plane inclined at an angle of 60 deg. with the horizontal. The coefficient of friction is 0.30. (See Prob. 936.) What is the angular velocity ω at this time?   *Ans.* $t = 0.867$ sec., $\omega = 11.17$ rad./sec.

1114. Find the torque M required to prevent the lawn sprinkler from rotating if the total flow rate is 18 gal./min. Each nozzle is inclined 10 deg. above the horizontal and has an opening $\frac{1}{4}$ in. in diameter.

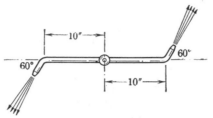

PROB. 1114

1115. In the centrifugal pump impeller shown water flows to the straight radial vanes in an axial direction and leaves the vanes with a velocity v whose tangential component is the rim speed of the impeller. If the pump handles 2000 gal./min. at a speed of 840 rev./min., what is the theoretical torque M

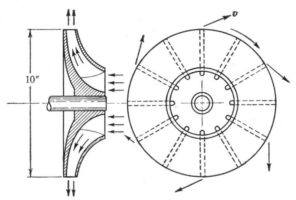

PROB. 1115

on the impeller shaft required to impart the angular momentum to the water? If the actual power required to run the pump is 30 h.p., what is the efficiency e of the pump?   *Ans.* $M = 132.0$ lb. ft., $e = 70.4$ per cent

1116. The two gears shown rotate about their mass centers with negligible friction. Gear A acquires a speed of 50 rad./sec. clockwise from rest under the action of a torque M. If the centroidal moments of inertia of A and B are 0.10 and 0.05 lb. ft. sec.^{2}, respectively, find the total angular momentum H of the system. Is it permissible to equate H to $\int M \, dt$?

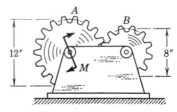

PROB. 1116

1117. In the rotating assembly of Prob. 759 the arm OB and attached motor frame A together weigh 10 lb. and have a radius of gyration about O of 7 in. The disk and attached motor armature together weigh 15 lb. and are mounted in bearings with negligible friction. A constant torque of 0.3 lb. ft. is applied to the shaft at O initially at rest, and, as the arm OB rotates, the disk moves with curvilinear translation with the motor A turned off. Determine the angular velocity ω of OB when the torque on the shaft at O has been applied for 10 sec.
Ans. $\omega = 8.16$ rad./sec.

1118. In the gear and rack unit of Prob. 905 the gear weighs 10 lb. with a radius of gyration of 4 in. Each rack weighs 12 lb., and there is negligible friction in the unit. Determine the constant torque M applied to the gear for $\frac{3}{4}$ sec. which is required to reverse the motion of each rack from a velocity of 4 ft./sec. in one direction to a velocity of 4 ft./sec. in the opposite direction.

1119. In the position shown the center O of the wheel has a velocity of 6 ft./sec. to the right. The wheel weighs 20 lb. with center of gravity at G and has a radius of gyration about G of 8 in. At this instant determine the linear momentum G of the wheel and its angular momentum H about O if the wheel rolls without slipping. *Ans.* $G = 5.21$ lb. sec., $H_O = 3.98$ lb. ft. sec.

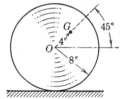

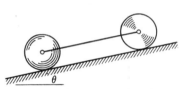

PROB. 1119   PROB. 1120

1120. The sphere and cylinder are made from a homogeneous material and have the same weight W and radius r. The two are attached by a cord between their axles and are released from rest on the incline with no slack in the cord and with the sphere in the lead. Find their common velocity v in terms of the time t from rest. Solve by applying the impulse-momentum equations, first, for the sphere and cylinder isolated separately and, second, for the two taken together as a single system.

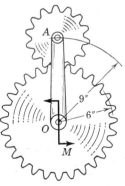

* **1121.** The small gear is made to rotate in a horizontal plane about the large stationary gear by means of the torque M applied to the arm OA. The small gear weighs 6 lb. and may be treated as a circular disk. The arm OA weighs 4 lb. and has a radius of gyration about the fixed bearing at O of 6 in. Determine the constant torque M required to give the small gear an absolute angular velocity of 60 rad./sec. in 3 sec., starting from rest. Neglect friction and analyze the system consisting of the arm OA and the small

PROB. 1121   gear together. *Ans.* **$M = 1.256$ lb. ft.**

* **1122.** The centrifugal pump handles water at the rate of 4000 gal./min. The inside diameter of both the inlet and discharge pipes at A and B is 4 in. The tension in each of the connecting pipes at sections A and B balances the force on the pump due to pressure in the water. The pump shaft turns clockwise at 2000 rev./min., and the driving motor supplies 50 h.p. With the pump filled but at rest the total force exerted on each of the mountings C and D is 60 lb. vertically up. Neglect any vertical restraint on the pump by the long connecting pipes and calculate the total vertical forces which act on the mountings while pumping. *Ans.* $C = 250$ lb. down, $D = 370$ lb. up

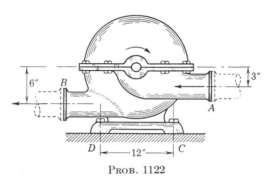

PROB. 1122

* **1123.** The integral gears of the machine in Prob. 752 weigh 20 lb. with a centroidal radius of gyration of 6 in., and each rack weighs 8 lb. Determine the angular velocity ω of the gears $\frac{3}{4}$ sec. after starting from rest under the simultaneous action of a 10 lb. force applied horizontally to each rack in the opposite direction. *Ans.* $\omega = 26.1$ rad./sec.

108. Conservation of Momentum. The principle of linear impulse and momentum for any mass system is expressed by Eqs. (101) and states that the resultant external force in any direction on the system equals the time rate of change of the linear momentum of the system in that direction. If the resultant force in, say, the x-direction is zero during any interval of time, it follows that the time rate of change of the momentum in that direction is also zero. Hence,

$$G_x = \Sigma m v_x = \text{constant,} \qquad (114)$$

where $\Sigma m v_x$ is the sum of the linear momenta of the several parts of the system in the x-direction. This statement expresses the *law of conservation of linear momentum.* Thus the linear momentum in any direction for a system of bodies remains constant (is conserved) as long as there is no resultant external force on the system in that direction. This principle finds particular use in describing the interactions of bodies such as the recoil of a gun or the collision of two objects.

The principle of angular impulse and momentum about a fixed axis for any system of bodies is expressed by Eq. (113) and states that the resultant moment about a fixed axis O equals the time rate of change of angular momentum of the system about that axis. If the resultant moment about any such axis is zero during an interval of time, it follows that the time rate of change of angular momentum about that axis is also zero. Hence

$$H_O = \Sigma I_O \omega = \text{constant}, \tag{115}$$

where $\Sigma I_O \omega$ is the sum of the angular momenta of all parts of the system about O. This statement expresses the *law of conservation of angular momentum*. Thus, when there are no externally applied moments on any system about a fixed axis, the angular momentum of each part may change, but the total angular momentum of the system about this axis remains constant (is conserved). Since Eq. (113) also applies to a moving axis through the mass center, it follows that the principle of conservation of angular momentum also holds for a moving centroidal axis.

SAMPLE PROBLEMS

1124. The 2 oz. bullet is fired at the center of the 4 oz. washer whose hole is small enough to cause the bullet to wedge solidly in the washer. If the washer is free to move and the velocity of the bullet is 2000 ft./sec. before impact, find the common velocity v of bullet and washer immediately after impact.

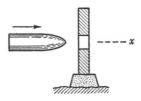

PROB. 1124

Solution: The only forces acting on the system in the direction of motion are the internal action and reaction between the bullet and washer. Therefore the linear momentum of the system consisting of the two bodies remains constant, and

$$[\Delta G_x = 0] \qquad 2 \times 2000 = (2 + 4)v, \qquad v = 667 \text{ ft./sec.} \qquad Ans.$$

The acceleration of gravity g cancels and need not be included.

1125. The circular disk A weighs 20 lb. and is spinning freely at 400 rev./min. about the vertical shaft. Disk B weighs 10 lb. with a radius of gyration of 4 in. If disk B slides freely on the shaft and is dropped from rest onto disk A, determine the final common velocity N of the two after slipping ceases.

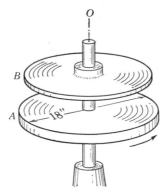

PROB. 1125

Solution: Angular momentum about the fixed shaft is clearly conserved since there are no external moments applied to the system.   Thus

$$[\Delta H_O = 0] \qquad \frac{1}{2}\frac{20}{g}\left(\frac{9}{12}\right)^2 400 = \left[\frac{1}{2}\frac{20}{g}\left(\frac{9}{12}\right)^2 + \frac{10}{g}\left(\frac{4}{12}\right)^2\right] N,$$

$$N = 334 \text{ rev./min.} \qquad\qquad\qquad\qquad Ans.$$

PROBLEMS

1126. Determine the loss of energy ΔE for the interaction in (*a*) Sample Prob. 1124 and (*b*) Sample Prob. 1125.

1127. If the bullet of Sample Prob. 1124 picks up five additional 4 oz. washers mounted in line with the trajectory over a short distance, what is the final common velocity v of the bullet and its six washers?   *Ans.* $v = 153.8$ ft./sec.

1128. If the bullet in Sample Prob. 1124 passed through the washer and emerged with a velocity of 1500 ft./sec., what would be the velocity v of the washer?

1129. If disk B in Sample Prob. 1125 were revolving initially at a speed of 1000 rev./min. in the opposite direction to the rotation of disk A, what would be the final angular speed N of the disks when they stopped slipping after B was allowed to drop on A?   *Ans.* $N = 169.1$ rev./min.

1130. The barrel and breech of a 3 in. anti-aircraft gun weigh 1800 lb.   The projectile weighs 15 lb. and has a muzzle velocity of 3000 ft./sec.   The recoil of the gun is checked by a combination of springs and oil dampers so that the force F of the recoil mechanism on the moving barrel is essentially constant. Determine F if the recoil distance is 16 in.   Neglect the weight of the gases and assume that the gun acquires its full recoil velocity before the recoil mechanism begins to act.

1131. For a powder charge of 5 lb. in the anti-aircraft gun of Prob. 1130 determine the recoil velocity of the gun as the projectile leaves the muzzle.   The center of gravity of the corresponding weight of gases may be assumed to have a velocity of one half that of the shell.   *Ans.* $v = 29.2$ ft./sec.

1132. A ballistic pendulum consists of a 100 lb. box of sand suspended by a wire as shown.   A 2 oz. bullet traveling horizontally is embedded in the sand, and the pendulum is observed to swing through an angle $\theta = 10$ deg.   Determine the initial velocity v of the bullet.   What percentage e of the energy of the bullet is lost from the system?

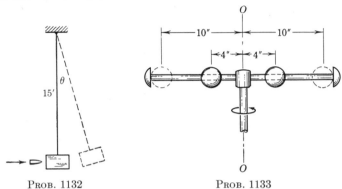

PROB. 1132   PROB. 1133

1133. The horizontal rod has a moment of inertia about the vertical axis of 0.080 lb. ft. sec.², and each of the sliding balls with negligible dimensions weighs 2 lb.   The assembly is rotating freely about O–O at an angular velocity of 20 rad./sec. with the balls latched in the positions shown.   If the latches are released, determine the new angular velocity of the system after the balls have come to rest against the stops.   Find the loss of kinetic energy ΔE.

                    Ans. $\omega = 11.29$ rad./sec., $\Delta E = 8.17$ ft. lb.

1134. The 2 oz. bullet traveling at 2000 ft./sec. strikes the 10 lb. block centrally and is embedded within it.   If the block is sliding on a smooth horizontal

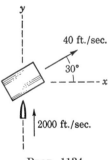

PROB. 1134

plane with a velocity of 40 ft./sec. in the direction shown just before impact, determine the velocity v of the block immediately after impact.

1135. A 2 oz. bullet is fired with a velocity of 1000 ft./sec. in the direction shown and embeds itself into the uniform slender rod which weighs 50 lb. and is initially at rest. Determine the angle θ through which the bar swings if it is freely pivoted at O. (*Note:* The angular momentum of the system about O is unchanged.)

Ans. $\theta = 10° 46'$

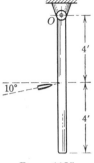

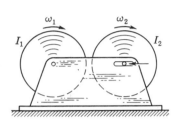

PROB. 1135   PROB. 1136

1136. The two wheels shown are spinning freely with the angular velocities indicated. The axle of the right-hand wheel is moved to the left so that interference and slipping occur for a short period, and then the wheels are separated. Discuss the application of the principle of conservation of angular momentum to this situation. (*Hint:* Be certain to define and isolate clearly the system under consideration.)

* 1137. A turntable of radius r is initially at rest but is free to rotate about its central vertical axis about which its moment of inertia is I. A man of weight W starts from rest at point A marked on the rim and walks around the rim until he meets point A again. Through what angle θ has the disk turned during this interval?

Ans. $\theta = \dfrac{2\pi}{1 + (Ig/Wr^2)}$

* 1138. A 150 lb. man starts from rest at A and walks along the chord AB of the circular platform with a speed of 4 ft./sec. (relative to the platform). If the platform has a moment of inertia about O of 200 lb. ft. sec.^{2}, is free to turn about a vertical axis through O, and was at rest when the man started to walk, find its angular velocity ω when the man reaches point C.

Ans. $\omega = 0.262$ rad./sec.

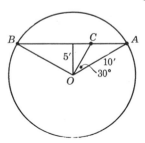

PROB. 1138

109. Impact. The collision between two bodies where relatively large contact forces exist during a very short interval of time is called *impact*. Experimental verification of impact theory is difficult by reason of the extremely short time during which the contact forces act. Consequently reliable data for the description of impact phenomena are difficult to obtain.

As an introduction to impact consider the collinear motion of two spheres of masses m_1 and m_2, Fig. 139a, traveling with velocities v_1 and

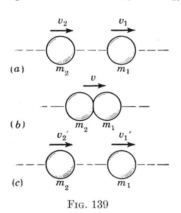

(a)

(b)

(c)

Fig. 139

v_2. If v_2 is greater than v_1, collision occurs, and a short period of deformation takes place, Fig. 139b, until the contact area between the spheres ceases to increase. After this deformation a period of restoration takes place, and the spheres regain their original shape if the blow is not too severe or else retain a deformed shape if the impact is more severe. The spheres then continue to move with final velocities v_1' and v_2' as in Fig. 139c. Inasmuch as the contact forces are equal and opposite, the linear momentum of the system remains unchanged. Thus the law of conservation of momentum applies, and

$$m_1v_1 + m_2v_2 = m_1v_1' + m_2v_2'.$$

All velocities are arbitrarily assumed positive to the right so that a negative sign will describe a velocity to the left.

In addition to the conservation of momentum, the energy of the colliding masses must be accounted for. The initial kinetic energy of the system before impact is divided into three parts after impact. First, some of the energy is retained in the form of kinetic energy on account of the rebound velocities of the spheres as a whole. Second, some of the initial energy is lost as a result of the generation of heat if the spheres are permanently deformed. Third, the impact forces cause internal vibrations of the spheres, and the resulting propagation and rebound of elastic waves within the spheres consume some of the initial energy. This third part of the total energy is usually difficult to account for and is by no means negligible in many impact problems involving bodies whose shapes are other than spherical.

The classical theory of impact as presented in most treatments on mechanics neglects the internal energy of vibration. With this neglect and for the case of perfectly elastic impact the final kinetic energy must equal the initial kinetic energy. Thus

$$\tfrac{1}{2}m_1v_1{}^2 + \tfrac{1}{2}m_2v_2{}^2 = \tfrac{1}{2}m_1v_1{}'^2 + \tfrac{1}{2}m_2v_2{}'^2,$$

or

$$m_1(v_1 + v_1')(v_1 - v_1') = m_2(v_2 + v_2')(v_2' - v_2).$$

The equation for the conservation of momentum may be written

$$m_1(v_1 - v_1') = m_2(v_2' - v_2).$$

Dividing the energy equation by the momentum equation gives

$$v_1 + v_1' = v_2 + v_2' \qquad \text{or} \qquad v_2 - v_1 = v_1' - v_2',$$

which shows that the relative velocity of approach equals the relative velocity of separation if the energy is conserved.

In most impact problems a rather large percentage of the energy of the system is lost, and the equation for the velocity difference is written

$$e(v_2 - v_1) = (v_1' - v_2').$$

The factor e, which may vary between zero and unity, is known as the *coefficient of restitution* and equals the ratio of the relative velocity of separation to the relative velocity of approach. If the impact occurs obliquely, then only the components of the velocities in the direction of the force of impact should be used with the coefficient of restitution. In the classical theory of impact a coefficient of restitution of unity means *elastic impact* with no energy loss, and a coefficient of restitution of zero means an *inelastic* or *plastic impact*, where the bodies cling together after collision and the energy loss is a maximum.

Experimental determination of coefficients of restitution for spheres of various materials indicates that e varies greatly with the impact velocity but approaches unity when this velocity approaches zero. This condition is explained on the basis that the energy loss due to permanent deformation becomes less as the impact velocity decreases. Experiment also has shown that for given materials and for a given impact velocity the coefficient of restitution changes appreciably with the size and shape of the colliding bodies. This effect is due to the corresponding change in induced internal energy of vibration. A handbook value for a coefficient of restitution is generally unreliable * unless conditions identical to those under which the measurement was made are known to exist.

---

* Most of the values for coefficients of restitution reported in handbooks and in books on mechanics are taken directly from the early experiments by Eaton Hodgkinson in 1834 and P. G. Tait in 1890.

SAMPLE PROBLEM

1139. Two smooth steel spheres moving with the initial velocities shown collide with the line joining their centers in the direction of the velocity v_2. From previous experiments it is known that the coefficient of restitution for these conditions is 0.70. Determine the final velocity v of each sphere and the percentage loss of kinetic energy.

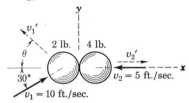

PROB. 1139

Solution: The equal and opposite force of contact on each sphere is along the x-direction so that the linear momentum of the system is conserved in that direction. Also, since there is no force on either sphere in the y-direction, there is no change in the y-component of either velocity. Thus

$$[\Delta G_x = 0]_{\text{system}} \qquad 2 \times 10 \times 0.866 - 4 \times 5 = 4v_2' - 2v_1' \cos \theta,$$

$$[\Delta v_y = 0]_{\text{each sphere}} \qquad v_1' \sin \theta = 10 \times 0.5, \qquad v_{2_y}' = 0.$$

The coefficient of restitution is the ratio of relative separation velocity to relative approach velocity both measured in the direction of the impact force. Therefore

$$\left[e = \left| \frac{\Delta v_x'}{\Delta v_x} \right| \right] \qquad\qquad 0.70 = \frac{v_2' + v_1' \cos \theta}{5 + 10 \times 0.866}.$$

The simultaneous solution of these three equations gives

$$v_1' = 8.46 \text{ ft./sec.}, \qquad \theta = 36° 14', \qquad v_2' = 2.74 \text{ ft./sec.} \qquad Ans.$$

The initial kinetic energy of the system is

$$\frac{1}{2} \frac{2}{32.2} (10)^2 + \frac{1}{2} \frac{4}{32.2} 5^2 = 4.66 \text{ ft. lb.}$$

The final kinetic energy is

$$\frac{1}{2} \frac{2}{32.2} (8.46)^2 + \frac{1}{2} \frac{4}{32.2} (2.74)^2 = 2.69 \text{ ft. lb.}$$

The percentage loss is

$$\frac{4.66 - 2.69}{4.66} 100 = 42.3 \text{ per cent.} \qquad Ans.$$

PROBLEMS

1140. A 24,000 lb. bus traveling at 30 mi./hr. collides head on with a 3300 lb. car going in the opposite direction at 40 mi./hr. Because of the extent of deformation involved there is no rebound of the vehicles as a whole. Determine the common velocity v immediately after impact, and find the loss of kinetic energy ΔE.

1141. A steel ball is dropped from rest from a height h above a horizontal steel plate of large weight and rebounds to a height h'. Determine the coefficient of restitution e.

$$Ans. \quad e = \sqrt{\frac{h'}{h}}$$

1142. Show that the moving billiard ball A transfers all of its kinetic energy to the identical ball B initially at rest. Assume direct central impact without permanent deformation or contact friction and neglect internal vibrational energy.

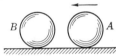

1143. Describe the conditions under which elastic impact occurs with a coefficient of restitution of less than unity. Consider all energies involved.

PROB. 1142

1144. If the steel plate of Prob. 1141 is tilted through an angle θ as shown, determine the direction α of the rebound velocity in terms of the restitution coefficient e which applies. $Ans.$ $\tan \alpha = e \operatorname{ctn} \theta$

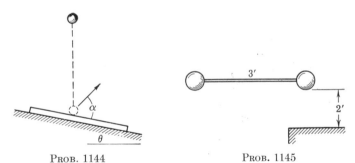

PROB. 1144   PROB. 1145

1145. Two steel balls each weighing 4 lb. and connected 3 ft. apart by a light rod are dropped from rest in the position shown. The right-hand ball strikes a horizontal steel plate of considerable mass and suffers a rebound for which the coefficient of restitution is 0.60. Determine the angular velocity ω of the bar (a) at the instant of maximum deformation of the right-hand ball and (b) an instant after impact.

1146. A pile driver consists of a 1200 lb. weight which falls freely through a height of 5 ft. above the top of a 300 lb. pile. Upon impact the weight is seen to move with the pile with no appreciable rebound, and the pile penetrates 15 in. into the ground at each blow. Determine the average resistance R to penetration of the pile. $Ans.$ $R = 5340$ lb.

* **1147.** Show that the loss of energy due to direct central impact of two masses m_1 and m_2 having velocities v_1 and v_2 directed toward each other is given by

$$\Delta E = \frac{1 - e^2}{2} \frac{m_1 m_2}{m_1 + m_2} (v_1 + v_2)^2,$$

where e is the coefficient of restitution for these particular impact conditions and the internal vibrational energy is neglected. (*Hint:* The energy loss depends on the relative impact velocity $v_1 + v_2$. Thus the center of gravity of the system may be taken at rest to simplify the algebra so that $m_1 v_1 = m_2 v_2$.)

110. Gyroscopic Motion. One of the most interesting of all problems in dynamics is that of the gyroscope, which involves the rotation of a

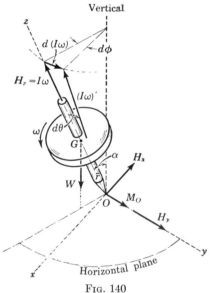

FIG. 140

body about an axis which itself is rotating. This problem is three-dimensional and may be described by the general principle of angular impulse and momentum for a rigid body with respect to a fixed point as given by Eq. (113).

Consider the rotor in Fig. 140, which is pivoted at its point O with negligible friction and which has an angular velocity of spin ω about its own axis. The motion of this rotor under the action of its weight W and the pivot reaction will be described. The total angular momentum of the rotor about the fixed point O may be represented by its three vector components in the orthogonal x–y–z directions. The z-component is $H_z = I\omega$, where I is the moment of inertia of the rotor about the z-axis and the vector stems from O. The component $H_y = I_y(d\alpha/dt)$ is due to rotation of the rotor axis about the y-axis at the instant represented, and likewise the component $H_x = I_x(d\theta/dt)$ is due to rotation about the x-axis. The resultant angular momentum about O is the vector sum of these three components. The resultant moment about O is $M_O = W\bar{r}\sin\alpha$ and is in the y-direction. Equation (113) requires that this moment be equal in magnitude and direction to the time rate of change of the total angular momentum vector. Evaluation of this time rate of change where all three components of H_O are accounted for is necessary for a complete description of the motion.

The engineering aspects of the problem can be adequately explained by examining only the case where $H_z = I\omega$ is very large compared with H_y and H_x. This condition occurs for a large rate of spin ω. Thus only the one component of angular momentum will be considered. With this simplification Eq. (113) may be written as

$$M_O \, dt = dH_O = d(I\omega),$$

where the moment about O is $M_O = W\bar{r} \sin \alpha$. This relation states that the change in angular momentum is equal in magnitude and direction to the applied angular impulse. This impulse has the direction of M_O, which, vectorially, is along the y-axis, and, hence, $d(I\omega)$ has the same direction. Thus the change in angular momentum is at right angles to the momentum or spin axis. Adding this change to $I\omega$ gives the new angular momentum $(I\omega)'$ after time dt. The momentum or spin axis of the rotor has moved through the angle $d\theta$ which is given by

$$d\theta = \frac{d(I\omega)}{I\omega}.$$

Combination with the preceding equation gives

$$M_O \, dt = I\omega \, d\theta \qquad \text{or} \qquad M_O = I\frac{d\theta}{dt}\omega.$$

From the figure it is seen that $d\theta = d\phi \sin \alpha$, and thus the resulting equation may be written also as

$$W\bar{r} \sin \alpha = I\left(\frac{d\phi}{dt}\sin \alpha\right)\omega,$$

or

$$W\bar{r} = I\frac{d\phi}{dt}\omega,$$

where $d\phi/dt$ is the rate of *precession* of the rotor axis about the vertical. This relation shows that for a given rotor and given spin velocity the rate of precession about the vertical is the same for any value of α.

The reason that the rotor axis revolves about the vertical at a constant angle α instead of falling toward the x–y plane lies in the fact that the precession described is the only motion which will make the vector change in angular momentum have the same direction as the applied moment and angular impulse. If the rotor had no spin velocity, it would indeed fall. Actually as the spin velocity decreases because of friction, the rotor axis will drop toward the horizontal plane in a rather complex manner which requires the retention of the momentum components H_x and H_y for description. In understanding the gyroscopic effect it is helpful to note that precession of the axis of spin occurs when a moment is applied whose vector is at *right angles* to the angular momentum vector. In the problem of plane motion, on the other hand, the moment and angular momentum vectors are *parallel*.

In most engineering applications of gyroscopes the moment, spin, and precession axes are mutually perpendicular. This situation is illustrated in Fig. 141a where the axis of the rotor of the previous figure is now horizontal. The momentum equation becomes

$$M = I\Omega\omega, \tag{116}$$

where Ω is the rate of precession $d\phi/dt$ about the vertical and M is the moment $W\bar{r}$ of the weight about O. The moment vector M in Eq. (116)

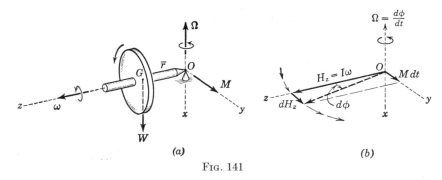

(a)   *(b)*

FIG. 141

is normal to both the spin axis (ω) and the precession axis (Ω) and represents the moment in this direction about the pivot O due to *all* forces acting *on* the gyro rotor. For the rotor illustrated Eq. (116) is not exact since it accounts for only the predominant momentum change in the direction of M. The error is exceedingly small, however, for the relatively high spin velocities normally used.

Equation (116) and the corresponding relationship between the senses of the three vectors M, Ω, and ω will now be determined directly for the case illustrated in Fig. 141a as further aid to correct interpretation of the gyroscopic equation. Equation (113) requires that the angular impulse $M\,dt$ during time dt about the y-axis through the fixed point O must equal the change dH_z in angular momentum both in magnitude and direction. These vectors are shown in Fig. 141b, and it is seen that during the time dt the momentum or spin axis has swung through the angle $d\phi$ in order that dH_z equal $M\,dt$. It follows, then, that $M\,dt = dH_z = I\omega\,d\phi$, and division by dt yields $M = I\Omega\omega$.

It should be carefully noted that the direction of the precession is determined by the fact that the vector change dH_z in angular momentum has the same sense as the applied moment M, and, hence, the spin axis will always rotate *toward* the moment axis. The three vectors M, Ω, and ω constitute a right-handed set of axes. Thus in rotating from the M-axis to the Ω-axis through the 90 deg. angle, advancement for a right-hand screw is along the ω-axis. Likewise a right-hand screw would advance in the M-direction when rotated from the Ω-axis to the ω-axis or would advance in the Ω-direction when rotated from the ω-axis to the M-axis. Use of this right-hand rule requires memory of the sequence M-Ω-ω of these vectors. This sequence can be established quickly by recognizing, basically, that the momentum axis rotates toward the moment axis since the vector change in the spin momentum must have the same sense as the applied moment.

In the event an additional moment about O is applied to the rotor a corresponding additional precession will occur which obeys the rules just cited. Thus, if a force F were applied to the rotating end of the rotor shaft, Fig. 142, in the positive y-direction, the corresponding moment vector would be in the negative x-direction. The momentum or spin axis (ω) would have a vector change in the direction of the moment axis (M) which is vertically up, and

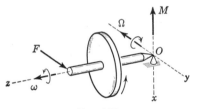

Fig. 142

the spin axis would rise. Conversely, if a force were applied to the end of the rotor shaft in the direction to oppose the precession (negative y-direction), the spin axis would fall.

If the rotor axis of a gyro precesses in a given plane, then the center of gravity of the rotor remains in that plane and can have no acceleration normal to it. It follows that the resultant of *all* forces acting *on* the rotor in a plane normal to the precession plane and containing the rotor axis cannot be a force and, if not zero, must be a couple. Thus the moment M in Eq. (116) is a couple and is known as the *gyroscopic couple*. Since the value of a couple is independent of which parallel axis is chosen for evaluating its moment, a moment summation about *any* axis normal to the rotor axis and lying in the precession plane may be used for evaluating M. Thus for the rotor in Fig. 141a, there is no vertical acceleration of G during the horizontal precession, and the upward force exerted by the pivot on the rotor at O equals the weight W and together with the weight constitute the gyroscopic couple $W\bar{r}$. The correct value of the couple may be obtained by taking moments about an axis parallel to the y-axis through O, G, or any other point.

When ω becomes small for the rotor of Fig. 141a, the axis begins to droop, and Eq. (116) is no longer a good approximation. On the other hand, if the rotor axis is confined to rotate in the horizontal plane about the vertical by some type of restraining guides, then there can be no angular momentum about the y-axis at all, and the only change in angular momentum in the y-direction comes from the directional change in $H_z = I\omega$ as expressed by Eq. (116). Therefore Eq. (116) is *exact* whenever the axis of a symmetrical rotor is confined to precess exclusively in one plane. If the end of the rotor axis in Fig. 142 were constrained by smooth guides (not shown) to move only in the horizontal y-z plane, then the force F would cause accelerated rotation of the shaft about the x-axis given by $Fl = I_x \alpha$ where l is the moment arm to O, α is the angular acceleration of the shaft axis about the vertical, and I_x is the moment of inertia of the rotor about the vertical. Accompanying this rotation there would be a downward force exerted by the guide on the shaft whose moment M about O obeys Eq. (116) exactly at any instant.

In addition to being a toy the gyroscope has important engineering application. First it is used extensively as a directional device. With a mounting in gimbal rings, Fig. 143, the gyroscope is free from external

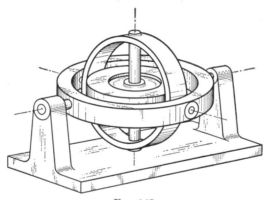

Fig. 143

moments, and its axis will retain a fixed direction irrespective of the rotational movement of its base. Independence from the rotational movement of the surroundings is used as a positioning control device. By adding a pendulous weight to the inner gimbal ring the attraction of the earth may be used to cause precession of the gyro so that the spin axis always points north. This action forms the basis of the gyro compass. The gyroscope has found important use as a stabilizing device. The controlled precession of a large gyro mounted in a ship is used to produce a moment to counteract the rolling of the ship at sea. The gyroscopic effect is an extremely important consideration in the design of bearings for the shafts of rotors subject to forced precession.

SAMPLE PROBLEM

1148. The turbine rotor in a ship's power plant weighs 2600 lb. with center of gravity at G and has a radius of gyration of 8 in. The rotor is mounted in bearings A and B with its axis in the horizontal fore-and-aft direction and turns counterclockwise at 5000 rev./min. when viewed from the stern. Determine the vertical components of the bearing reactions at A and B if the ship is making a turn to port (left) of 400 yd. radius at a speed of 22 knots (1 knot = 1.152 mi./hr.).

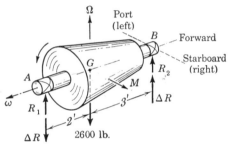

Prob. 1148

Solution: The vertical components of the bearing reactions will equal the static reactions R_1 and R_2 plus or minus the increment ΔR due to the gyroscopic effect. The moment principle easily gives $R_1 = 1560$ lb. and $R_2 = 1040$ lb. The direction of the spin velocity ω and the precessional velocity Ω are indicated with the free-body diagram. Use of the right-handed sequence shows that the couple due to the ΔR's points in the starboard direction, and, thus, the reaction at B is $R_2 + \Delta R$ and that at A is $R_1 - \Delta R$. Equation (116) is applied about the center of gravity of the rotor and gives

$$[M = I\Omega\omega] \qquad 5\Delta R = \frac{2600}{32.2}\left(\frac{8}{12}\right)^2\left(\frac{22 \times 1.152 \times 44}{400 \times 3 \times 30}\right)\left(\frac{5000 \times 2\pi}{60}\right),$$

$$\Delta R = 116 \text{ lb.}$$

The required reactions are then

$$A = 1560 - 116 = 1444 \text{ lb.}, \qquad B = 1040 + 116 = 1156 \text{ lb.} \qquad *Ans.*$$

The horizontal components of the bearing reactions necessary to give the rotor its centripetal acceleration in the turn may be computed, and each total bearing reaction determined if desired.

PROBLEMS

1149. If the bow of the ship of Sample Prob. 1148 is rising as a wave passes under it, determine the direction of the gyroscopic moment exerted *by* the turbine rotor *on* the hull structure.

1150. A pair of locomotive drivers 78 in. in diameter together with the axle weigh 6600 lb. and have a combined radius of gyration of 26 in. Compute the change in force ΔP between the inner rail and the wheel due to the gyroscopic effect alone if the engine is rounding a curve of 720 ft. radius at a speed of 50 mi./hr. Neglect the banking of the curve and use the standard gage of 4 ft. 8½ in. between rails.   *Ans.* $\Delta P = 470$ lb. decrease

1151. One type of aircraft engine supercharger consists of the 4.10 lb. blower A with a radius of gyration of 2.90 in. which is driven at 18,000 rev./min. by the 12.20 lb. exhaust turbine B with a radius of gyration of 2.75 in. Deter-

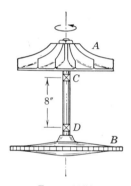

Prob. 1151

mine the radial forces on the bearings C and D if the shaft is mounted in a vertical position and the airplane is rolling (turning about the horizontal flight axis) at the rate of 3 rad./sec.

1152. The 4-bladed propeller of a single-engined airplane weighs 400 lb. with a radius of gyration of 3.80 ft. and rotates counterclockwise at a speed of 1500 rev./min. when viewed from the rear. When the airplane reaches the bottom of a vertical loop of 1500 ft. radius at a speed of 400 mi./hr., determine the gyroscopic moment M on the propeller bearing. In what direction will the tail of the airplane tend to move because of the gyroscopic effect?

        Ans. $M = 11,020$ lb. ft.; tail swings right

1153. In the figure is shown one of three gyros mounted with vertical axis and used to stabilize a large ship against rolling. The motor A turns the pinion which precesses the gyro by rotating the large precession gear B and attached rotor assembly about a horizontal transverse axis in the ship. The rotor turns inside the housing at a clockwise speed of 800 rev./min. when viewed from the top and has a weight of 100 tons with a radius of gyration of 4.85 ft. Determine the moment exerted on the hull structure by the gyro if the motor turns the precession gear at the rate of 0.420 rad./sec. In which of the two directions, (*a*) or (*b*), should the motor turn to counteract a roll of the ship to starboard?

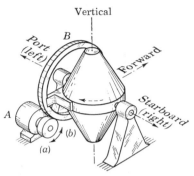

PROB. 1153

1154. The two identical disks are rotating freely on the shaft with angular velocities equal in magnitude and opposite in direction as shown. The shaft in turn is caused to rotate about the vertical axis in the sense indicated. Prove whether the shaft bends as in *A* or as in *B*. *Ans. A*

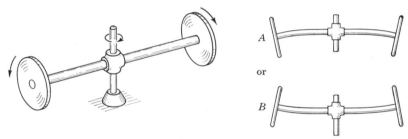

PROB. 1154

1155. The rotor axis of a gyro which is pivoted about its center of gravity like the one shown in Fig. 143 is in the vertical position at 12:00 noon. What angle α will the axis make with the vertical at 2:00 P.M. if the gyro is at a latitude of 40 deg. N and if the rotor is kept spinning at high speed with negligible friction in its gimbal bearings? *Ans.* $\alpha = 23.0$ deg.

1156. An experimental car is equipped with a gyro stabilizer to counteract completely the tendency of the car to tip when rounding a curve (no change in force between tires and road). The rotor of the gyro has a weight w and a radius of gyration k, and is mounted in fixed bearings on a shaft which is parallel to the rear axle of the car. The center of gravity of the car is a distance h above the road, and the car is rounding an unbanked level turn at a speed v. At what speed ω should the rotor turn and in what direction to counteract completely the tendency of the car to overturn for either a right or a left turn?

* **1157.** A solid cone of weight W, base radius r, and altitude h is set to spinning about its own axis with a high rate of spin ω. If the cone is released with its point supported at O, determine the direction of the precession and the period τ of one complete rotation about the vertical.

Ans. $\tau = \dfrac{4\pi\omega r^2}{5gh}$

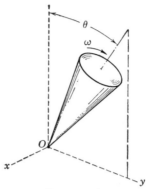

PROB. 1157

* **1158.** If the tip of the spinning cone or top shown in Prob. 1157 is slightly rounded (as would actually be the case) and if the top is spinning on a horizontal surface with some friction present, show why the spin axis rises to the vertical position.

CHAPTER XIV

Periodic Motion

111. Introduction. Any motion which repeats itself after a certain time interval is said to be *periodic*. All oscillations and vibrations of bodies come under this heading and constitute one of the most important applications of dynamics. In particular the rapid increase in recent years in the operating speeds of machinery has called attention to the necessity for an understanding of the mechanics of vibrations.

Most vibrations in machinery are detrimental to the performance and life of the machine, and effort is made to avoid or reduce them as much as possible. In a few instances vibrations are useful, as in the reduction of friction in delicate instruments by continued vibratory movement.

Vibrations are of two types, free and forced. A *free vibration* is one which is sustained by internal elastic forces and gravity forces such as in the vibration of an elastic beam. A *forced vibration* is one which is sustained by an external periodic force. Vibrations are also classified as to the number of possible modes of motion. The number of independent coordinates needed to specify completely the configuration of the system at any instant is known as the number of *degrees of freedom* of the system. In general, motion with more than a single degree of freedom calls for methods beyond the scope of this book, so that discussion will be confined to motion with a single degree of freedom, where only one independent coordinate is needed to specify the position of the vibrating body at any instant.

The dynamics of periodic motion is based on the same fundamental laws discussed and illustrated in the previous chapters but differs somewhat in the method of solution, and, consequently, has been placed in this separate chapter. The analysis of this type of motion is handled by the solution of a differential equation which will be illustrated in detail for several cases.

112. Free Vibrations. Consider a body of weight W, Fig. 144a, which is suspended by an elastic spring of negligible weight and of stiffness k. In the equilibrium position of the body the spring has a static deflection

$\delta = W/k$. If the body is pulled downward a distance x_0 from the equilibrium position and released from rest, it will vibrate in the vertical direction between the limits x_0 and $-x_0$. The free-body diagram of the weight at any position x during its motion shows the weight W and the force $k(\delta + x) = W + kx$ exerted by the spring. The equation of motion in the x-direction is $\Sigma F_x = ma_x$, which becomes

$$W - (W + kx) = \frac{W}{g}\frac{d^2x}{dt^2},$$

or

$$\frac{d^2x}{dt^2} + \frac{kg}{W}x = 0. \tag{117}$$

Equation (117) is the equation of motion for W written as a differential equation, and its solution will give the displacement x as a function of

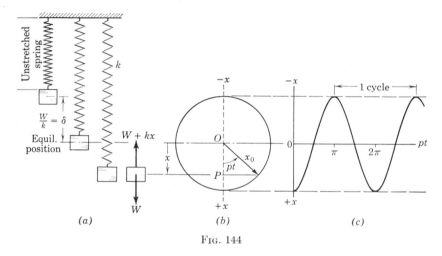

Fig. 144

the time t. It should be noted that, since x is taken positive down, d^2x/dt^2 will also be positive down. In writing the differential equation of motion it is necessary to be consistent with the arbitrary convention of sign.

The differential equation is of *second order*, so *two* integration constants will appear in its general solution. For this relatively simple physical problem it is not difficult to guess at the form of the solution and then to verify the assumption by direct substitution. The expression to be tried will be a periodic function of time

$$x = A \cos pt + B \sin pt.$$

The constants A and B are arbitrary, and p is a constant quantity having the dimensions of angular velocity to make the argument of the sine and cosine a dimensionless angle. Substitution into the differential equation requires two differentiations. The first is

$$\frac{dx}{dt} = -Ap \sin pt + Bp \cos pt,$$

and the second is

$$\frac{d^2x}{dt^2} = -Ap^2 \cos pt - Bp^2 \sin pt.$$

Substitution into Eq. (117) and grouping terms give

$$A\left(-p^2 + \frac{kg}{W}\right) \cos pt + B\left(-p^2 + \frac{kg}{W}\right) \sin pt = 0.$$

If the assumed solution is valid, then the expression just obtained must hold for *all* values of the time. The only way in which this expression can hold for all t is for the coefficients of both the sine and cosine terms to vanish at all times. Since both A and B cannot be zero, the requirement yields

$$-p^2 + \frac{kg}{W} = 0 \quad \text{or} \quad p = \sqrt{\frac{kg}{W}}.$$

With this constant value of p the assumed relation will satisfy Eq. (117) for all values of the time, and, consequently, is the general solution to the differential equation.

To give a simple interpretation to the solution just obtained assume that the time t is measured from the instant of release from rest at $x = x_0$. Thus the two boundary conditions needed to evaluate the two arbitrary constants A and B are $dx/dt = 0$ when $t = 0$ and $x = x_0$ when $t = 0$. Substitution of the first condition into the expression for dx/dt requires

$$0 = 0 + Bp, \qquad B = 0.$$

The solution is reduced to $x = A \cos pt$, and the second condition gives $A = x_0$. Hence for the boundary conditions imposed the solution is

$$x = x_0 \cos pt \quad \text{where } p = \sqrt{\frac{kg}{W}}. \tag{118}$$

The significance of this solution may be seen graphically in Figs. 144*b* and *c*, where the variation of x with pt is shown. The displacement x

may be viewed as the projection P on the x-axis of a vector of length x_0 which rotates counterclockwise with an angular velocity p. The motion of W is that of this projection and is known as *simple harmonic motion*. Simple harmonic motion may be defined as that motion wherein the acceleration is proportional to the displacement and is directed opposite to the displacement as described by Eq. (117). The maximum displacement x_0 from the neutral position is known as the *amplitude* of the motion. The time for one complete cycle is the *period* τ and is the time required to change the argument of the cosine term by 2π. Also the number of cycles per unit time is the *frequency* f and is the reciprocal of the period. Thus

$$\tau = \frac{2\pi}{p} = 2\pi \sqrt{\frac{W}{kg}} \quad \text{and} \quad f = \frac{1}{\tau} = \frac{p}{2\pi} = \frac{1}{2\pi} \sqrt{\frac{kg}{W}}.$$

The angular velocity p of the rotating reference vector is known as the *circular frequency*.

If this same vibration is described by counting time from the instant the body passes the origin with the velocity v_0, then the boundary conditions are $x = 0$ when $t = 0$ and $dx/dt = v_0$ when $t = 0$. By substitution into the expressions for x and dx/dt the first condition gives $A = 0$ and the second yields $B = v_0/p = x_0$ where x_0 is the amplitude of the vibration. Thus

$$x = x_0 \sin pt,$$

which, of course, has the same period and frequency as the cosine expression.

If time is counted from some other position, as shown in Fig. 145, the solution for this same vibration may be expressed as

$$x = x_0 \sin (pt + \phi),$$

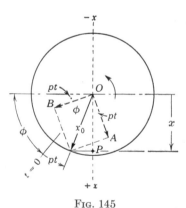

Fig. 145

where ϕ is a *phase angle*. For this condition both the constants A and B must be retained in the general solution, and it may be seen from the figure that $x_0 = \sqrt{A^2 + B^2}$ and $\phi = \tan^{-1}(A/B)$.

Equation (117) is the basic equation which describes simple harmonic motion. This equation together with its solution and the expressions for the period and frequency are common to many types of oscillatory motion which occur in engineering. Once the governing equation of motion for a given problem has been shown to be of the form of Eq. (117), it is then known that the solution will be the same as that for Eq. (117) except for whatever change of symbols is called for.

SAMPLE PROBLEMS

1159. Determine the natural frequency f for small vibrations of the system about the equilibrium position shown. Each spring has a constant k.

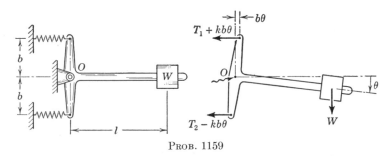

PROB. 1159

Solution: The free-body diagram of the system is represented for a small angular displacement θ away from the equilibrium position. The tension in the top spring is its initial equilibrium value T_1 plus the increment $kb\theta$ due to the stretch $b\theta$. The arc length $b\theta$ is a good approximation to the actual stretch for a small angle. Likewise the tension in the bottom spring is the initial equilibrium value T_2 minus the increment $kb\theta$.

The motion is one of rotation about the fixed point O, so the equation of motion $\Sigma M_O = I_O \alpha$ must be used. This equation gives

$$Wl + (T_2 - kb\theta)b - (T_1 + kb\theta)b = \frac{W}{g} l^2 \frac{d^2\theta}{dt^2}.$$

In using the moment arm l for W the difference between $\cos\theta$ and unity is neglected for small angular movements. The initial tensions are found from the balance of statical moments for the equilibrium position which gives

$$Wl = (T_1 - T_2)b.$$

Substitution into the equation of motion and rearrangement of terms give

$$\frac{d^2\theta}{dt^2} + 2\frac{kg}{W}\left(\frac{b}{l}\right)^2 \theta = 0.$$

This equation is seen to be of the same mathematical form as Eq. (117), and the circular frequency of this simple harmonic motion is

$$p = \sqrt{2\frac{kg}{W}\left(\frac{b}{l}\right)^2}.$$

Thus the natural frequency for small vibrations is

$$f = \frac{p}{2\pi} = \frac{1}{\pi\sqrt{2}} \frac{b}{l} \sqrt{\frac{kg}{W}}.$$ *Ans.*

For large amplitudes the geometrical approximations made become invalid.

1160. A homogeneous solid cylinder of weight W and radius r rolls without slipping during its oscillation on the circular surface of radius R. If the motion is confined to small amplitudes, determine the period τ of oscillation and the angular velocity ω of the cylinder as it crosses the vertical. The amplitude of motion is $\theta = \theta_0$.

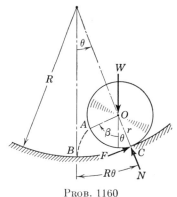

PROB. 1160

Solution: The free-body diagram of the cylinder in a displaced position is shown. The angular displacement of the wheel is the angular displacement β of line OA which was in the vertical position for $\theta = 0$. With the clockwise direction of β as positive the equation of motion $\Sigma M_C = I_C \alpha$ about the instant center C gives

$$-Wr \sin \theta = I_C \frac{d^2\beta}{dt^2}.$$

The relation between β and θ is obtained by equating the arc lengths AC and BC which gives

$$R\theta = r(\theta + \beta) \qquad \text{or} \qquad \beta = \frac{R - r}{r} \theta.$$

This substitution together with the expression $I_C = \frac{3}{2}mr^2$ and the replacement of $\sin \theta$ by θ for small movements gives

$$\frac{d^2\theta}{dt^2} + \frac{2g}{3(R - r)} \theta = 0.$$

The form of this equation is that of simple harmonic motion, and the circular frequency is

$$p = \sqrt{\frac{2g}{3(R - r)}}.$$

Thus the period for each complete small oscillation is

$$\tau = \frac{2\pi}{p} = 2\pi \sqrt{\frac{3(R-r)}{2g}}. \qquad Ans.$$

From Eq. (118) the displacement θ and the angular velocity $d\theta/dt$ may be written as

$$\theta = \theta_0 \cos pt \qquad \text{and} \qquad \frac{d\theta}{dt} = -\theta_0 p \sin pt,$$

where the time is measured from the extreme position θ_0. The maximum angular velocity of the cylinder occurs at $\theta = 0$ and is, therefore,

$$\omega = \left| \frac{d\beta}{dt} \right|_{\text{max.}} = \frac{R-r}{r} \left| \frac{d\theta}{dt} \right|_{\text{max.}} = \frac{R-r}{r} \theta_0 p = \frac{\theta_0}{r} \sqrt{\frac{2g(R-r)}{3}}. \quad Ans.$$

PROBLEMS

Neglect the weight of all springs in the following problems.

1161. A 50 lb. electric motor is symmetrically mounted on four identical spring pads and is observed to have a natural frequency of vertical vibration of 4 cycles/sec. Determine the constant k of each pad.

1162. Replace the springs in each of the two cases shown by a single spring of constant k (equivalent spring constant) which will cause each weight to vibrate with its original frequency. *Ans.* (a) $k = k_1 + k_2$, (b) $\dfrac{1}{k} = \dfrac{1}{k_1} + \dfrac{1}{k_2}$

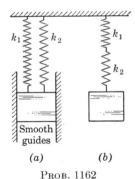

(a)   (b)

Prob. 1162

1163. The weight of the elastic cantilever beam is negligible compared with the weight $W = 20$ lb. If a force F of 6 lb. causes a static deflection $y = 0.03$ in., find the natural frequency f for small vibrations of the beam caused by a sudden removal of the force. *Ans.* $f = 9.90$ cycles/sec.

Prob. 1163

1164. Find the period τ of the simple pendulum for small amplitudes of motion.

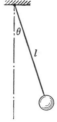

PROB. 1164

1165. A compound pendulum in the form of a slender rod of length l pivoted freely about one end oscillates with a small angular displacement under the action of its own weight. Find the period τ of its motion.

1166. The ring of radius r and negligible thickness oscillates with a small amplitude about the pivot at O. Determine the period τ of the motion.

$$Ans. \quad \tau = 2\pi \sqrt{\frac{2r}{g}}$$

PROB. 1166

1167. The plunger weighs 5 lb. and is subjected to the action of the two springs. Determine the natural frequency f of the vertical vibration if friction in the guide is negligible and both springs remain in compression at all times. $Ans. \quad f = 7.67$ cycles/sec.

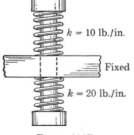

PROB. 1167

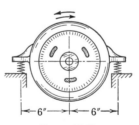

PROB. 1168

1168. The motor shown weighs 50 lb. and is set into small angular oscillation about its center of gravity which lies on the shaft axis. Each of the four identical spring pads (two on a side) has a modulus of 18 lb./in., and the measured frequency of oscillation is 4 cycles/sec. Determine the centroidal radius of gyration $\bar{k}$ of the motor.

1169. Determine the frequency f of natural vibration of the system for a small amplitude of motion about the equilibrium position shown.   Neglect the weights of the bars compared with W.   Each of the identical springs has a stiffness k.

$$Ans. \quad f = \frac{1}{2\pi} \sqrt{\frac{g}{l} + \frac{2kgb^2}{Wl^2}}$$

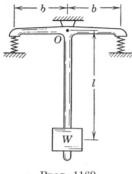

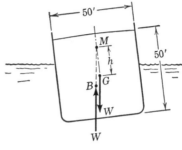

PROB. 1169   PROB. 1170

1170. The center of gravity G of the ship may be assumed to be at the center of the equivalent 50 ft. square section.   The metacentric height h, determined from the intersection M of the force W acting through the center of buoyancy B with the center line of the ship, is 3 ft.   Determine the period τ of one complete roll of the ship if the amplitude is small and the resistance of the water is neglected.   Neglect also the change in cross section of the ship at the bow and stern and treat the ship as a uniform solid block of square section.

$Ans. \quad \tau = 13.06$ sec.

1171. Each end of the connecting rod is "weighed" as shown.   The scales register 0.83 lb. for end A and 1.38 lb. for end B.   Next the rod is suspended from a knife edge in the wrist pin bearing at O and a period of 0.920 sec. is measured for small free oscillations.   Determine the centroidal radius of gyration $\bar{k}$ for the rod.

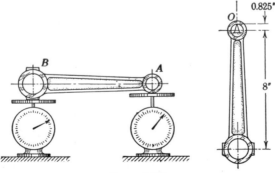

PROB. 1171

* **1172.** A compound pendulum with center of gravity at G and with centroidal radius of gyration $\bar{k}$ is freely suspended, first, at O_1, and second, at O_2. Determine the relation between $\bar{r}_1$ and $\bar{r}_2$ (other than the obvious one $\bar{r}_1 = \bar{r}_2$) which will make the period for small oscillations the same for each suspension point.   *Ans.* $\bar{r}_1\bar{r}_2 = \bar{k}^2$

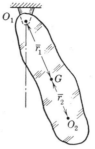

PROB. 1172

* **1173.** The two blocks of equal weight W are at rest on a smooth surface in the position shown where the connecting spring of stiffness k is unstretched. If a constant force P is applied as indicated, determine the acceleration a of each block as a function of the time t.

$$\textit{Ans.} \quad a = \frac{Pg}{2W}\left(1 \pm \cos \sqrt{\frac{2kg}{W}}\, t\right); \text{ plus for 2, minus for 1}$$

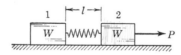

PROB. 1173

113. Torsional Vibrations. Consider a body suspended at its center of gravity by a light rod of small cross section, Fig. 146. The rod is assumed to be elastic within the range of angles through which it is twisted.

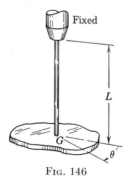

FIG. 146

In this event the resisting moment M is proportional to the angle θ through which the suspended body is twisted. From elementary elasticity theory the magnitude of this moment is found to be $(JG/L)\theta$, where J is the polar moment of inertia of the cross section of the rod and G is the shear modulus (resistance to shear stress) of the shaft. If the body is twisted through a small angle and then released, angular oscillation will take place. For any position for which the angular displacement is θ the moment applied to the body in the direction of θ is $M = -JG\theta/L$.   If the moment of inertia of the body about the centroidal axis is I, the equation of motion $\Sigma M = I\alpha$ applied in the arbitrary direction of positive θ gives

$$-\frac{JG}{L}\theta = I\frac{d^2\theta}{dt^2} \quad \text{or} \quad \frac{d^2\theta}{dt^2} + \frac{JG}{IL}\theta = 0.$$

This equation is of the form of Eq. (117) and so describes simple harmonic motion with a period

$$\tau = \frac{2\pi}{p} = 2\pi\sqrt{\frac{IL}{JG}}.$$

The unknown moment of inertia of a body may be determined experimentally by measurement of the period τ for the body suspended as in Fig. 146 from a wire of known properties and by substitution into the expression for τ.

Torsional vibrations are commonly encountered when two rotors are connected by a shaft as in Fig. 147.   If the rotors are twisted in the opposite directions and then released, a torsional vibration will occur.   The resulting motion may be analyzed by neglecting the mass of the shaft compared with that of the rotors.   There will be some section N, known as the *nodal section*, which will have no angular motion. The periods of both rotors will be equal since the periodic twisting moment acting on one rotor is transmitted through the shaft and acts equally on the other rotor but in the opposite sense.   By reason of equal periods the expression for τ gives

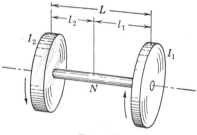

Fig. 147

$$I_1l_1 = I_2l_2.$$

Combination with $l_1 + l_2 = L$ yields

$$l_1 = \frac{I_2}{I_1 + I_2}L \quad \text{and} \quad l_2 = \frac{I_1}{I_1 + I_2}L.$$

The natural period of vibration for either rotor now becomes

$$\tau = 2\pi\sqrt{\frac{I_1I_2L}{(I_1 + I_2)JG}}.$$

PROBLEMS

1174. A steel bar 12 in. long with a 1 in. square cross section is suspended from its middle point by a $\frac{1}{16}$ in. diameter steel wire 24 in. long. The shear modulus G for the wire is 11.4×10^6 lb./in.^{2} Determine the frequency f of torsional vibration of the wire.

1175. The generator A is driven by the motor B through the 1 in. diameter shaft C which is 2 ft. long. The rotor of A weighs 40 lb. and has a radius of gyration of 3 in. The flywheel and rotating parts of B are equivalent to a single 80 lb. rotor with a radius of gyration of 6 in. The connecting steel shaft has a shear modulus of 11.4×10^6 lb./in.^{2} Find the speed N at which the system should not be run if this speed corresponds to the natural frequency of torsional vibration. *Ans.* $N = 2270$ rev./min.

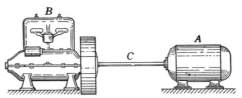

PROB. 1175

1176. The bar A weighs 12 lb. and may be considered a uniform slender rod fastened at its end to the short shaft. The shaft is supported freely in the bearing B and is fixed in a rigid support at C. If the shear modulus for the shaft is 11.4×10^6 lb./in.^{2}, determine the natural frequency f for small torsional vibration of the shaft when the bar is given an angular movement and then released. *Ans.* $f = 11.26$ cycles/sec.

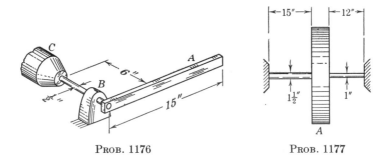

PROB. 1176   PROB. 1177

1177. The flywheel A weighs 60 lb. and has a radius of gyration of 12 in. The wheel is mounted rigidly to the two steel shafts shown whose ends, in turn, are rigidly clamped. Determine the natural frequency f of torsional vibration of the system. The shear modulus for each shaft is 11.4×10^6 lb./in.^{2}

1178. The motor armature of the computer mechanism shown with Prob. 908 has a moment of inertia of 0.008 lb. ft. sec.^{2} The shaft has a torsional stiffness of 2 lb. ft. per degree of twist between its ends. If the positive clutch is engaged at the instant the power to the motor is shut off from a speed of 1800 rev./min., determine the maximum amplitude θ_0 and the frequency f of the resulting torsional vibration. *Ans.* $\theta_0 = 90.2$ deg., $f = 19.05$ cycles/sec.

114. Work-Energy Solution. The equation of motion for a body which vibrates without energy loss may be obtained by the principle of conservation of energy. For any conservative vibrating system the total energy remains constant and at any general position is partly kinetic and partly potential. The potential energy will include both potential energy of position V_g, if there is motion in the vertical direction, and elastic potential energy V_e of the supporting members. Thus

$$T + V = \text{constant} \quad \text{and} \quad \frac{d}{dt}(T + V) = 0.$$

For the simple vibrating weight in Fig. 144a the kinetic energy at any displacement x is

$$T = \frac{1}{2}\frac{W}{g}\left(\frac{dx}{dt}\right)^2.$$

If $x = 0$ is selected as the position for zero potential energy, the elastic potential energy of the spring due to the stretch x is

$$V_e = \int_0^x (W + kx)\,dx = Wx + \tfrac{1}{2}kx^2,$$

and the potential energy of position is $V_g = -Wx$. Thus $V = V_e + V_g = \tfrac{1}{2}kx^2$, and the total energy is

$$\frac{1}{2}\frac{W}{g}\left(\frac{dx}{dt}\right)^2 + \frac{1}{2}kx^2 = \text{constant}.$$

Differentiation of this total constant energy with respect to the time gives

$$\frac{W}{g}\frac{dx}{dt}\frac{d^2x}{dt^2} + kx\frac{dx}{dt} = 0 \quad \text{or} \quad \frac{d^2x}{dt^2} + \frac{kg}{W}x = 0,$$

which is Eq. (117).

Work-energy consideration also leads directly to the determination of the frequency or period of a harmonic vibrating system. When the body reaches an extreme position, the entire energy is potential $V_{\text{max.}}$, and when the body passes the neutral or equilibrium position for which the potential energy is taken as zero, the energy is entirely kinetic $T_{\text{max.}}$. Conservation of energy requires, therefore, that

$$T_{\text{max.}} = V_{\text{max.}}.$$

This equality leads directly to the determination of the circular frequency for simple harmonic motion as may be shown for the vibrating body of Fig. 144a. Simple harmonic motion gives

$$x = x_0 \cos pt \qquad \text{and} \qquad \left| \frac{dx}{dt} \right|_{\text{max.}} = x_0 p.$$

Thus, for this type of motion, the maximum velocity equals the amplitude of motion multiplied by the circular frequency. The maximum kinetic energy becomes $T_{\text{max.}} = \frac{1}{2}(W/g)x_0^2 p^2$, and the maximum potential energy is $V_{\text{max.}} = \frac{1}{2}kx_0^2$. Hence

$$\frac{1}{2}\frac{W}{g}x_0^2 p^2 = \frac{1}{2}kx_0^2 \qquad \text{and} \qquad p = \sqrt{\frac{kg}{W}}.$$

The period and frequency are then obtained from p in the usual manner.

SAMPLE PROBLEM

1179. Determine the equation of motion and the period of motion for the rolling cylindrical disk of Sample Prob. 1160 by the energy method.

Solution: The kinetic energy at any position is

$$T = \frac{1}{2}I_C \omega^2 = \frac{1}{2}\left(\frac{3}{2}\frac{W}{g}r^2\right)\left(\frac{d\beta}{dt}\right)^2 = \frac{3}{4}\frac{W}{g}(R - r)^2\left(\frac{d\theta}{dt}\right)^2,$$

where the variable is changed to θ by the relation $\beta = (R - r)\theta/r$. The potential energy may be measured from the bottom position and is

$$V_g = W(R - r)(1 - \cos\theta).$$

The total energy of the system is

$$\frac{3}{4}\frac{W}{g}(R - r)^2\left(\frac{d\theta}{dt}\right)^2 + W(R - r)(1 - \cos\theta) = \text{constant},$$

and differentiation with respect to the time gives

$$\frac{3}{2}\frac{W}{g}(R - r)^2\frac{d\theta}{dt}\frac{d^2\theta}{dt^2} + W(R - r)\sin\theta\frac{d\theta}{dt} = 0.$$

Thus the equation of motion reduces to

$$\frac{d^2\theta}{dt^2} + \frac{2g}{3(R - r)}\theta = 0,$$

if motion is restricted to small angles for which sin θ is replaced by θ. This expression agrees with that obtained in Sample Prob. 1160.

The circular frequency is evident from the foregoing equation but could have been obtained at the outset by assuming simple harmonic motion for which $|\,d\beta/dt\,|_{\text{max.}} = \beta_0 p$, where β_0 is the amplitude of β. The maximum kinetic energy is, then,

$$T_{\text{max.}} = \frac{1}{2} I_c \omega^2 = \frac{1}{2}\left(\frac{3}{2}\frac{W}{g}r^2\right)(\beta_0 p)^2 = \frac{3}{4}\frac{W}{g}(R-r)^2 \theta_0^2 p^2.$$

The maximum potential energy is

$$V_{\text{max.}} = W(R-r)(1-\cos\theta_0) \approx W(R-r)\frac{\theta_0^2}{2},$$

where only the first two terms in the series expansion for $\cos\theta_0$ have been used for θ_0, a small angle. Equating the two energies gives

$$p = \sqrt{\frac{2g}{3(R-r)}},$$

which is the same expression as obtained previously.

PROBLEMS

1180. Determine the period τ for small oscillations of the supported ring of Prob. 1166 directly by the work-energy method.

1181. Neglect friction on the walls of the U-tube and determine the period τ of motion of the liquid if its total length in the tube is l.

$$Ans. \quad \tau = 2\pi\sqrt{\frac{l}{2g}}$$

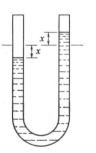

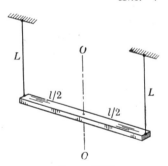

| PROB. 1181 | PROB. 1182 |

1182. The uniform slender bar of weight W is supported as a bifilar pendulum. Determine the period τ for small angular oscillations about the central vertical axis O–O.

1183. The flywheel A weighs 80 lb. with a radius of gyration of 6 in., and the friction in its bearing is negligible. A steel band connects A to a rigid wheel B, which is locked in position as shown. Each portion of the band between the wheels is under an initial tension of 200 lb. and undergoes a change of length of 2×10^{-4} in. per inch of length for every 100 lb. change in tension in the band. Determine the natural frequency f for small rotational vibration of wheel A if the band does not slip on either wheel.   *Ans.* $f = 85.2$ cycles/sec.

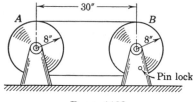

PROB. 1183

1184. Determine the natural frequency f for small vibrations of the system of Prob. 1169 directly by the work-energy method without obtaining the differential equation.

* 1185. The system shown is displaced from its equilibrium position and then released.   Find the natural frequency f of the resulting vibration if the **spring**

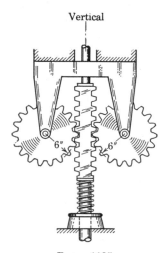

PROB. 1185

is in contact with the central rack at all times.   Each gear weighs 15 lb. with a radius of gyration of 4 in., the central rack weighs 12 lb., and the spring constant is 6 lb./in.   *Ans.* $f = 1.520$ cycles/sec.

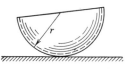

PROB. 1186

* 1186. The hemispherical bowl with negligible but uniform wall thickness rocks with a small amplitude on a horizontal surface.   Determine the period τ of motion by the energy method.

Ans. $\tau = 2\pi \sqrt{\dfrac{4r}{3g}}$

115. Damped Free Vibrations. Frictional retardation or damping is present to some degree in all vibrating systems, and the amplitude of any free vibration will diminish steadily with time. There are three sources of damping forces: *fluid damping*, which is caused by the frictional resistance offered by the surrounding fluid to motion; *Coulomb damping*, which is caused by kinetic friction force $F = fN$ between sliding dry surfaces; and *solid damping*, which is due to internal friction or *hysteresis* in the body which undergoes periodic change of shape. In the case of fluid damping moderate velocity through the fluid results in a frictional retardation

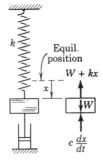

$$F_x = -c \frac{dx}{dt},$$

which is proportional to the first power of the velocity and which is in the direction opposite to the velocity. This type of damping is known as *viscous damping*, and the damping constant c depends on the viscous properties of the fluid.

FIG. 148

The free vibrations of a simple spring-mass system, Fig. 148, may be retarded with viscous damping by attaching the weight to the plunger of a dashpot. The equation of motion is applied to the free-body diagram and gives

$$W - (W + kx) - c \frac{dx}{dt} = \frac{W}{g} \frac{d^2x}{dt^2},$$

which becomes

$$\frac{d^2x}{dt^2} + \frac{cg}{W} \frac{dx}{dt} + \frac{kg}{W} x = 0. \tag{119}$$

The solution of Eq. (119) will involve a factor which diminishes with time, an oscillatory term for the vibration, and two integration constants. Assume, therefore, a solution of the form

$$x = A e^{-bt} \cos (pt - \phi). \tag{120}$$

By direct substitution it may be verified that this expression satisfies Eq. (119) for all values of the time where

$$b = \frac{cg}{2W} \quad \text{and} \quad p = \sqrt{\frac{kg}{W} - \left(\frac{cg}{2W}\right)^2}$$

and provided $kg/W > (cg/2W)^2$.

If the weight W is released from rest at a distance x_0 from the equilibrium position, the phase angle ϕ is zero and A is replaced by x_0. Thus the solution becomes

$$x = x_0 e^{-bt} \cos pt,$$

which is plotted in Fig. 149. The vibration has a period of

$$\tau = \frac{2\pi}{p} = \frac{2\pi}{\sqrt{\dfrac{kg}{W} - \left(\dfrac{cg}{2W}\right)^2}},$$

which is greater than that with no damping. The motion is limited between the two curves $x = x_0 e^{-bt}$ and $x = -x_0 e^{-bt}$.

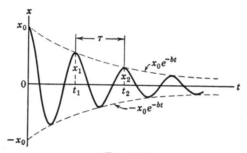

FIG. 149

The damping constant c may be determined from an experimental record of the vibration, as represented in Fig. 149, by the measurement of two successive amplitudes at times t_1 and $t_2 = t_1 + \tau$. These amplitudes are $x_1 = x_0 e^{-bt_1}$ and $x_2 = x_0 e^{-b(t_1+\tau)}$, and their ratio is

$$\frac{x_1}{x_2} = \frac{x_0 e^{-bt_1}}{x_0 e^{-b(t_1+\tau)}} = e^{b\tau}.$$

This expression may be written

$$b\tau = \log\frac{x_1}{x_2},$$

and $b\tau$ is known as the *logarithmic decrement*. Measurements of x_1, x_2, and τ enable the calculation of b and hence c to be made.

If $(cg/2W)^2 > kg/W$, the solution given by Eq. (120) does not hold. The correct solution for this case is

$$x = A_1 e^{-(b+K)t} + A_2 e^{-(b-K)t},$$

where $K = \sqrt{(cg/2W)^2 - (kg/W)}$. This motion is nonvibratory since both exponential terms are positive and represents the case of damping so severe that the body never crosses the equilibrium position when released from an initial displacement. If $(cg/2W)^2 = kg/W$, the motion is said to be critically damped, and this condition represents the transition between a damped vibration and an overdamped non-vibratory motion.

PROBLEM

* **1187.** Investigate the case of Coulomb damping for the block shown, where the coefficient of kinetic friction is f and each spring has a stiffness k. The

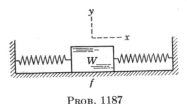

PROB. 1187

block is displaced a distance x_0 from the neutral position and released. Determine the differential equation of motion and solve. Plot the resulting vibration and indicate the rate of decay of amplitude with time.

$$Ans. \quad x = \left(x_0 - \frac{fW}{2k}\right) \cos \sqrt{\frac{2kg}{W}}\, t + \frac{fW}{2k}\; ; \text{ for the first half cycle}$$

116. Forced Vibrations. When the vibration of a system is generated and sustained by the application of an external periodic force or by the periodic movement of the foundation of the system, the vibration is said to be *forced*. Forced vibration constitutes the most important type of vibration found in engineering work.

In Fig. 150a is shown a simple spring-mass system subjected to an external alternating force $P \sin \omega t$. It is assumed that the system is constrained to move in the vertical direction, so that only the one coordinate x is needed to specify the position of the system. Also, damping forces are assumed absent for the time being. From the free-body diagram the equation of motion is seen to be

$$P \sin \omega t + W - (W + kx) = \frac{W}{g}\frac{d^2x}{dt^2},$$

or

$$\frac{d^2x}{dt^2} + \frac{kg}{W}x = \frac{Pg}{W}\sin \omega t. \tag{121}$$

In Fig. 150b is represented a spring-supported mass which is vibrating by reason of an assumed harmonic movement $\delta \sin \omega t$ of the foundation.

The net stretch of the spring in any general displaced position is $x - \delta \sin \omega t$, so that the equation of motion is

$$W - [W + k(x - \delta \sin \omega t)] = \frac{W}{g} \frac{d^2x}{dt^2},$$

or

$$\frac{d^2x}{dt^2} + \frac{kg}{W} x = \frac{kg}{W} \delta \sin \omega t. \tag{122}$$

Equations (121) and (122) are of the same form, so that solution of the first will apply to the second if $k\delta$ is substituted for P.

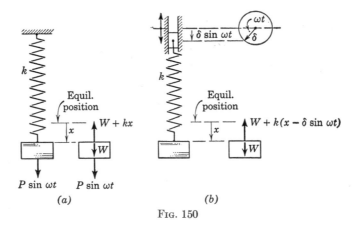

P sin ωt   P sin ωt

(a)   (b)

Fig. 150

When the right-hand side of a linear differential equation is not zero, the complete solution will equal the general solution x_c of the homogeneous equation (right side equal to zero) plus *any* particular solution x_p of the complete equation. The complementary solution is that for the free vibration of W and was found in Art. 112 to be

$$x_c = A \cos pt + B \sin pt, \quad \text{where } p = \sqrt{\frac{kg}{W}}.$$

For the particular solution of Eq. (121) try the expression

$$x_p = C \sin \omega t,$$

where C is a constant. The second time derivative of x_p is

$$\frac{d^2x_p}{dt^2} = -C\omega^2 \sin \omega t.$$

Substitution into Eq. (121) gives

$$C\left(-\omega^2 + \frac{kg}{W}\right)\sin \omega t = \frac{Pg}{W}\sin \omega t.$$

This expression is satisfied for all values of the time if the two coefficients of the sine terms are equal. Thus

$$C = \frac{Pg/W}{(kg/W) - \omega^2} = \frac{P/k}{1 - (\omega/p)^2}.$$

With this value for the constant C the assumed particular solution is valid, and the complete solution to Eq. (121) is $x = x_c + x_p$ or

$$x = A \cos pt + B \sin pt + \frac{P/k}{1 - (\omega/p)^2}\sin \omega t. \tag{123}$$

The constants A and B are dependent on the starting conditions as was shown in Art. 112 for the case of free vibrations.

The periodic force may also be expressed as $P \cos \omega t$ or as P times the sine or cosine of $\omega t - \phi$, where ϕ is a phase angle dependent on the exact instant at which the alternating force is first applied.

The first two terms of Eq. (123) represent the complementary or *transient* solution which disappears shortly because of the presence of even a small amount of damping as shown in Fig. 151. If a description

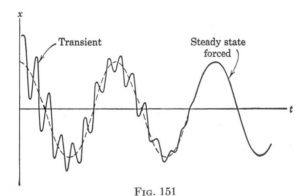

Fig. 151

is desired of the first few cycles immediately after application of the alternating force, it is necessary to know the exact phase at which the external force is applied at time $t = 0$ in order that the appropriate function $\sin \omega t$, $\cos \omega t$, or sine or cosine of $\omega t - \phi$ be employed.

After the initial or transient vibration has been damped out the particular solution

$$x_p = \frac{P/k}{1 - (\omega/p)^2} \sin \omega t \qquad (124)$$

remains and represents the *steady-state* forced vibration. When P/k is replaced by δ, Eq. (124) also represents the solution for the steady-state forced vibration due to harmonic movement of amplitude δ of the foundation of the spring-mass system in Fig. 150b. If the symbol δ is additionally used for the static deflection P/k of the spring due to a static load equal to P in the case of Fig. 150a, the amplitude x_0 of motion may be written in nondimensional form as

$$\frac{x_0}{\delta} = \frac{1}{1 - (\omega/p)^2}. \qquad (125)$$

The ratio x_0/δ is called the *magnification factor* and compares the actual amplitude x_0 with the static deflection δ. The term ω/p is known as the *frequency ratio* and compares the applied frequency with the natural frequency of free vibration. The magnification factor is plotted against the frequency ratio in the full line of Fig. 152. For the limiting

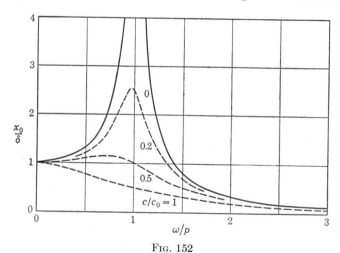

Fig. 152

case of zero damping the amplitude of the forced vibration is seen to approach infinity as ω approaches p. For values of ω greater than p the magnification factor is actually negative but is plotted above the axis for convenience. The negative value indicates that the resulting vibration is 180 deg. out of phase with the impressed force or foundation movement. The value $\omega = p$ is known as the *resonant frequency* or *critical speed* and clearly represents an operating condition to be avoided.

The effect of damping may be calculated by retaining the term $c(dx/dt)$ in the differential equation. The results of this analysis yield a steady-state motion of

$$x_p = \frac{P/k}{\sqrt{\left[1 - \left(\frac{\omega}{p}\right)^2\right]^2 + \left[\frac{c\omega}{k}\right]^2}} \sin(\omega t - \phi), \text{ where } \tan\phi = \frac{c\omega/k}{1 - \left(\frac{\omega}{p}\right)^2}.$$

The magnification factor becomes

$$\frac{x_0}{\delta} = \frac{1}{\sqrt{\left[1 - \left(\frac{\omega}{p}\right)^2\right]^2 + \left[2\frac{c\omega}{c_0 p}\right]^2}},$$

where c/c_0 is the damping factor and $c_0 = 2\sqrt{kW/g}$ is the critical damping constant. The curves for three values of c/c_0 are shown by the dotted lines in Fig. 152. Such curves are used to select suitable damping constants to limit the amplitude of motion when operation is in the critical range.

It is usually desirable to reduce as much as possible the forced vibrations which are generated in engineering structures and machines. Vibration reduction is normally accomplished in any of four ways: (1) elimination or reduction of the exciting force by balancing or other removal, (2) introduction of sufficient damping to limit the amplitude, (3) isolation of the body from the vibration source by providing elastic mountings of the proper stiffness, and (4) operation at a forced frequency sufficiently different from the natural frequency so as to avoid resonance.

The foregoing discussion of forced vibrations is only a brief introduction to this subject. Further study includes the analysis of systems with a number of degrees of freedom, and more advanced methods of solution are available.

SAMPLE PROBLEM

1188. The armature of an electric motor weighs 36 lb. and has a center of gravity midway between the two bearings and 0.015 in. off center from the bearing axis. The entire motor weighs 80 lb. and causes a static deflection of 0.125 in. in each of the four spring mounts under the base of the motor. Determine the speed N at which the motor should *not* be run and find the amplitude x_0 of vertical vibration of the motor when running at twice this speed.

Solution: The spring constant for an equivalent single spring is

$$k = \frac{F}{\delta} = \frac{80}{0.125} = 640 \text{ lb./in.}$$

Thus the critical frequency is

$$\frac{p}{2\pi} = \frac{1}{2\pi} \sqrt{\frac{kg}{W}} = \frac{1}{2\pi} \sqrt{\frac{640 \times 32.2 \times 12}{80}} = 8.84 \text{ cycles/sec.,}$$

or

$$N = 8.84 \times 60 = 530 \text{ rev./min.} \qquad\qquad Ans.$$

The amplitude of the applied harmonic force for a speed of 1060 rev./min. is

$$P = me\omega^2 = \frac{36}{32.2} \frac{0.015}{12} \left(\frac{1060 \times 2\pi}{60}\right)^2 = 17.22 \text{ lb.}$$

The equivalent static deflection due to this load is $\delta = P/k = 17.22/640 = 0.0269$ in.   The maximum amplitude of motion is, therefore,

$$x_0 = \left|\frac{\delta}{1 - (\omega/p)^2}\right| = \left|\frac{0.0269}{1 - (2)^2}\right| = 0.0090 \text{ in.} \qquad Ans.$$

PROBLEMS

1189. The overhanging motor shaft has a static deflection of 0.004 in. at its end due to the weight of the 10 lb. rotor A.   At what speed N would the vibration of the shaft become excessive for a small amount of unbalance of the rotor?

Ans. $N = 2970$ rev./min.

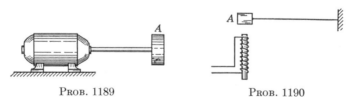

PROB. 1189   PROB. 1190

1190. When the electromagnet is energized by an alternating current with a frequency of 30 cycles/sec., the 2 oz. steel weight A is observed to vibrate in the vertical direction with a double amplitude of $\frac{1}{16}$ in. Determine the peak value of the alternating magnetic force if the stiffness of the light elastic beam is such that its end deflects 0.008 in. under a static force of 2 oz.

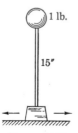

1191. The 1 lb. weight is attached to the end of the light elastic beam and deflects 0.250 in. because of a horizontal load of 8 oz. applied statically to the weight.   If the foundation is given a horizontal harmonic movement with a frequency of 4 cycles/sec. and an amplitude of $\frac{1}{8}$ in., find the amplitude x_0 of horizontal vibration of the weight.   *Ans.* $x_0 = 0.687$ in.

PROB. 1191

1192. It is desired to limit the amplitude of vertical vibration for the motor described in Sample Prob. 1188 to 0.010 in. when operating at a speed of 800 rev./min. by providing suitable viscous damping. Determine the necessary damping factor c/c_0.

1193. The electric motor weighs 50 lb. and causes a static deflection of 0.125 in. of the center of the light elastic beam. The armature of the motor weighs 20 lb. and its center of gravity is 0.002 in. off center. Determine the vertical amplitude x_0 of the forced vibration of the middle of the beam when the motor is running at 600 rev./min.

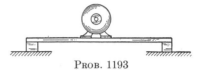
PROB. 1193

Ans. $x_0 = 0.00368$ in.

1194. The disk has a weight W and is mounted with a small eccentricity e in the middle of the light elastic shaft. When the shaft rotates at an angular velocity ω, the "centrifugal force" F deflects the shaft an amount r. This force equals kr, where k is the equivalent spring constant or lateral force required to produce a unit deflection of the middle of the shaft. Equate F and kr and find the relation between r and the natural circular frequency $p = \sqrt{kg/W}$ for lateral vibration of the shaft. At what angular velocity ω_c would the shaft vibrate excessively?

1195. In the case of an elastically mounted motor of total weight W, where the forced vibration is excited by the out-of-balance of its rotor of weight W', it is convenient to define the magnification factor as the ratio of Wx_0 to the product $W'e$, where e is the eccentricity or distance from the center of gravity of the rotor to the axis of revolution. With this definition derive and plot the relation between $Wx_0/W'e$ and the frequency ratio ω/p.

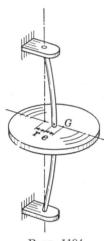
PROB. 1194

Ans. $\dfrac{Wx_0}{W'e} = \dfrac{(\omega/p)^2}{1 - (\omega/p)^2}$

1196. A delicate instrument weighing 6.50 lb. is rigidly mounted to an 8 lb. base which in turn must be suspended from the ceiling by four identical and symmetrically placed springs in order to isolate the instrument from building vibration caused by operation of heavy rotating machinery on a near-by floor. Measurements indicate that the ceiling of the room in which the instrument is to be suspended has a vertical amplitude of 0.003 in. at a frequency of 6 cycles/sec. Specify the maximum constant k of each of the four springs so that the corresponding amplitude of vibration of the instrument will be no greater than 0.0001 in. *Ans.* $k = 5.16$ lb./ft.

1197. A 60 lb. motor operates at 1250 rev./min. and has an unbalance in its rotor. When the motor is mounted on four identical spring pads, the alternating part of the force which is transmitted to the foundation is cut in half. Determine the constant k of each pad.

1198. The vibrometer shown is fastened to a ship's deck near the stern where the propeller vibration is most pronounced. The ship has a single 3-bladed propeller which turns at 125 rev./min. partly out of water, thus causing a shock as each blade breaks the surface. The natural frequency of vibration of the instrument is 2 cycles/sec., and the observed vertical amplitude of motion of the weight A relative to the frame and deck is 0.030 in. Find the amplitude δ of vibration of the deck. (*Hint:* Note that the vibration of the weight is 180 deg. out of phase with the deck for operation above the natural frequency of 2 cycles/sec.) *Ans.* $\delta = 0.0269$ in.

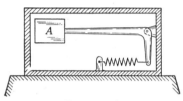

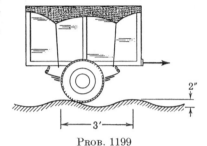

PROB. 1198

PROB. 1199

* **1199.** Determine the amplitude of vertical vibration of the spring-mounted trailer as it travels at a velocity of 15 mi./hr. over the corduroy road whose contour may be expressed by a sine or cosine term. The weight of the trailer is 800 lb., and that of the wheels alone may be neglected. During the loading each 100 lb. increment of load caused the trailer to sag $\frac{1}{8}$ in. on its springs. Assume that the wheels are in contact with the road at all times. At what critical speed v_c is the vibration of the trailer greatest?

Ans. $x_0 = 0.223$ in., $v_c = 6.4$ mi./hr.

* **1200.** A *seismic* type of vibration-recording instrument, represented schematically in the figure, consists of a spring-mounted mass within a case. The case

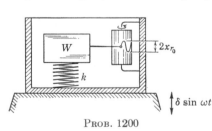

PROB. 1200

in turn is secured to the body whose vibration is to be determined, and the *relative* movement x_r between the mass and the case is measured and recorded. Derive the equation of motion for the mass in terms of x_r and obtain the expression for the ratio of the amplitude x_{r_0} to the amplitude δ of the given body vibration. Note that the equation derived for the system in Fig. 150b needs to be modified only by the change of variable from x to x_r. Represent the relation between x_{r_0}/δ and ω/p graphically and indicate the conditions under which the measurement x_r may be used with satisfactory accuracy to represent δ.

Ans. $\dfrac{x_{r_0}}{\delta} = \dfrac{(\omega/p)^2}{1 - (\omega/p)^2}$

Appendix A

Moments of Inertia

I. MOMENTS OF INERTIA OF AREAS

A1. Definitions. In the analysis of the distribution of stress over the cross-sectional areas of structural and machine members an expression of the form $\int y^2 \, dA$ is encountered, where y is the distance from an element dA of the area to an axis which is either in or normal to the plane of the area. Expressions of this type also appear in other engineering problems. By reason of the frequent occurrence of these integrals it is convenient to develop them for some of the more common areas and to tabulate the results.

The integral to which reference is made is generally called the *moment of inertia* of the area about the axis in question. A more fitting term is the *second moment of area* since the first moment $y \, dA$ is multiplied again by the moment arm y to obtain the result for the element dA. The word *inertia* appears in the terminology by reason of the similarity between the mathematical form of the integrals for second moments of areas and those for the resultant moments of the inertia forces in the case of rotating bodies. The moment of inertia of an area is a purely mathematical property of the area and in itself has no physical significance.

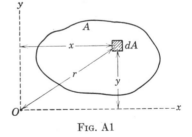

Fig. A1

Consider the area A in the x–y plane, Fig. A1. The moments of inertia of the element dA about the x- and y-axes are, by definition, $dI_x = y^2 \, dA$ and $dI_y = x^2 \, dA$, respectively. Therefore the moments of inertia of A about the same axes are

$$I_x = \int y^2 \, dA,$$

$$I_y = \int x^2 \, dA,$$

$$(A1)$$

where the integration covers the entire area. The moment of inertia of

dA about the pole O (z-axis) is, by similar definition, $dJ_z = r^2\,dA$, and the moment of inertia of the entire area about O is

$$J_z = \int r^2\,dA. \tag{A2}$$

The expressions defined by Eqs. (A1) are known as *rectangular* moments of inertia, whereas the expression of Eq. (A2) is known as the *polar* moment of inertia. Since $x^2 + y^2 = r^2$, it is clear that

$$J_z = I_x + I_y. \tag{A3}$$

A polar moment of inertia for an area whose boundaries are more simply described in rectangular coordinates than in polar coordinates is easily calculated with the aid of Eq. (A3).

It should be noted that the moment of inertia of an element involves the square of the distance from the inertia axis to the element. An element whose coordinate is negative contributes as much to the moment of inertia as does an element with a positive coordinate of the same magnitude. Consequently the moment of inertia of an area about any axis is always a positive quantity. In contrast, the first moment of the area, which was involved in the computations of centroids, could be either positive or negative.

The dimensions of moments of inertia of areas are clearly L^4, where L stands for the dimension of length. Thus the units for area moments of inertia are expressed as quartic inches (in.^{4}) or quartic feet (ft.^{4}).

The choice of the coordinates to use for the calculation of moments of inertia is important. Rectangular coordinates should be used for shapes whose boundaries are most easily expressed in these coordinates. Polar coordinates will usually simplify problems involving boundaries which are easily described in r and θ. The choice of an element of area which simplifies the integration as much as possible is also important. These considerations are quite analogous to those discussed and illustrated in Chapter V in the calculation of centroids.

A2. Radius of Gyration. The moment of inertia of an area is a measure of the distribution of the area from the axis in question. Assume all the area A, Fig. A2, to be concentrated into a strip of negligible thickness at a distance k_x from the x-axis such that the product $k_x^2 A$ equals the moment of inertia about the axis. The distance k_x, called the *radius of gyration*, is then a measure of the distribution of area from the inertia axis. By definition, then, for any axis

$$I = k^2 A \qquad \text{or} \qquad k = \sqrt{\frac{I}{A}}. \tag{A4}$$

When this definition is substituted in each of the three terms in Eq. (A3), there results

$$k_z{}^2 = k_x{}^2 + k_y{}^2. \tag{A5}$$

Thus the square of the radius of gyration about a polar axis equals the sum of the squares of the radii of gyration about the two corresponding rectangular axes.

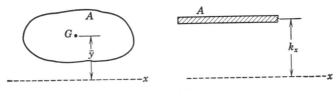

Fɪɢ. A2

It is imperative that there be no confusion between the coordinate to the centroid of the area and the radius of gyration k. The square of the centroidal distance, Fig. A2, is $\bar{y}^2$ and is the square of the mean value of the distances y from the elements dA to the axis. The quantity $k_x{}^2$, on the other hand, is the mean of the squares of these distances. The moment of inertia is *not* equal to $A\bar{y}^2$ since the square of the mean is not equal to the mean of the squares.

A3. Transfer of Axes. The moment of inertia of an area about a noncentroidal axis may be easily expressed in terms of the moment of inertia about a parallel centroidal axis. In Fig. A3 the x_o–y_o axes pass through the centroid G of the area. Let it be desired to determine the

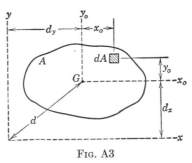

Fɪɢ. A3

moments of inertia of the area about the parallel x–y axes. By definition the moment of inertia of the element dA about the x-axis is

$$dI_x = (y_o + d_x)^2 \, dA.$$

Expanding and integrating give

$$I_x = \int y_o{}^2 \, dA + 2d_x \int y_o \, dA + d_x{}^2 \int dA.$$

The first integral is the moment of inertia $\bar{I}_x$ about the centroidal x_o-axis. The second integral is zero since $A\bar{y}_o = \int y_o \, dA$ and $\bar{y}_o$ is automatically zero. The third integral is simply $A d_x{}^2$. Thus the expression for I_x and the similar expression for I_y become

$$I_x = \bar{I}_x + A d_x{}^2,$$
$$I_y = \bar{I}_y + A d_y{}^2. \tag{A6}$$

By Eq. (A3) the sum of these two equations gives

$$J_z = \bar{J}_z + A d^2. \tag{A6a}$$

Equations (A6) and (A6a) are the so-called *parallel-axis theorems*. Two points in particular should be noted. First, the axes between which the transfer is made must be parallel, and, second, one of the axes must pass through the centroid of the area.

If a transfer between two parallel axes neither one of which passes through the centroid is desired, it is first necessary to transfer from one axis to the parallel centroidal axis and then to transfer from the centroidal axis to the second axis.

The parallel-axis theorems also hold for radii of gyration. With substitution of the definition of k into Eqs. (A6), the transfer relation becomes

$$k^2 = \bar{k}^2 + d^2, \tag{A6b}$$

where $\bar{k}$ is the radius of gyration about a centroidal axis parallel to the axis about which k applies and d is the distance between the two axes. The axes may be either in the plane or normal to the plane of the area.

A summary of the moment of inertia relations for some of the common plane figures is given in Table B5, Appendix B.

SAMPLE PROBLEMS

A1. Determine the moments of inertia of the rectangular area about the centroidal x_o–y_o axes, the centroidal polar axis G, the x-axis, and the polar axis O.

Solution: For the calculation of the moment of inertia $\bar{I}_x$ about the x_o-axis a horizontal strip of area $b\, dy$ is chosen so that all elements of the strip have the same y-coordinate. Thus

$$[I_x = \int y^2\, dA] \qquad \bar{I}_x = \int_{-h/2}^{h/2} y^2 b\, dy = \tfrac{1}{12}\, bh^3. \qquad Ans.$$

By interchanging symbols the moment of inertia about the centroidal y_o-axis is

$$\bar{I}_y = \tfrac{1}{12}\, hb^3. \qquad Ans.$$

The centroidal polar moment of inertia is

$$[J_z = I_x + I_y] \qquad \bar{J}_z = \tfrac{1}{12}(bh^3 + hb^3) = \tfrac{1}{12} A(b^2 + h^2). \qquad Ans.$$

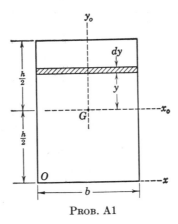

PROB. A1

By the parallel-axis theorem the moment of inertia about the x-axis is

$$[I_x = \bar{I}_x + A d_x^2] \qquad I_x = \tfrac{1}{12} bh^3 + bh \left(\frac{h}{2}\right)^2 = \tfrac{1}{3} bh^3 = \tfrac{1}{3} A h^2. \qquad Ans.$$

The polar moment of inertia about O may also be obtained by the parallel-axis theorem. Thus

$$[J_z = \bar{J}_z + A d^2] \qquad J_z = \tfrac{1}{12} A(b^2 + h^2) + A \left[\left(\frac{b}{2}\right)^2 + \left(\frac{h}{2}\right)^2\right],$$

$$J_z = \tfrac{1}{3} A(b^2 + h^2). \qquad Ans.$$

A2. Calculate the moments of inertia of the area of the circle about a diametral axis and about the polar axis through the center. Specify the radii of gyration.

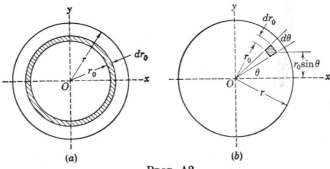

(a)   (b)

PROB. A2

Solution: An element of area in the form of a circular ring, shown in the *a*-part of the figure, may be used for the calculation of the moment of inertia about the polar z-axis through O since all elements of the ring are equidistant from O.   The elemental area is $dA = 2\pi r_o\, dr_o$, and thus

$$[J_z = \int r^2\, dA] \qquad\qquad J_z = \int_0^r r_o{}^2(2\pi r_o\, dr_o) = \frac{\pi r^4}{2} = \tfrac{1}{2}Ar^2. \qquad\qquad Ans.$$

The polar radius of gyration is

$$\left[k = \sqrt{\frac{J}{A}}\right] \qquad\qquad k_z = \frac{r}{\sqrt{2}}. \qquad\qquad Ans.$$

By symmetry $I_x = I_y$, so that from Eq. (A3)

$$[J_z = I_x + I_y] \qquad\qquad I_x = \tfrac{1}{2}J_z = \frac{\pi r^4}{4} = \tfrac{1}{4}\,Ar^2. \qquad\qquad Ans.$$

The radius of gyration about the diametral axis is

$$\left[k = \sqrt{\frac{I}{A}}\right] \qquad\qquad k_x = \frac{r}{2}. \qquad\qquad Ans.$$

The foregoing determination of I_x is the simplest possible.   The result may also be obtained by direct integration, using the element of area $dA = r_o\, dr_o\, d\theta$ shown in the b-part of the figure.   By definition

$$[I_x = \int y^2\, dA] \qquad I_x = \int_0^{2\pi}\int_0^r (r_o \sin\theta)^2 r_o\, dr_o\, d\theta,$$

$$= \int_0^{2\pi} \frac{r^4 \sin^2\theta}{4}\, d\theta = \frac{r^4}{4}\frac{1}{2}\left[\theta - \frac{\sin 2\theta}{2}\right]_0^{2\pi} = \frac{\pi r^4}{4}. \qquad Ans.$$

A3. Determine the moments of inertia of the triangular area about its base and about parallel axes through its centroid and vertex.

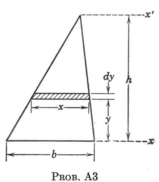

PROB. A3

Solution: A strip of area parallel to the base is selected as shown in the figure, and it has the area $dA = x\, dy = [(h - y)b/h]\, dy$.   By definition

$$[I_x = \int y^2\, dA] \qquad I_x = \int_0^h y^2 \frac{h - y}{h}\, b\, dy = b\left[\frac{y^3}{3} - \frac{y^4}{4h}\right]_0^h = \frac{bh^3}{12}. \qquad Ans.$$

By the parallel-axis theorem the moment of inertia $\bar{I}$ about an axis through the centroid, a distance $h/3$ above the x-axis, is

$[\bar{I} = I - Ad^2]$ $\bar{I} = \dfrac{bh^3}{12} - \left(\dfrac{bh}{2}\right)\left(\dfrac{h}{3}\right)^2 = \dfrac{bh^3}{36}.$ *Ans.*

A transfer from the centroidal axis to the x'-axis through the vertex gives

$[I = \bar{I} + Ad^2]$ $I_{x'} = \dfrac{bh^3}{36} + \left(\dfrac{bh}{2}\right)\left(\dfrac{2h}{3}\right)^2 = \dfrac{bh^3}{4}.$ *Ans.*

A4. Determine the moment of inertia about the x-axis of the semicircular area shown.

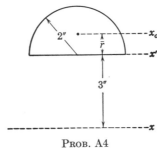

Prob. A4

Solution: The moment of inertia of the semicircular area about the x'-axis is one half of that for a complete circle about the same axis. Thus from the results of Prob. A2

$$I_{x'} = \frac{1}{2}\frac{\pi r^4}{4} = \frac{2^4\pi}{8} = 2\pi \text{ in.}^4$$

The moment of inertia $\bar{I}$ about the parallel centroidal axis x_o is obtained next. Transfer is made through the distance $\bar{r} = 4r/3\pi = (4 \times 2)/3\pi = 8/(3\pi)$ in. by the parallel-axis theorem. Hence

$[\bar{I} = I - Ad^2]$ $\bar{I} = 2\pi - \left(\dfrac{2^2\pi}{2}\right)\left(\dfrac{8}{3\pi}\right)^2 = 1.755 \text{ in.}^4$

Finally, transfer is made from the centroidal x_o-axis to the x-axis, which gives

$[I = \bar{I} + Ad^2]$ $I_z = 1.755 + \left(\dfrac{2^2\pi}{2}\right)\left(3 + \dfrac{8}{3\pi}\right)^2,$

$$= 1.755 + 93.1 = 94.9 \text{ in.}^4$$ *Ans.*

PROBLEMS

A5. Find the moments of inertia of the area of the quarter circle shown about the diametral x-axis and the polar axis through O.   *Ans.* $I_x = \dfrac{\pi r^4}{16}, J_z = \dfrac{\pi r^4}{8}$

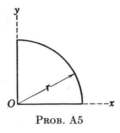

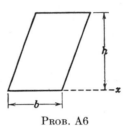

Prob. A5   Prob. A6

A6. Find the moments of inertia of the area of the parallelogram about the base (x-axis) and about a parallel centroidal axis. (Compare with Sample Prob. A1.)

A7. Approximate the result for the moment of inertia of a circular area about a diameter by dividing the circle into strips parallel to the inertia axis and of width $r/5$. Treat the moment of inertia of each strip as its area times the square of the distance from its center to the axis.

A8. Find the radius of gyration k of a square of side b about one diagonal.

Ans. $k = \dfrac{b}{2\sqrt{3}}$

A9. Find the moment of inertia of the shaded area about the x-axis by taking a horizontal strip of area dA.   *Ans.* $I_x = \frac{4}{15}ab^3$

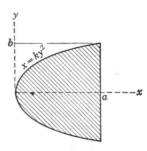

Prob. A9

A10. Solve Prob. A9 by choosing a vertical strip of area dA and applying the results of Sample Prob. A1 to this element.

A11. Find the moment of inertia of the figure in Prob. A9 about the y-axis.

Ans. $I_y = \frac{4}{7}a^3b$

A12. Calculate the moments of inertia of the elliptical area about the major axes and the central polar axis.

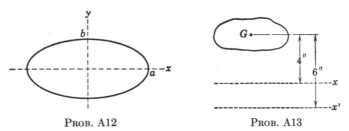

PROB. A12   PROB. A13

A13. The x- and x'-axes are located from the centroid G of the irregular area as shown. If the moments of inertia about these axes are $I_x = 1800$ in.^{4} and $I_{x'} = 2200$ in.^{4}, determine the area A of the figure.   *Ans.* $A = 20$ in.^{2}

A14. Use the results of Probs. A9 and A11 to find the polar moment of inertia J of the figure in Prob. A9 about the point $(a, 0)$. (The centroid is a distance $3a/5$ from the origin, and the area of the figure is $4ab/3$.)

A15. Determine the moments of inertia of the area of the circular sector about the x- and y-axes.   *Ans.* $I_x = \dfrac{r^4}{4}\left(\alpha - \dfrac{\sin 2\alpha}{2}\right), I_y = \dfrac{r^4}{4}\left(\alpha + \dfrac{\sin 2\alpha}{2}\right)$

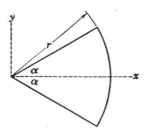

PROB. A15

A16. The area of a circular ring of inside radius r and outside radius $r + \Delta r$ is approximately equal to the circumference at the mean radius times the thickness Δr. The polar moment of inertia of the ring may be approximated by multiplying this area by the square of the mean radius. What per cent error is involved if $\Delta r = r/10$?   *Ans.*   Error $= 0.226\%$

A4. Composite Areas. The moment of inertia of a composite area about a particular axis is the algebraic sum of the moments of inertia of the various parts about the same axis. The results of the problems in Art. A3 and the tabulation of results in Table B5, Appendix B, may be used to determine the moments of inertia for component parts of the shapes given. It is often convenient to regard a composite area as composed of positive and negative parts. The moment of inertia of a negative area is a minus quantity.

When the section is composed of a large number of parts, it is convenient to tabulate the results for the parts in terms of the area A, centroidal moment of inertia $\bar{I}$, distance d from the centroidal axis to the axis about which the moment of inertia of the entire section is being computed, and the product Ad^2. For any one of the parts the desired moment of inertia is $\bar{I} + Ad^2$, and thus for the entire section the desired moment of inertia may be expressed as $I = \Sigma\bar{I} + \Sigma Ad^2$.

SAMPLE PROBLEM

A17. Compute the moment of inertia and radius of gyration about the x-axis for the cross section shown.

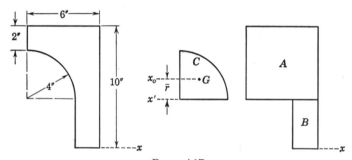

PROB. A17

Solution: The composite area may be considered as composed of the two rectangles A and B and the negative quarter circular area C. For the rectangle A the moment of inertia about the x-axis is

$$[I = \bar{I} + Ad^2] \qquad I_x = \tfrac{1}{12} \times 6 \times 6^3 + 6^2 \times 7^2 = 1872 \text{ in.}^4$$

The moment of inertia of B about the x-axis is

$$I_x = \tfrac{1}{3} \times 2 \times 4^3 = 42.67 \text{ in.}^4$$

The moment of inertia of the negative quarter circle C about its horizontal diameter is

$$I_{x'} = -\tfrac{1}{4} \times \tfrac{1}{4}\pi \times 4^4 = -50.27 \text{ in.}^4$$

Transfer of this result through the distance $\bar{r} = 4r/3\pi = (4 \times 4)/3\pi = 1.697$ in. gives for the centroidal moment of inertia of C

$$[\bar{I} = I - Ad^2] \qquad \bar{I} = -50.27 - \left(-\frac{\pi}{4} \times 4^2\right)(1.697)^2 = -14.07 \text{ in.}^4$$

The moment of inertia of C may now be found with respect to the x-axis, and the transfer from the centroidal axis gives

$$[I = \bar{I} + Ad^2] \qquad I_x = -14.07 + \left(-\frac{\pi}{4} \times 4^2\right)(4 + 1.697)^2 = -422 \text{ in.}^4$$

The moment of inertia of the net section about the x-axis is the sum of moments of inertia of its component parts. Thus

$$I_x = 1872 + 42.7 - 422 = 1493 \text{ in.}^4, \qquad \qquad Ans.$$

and

$$k_x = \sqrt{\frac{I_x}{A}} = \sqrt{\frac{1493}{31.43}} = 6.89 \text{ in.} \qquad \qquad Ans.$$

PROBLEMS

A18. Determine the polar moment of inertia J for the section about point O.

$$Ans. \quad J = 138.9 \text{ in.}^4$$

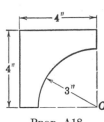

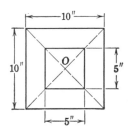

PROB. A18   PROB. A19

A19. Find the polar moment of inertia J about point O for the cross section bounded by the two squares.

A20. Find the polar moment of inertia of the net area about O.

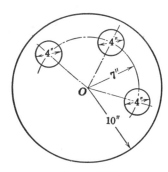

PROB. A20

A21. Determine the moment of inertia of the area of a rectangle of sides a and b about a diagonal.

$$Ans. \quad I = \frac{a^3 b^3}{6(a^2 + b^2)}$$

A22. Find the moment of inertia about the x-axis of the area between the curves $x = y^2$ and $x = y$ from $x = 0$ to $x = 1$, where x and y are in inches.

A23. Determine the moments of inertia of the Z-section about the centroidal x_o- and y_o-axes.

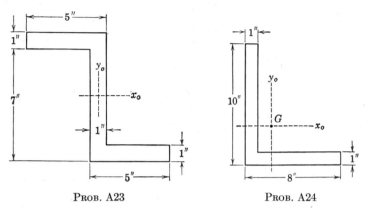

PROB. A23   PROB. A24

A24. Determine the moment of inertia of the angle section about its horizontal centroidal axis x_o.   *Ans.* $\bar{I}_x = 167.3$ in.⁴

A25. Determine the moment of inertia of the area of the hexagon of side b about the x-axis.

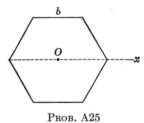

PROB. A25

A26. Determine the polar moment of inertia J of the hexagonal area of Prob. A25 about O.

$$Ans. \quad J = \frac{5\sqrt{3}}{8} b^4$$

A27. Determine the radius of gyration of the section about the 45 deg. axis of symmetry. (*Hint:* Use the results of Prob. A15.)

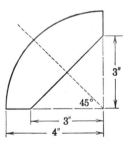

PROB. A27

A28. In the calculation of the stability of a ship's hull it is necessary to know the moment of inertia about the longitudinal center line of the area of the horizontal cross section of the hull at the waterline. Estimate this moment of inertia for the waterline shape reproduced here by dividing the area into a number of approximating strips. *Ans.* $I \cong 53,000$ ft.[4]

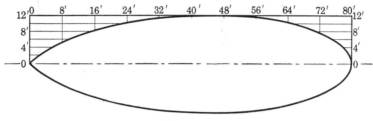

PROB. A28

A29. Determine the moment of inertia of the built-up structural section about its centroidal x_o-axis.

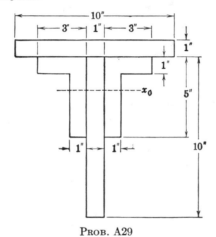

PROB. A29

A30. Calculate the moment of inertia of the standard 12×4 in. channel section about the centroidal x_o-axis. Neglect the fillets and radii and compare with the handbook value of $\bar{I}_x = 16.0$ in.[4]

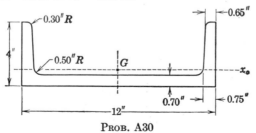

PROB. A30

A31. Determine the moment of inertia of the cross section shown about the x-axis.   *Ans.* $I_x = 1611$ in.^{4}

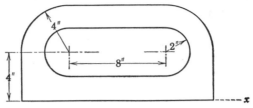

PROB. A31

A32. Determine the flange width b for the H-beam section such that the moments of inertia about the central x- and y-axes will be equal.

Ans. $b = 16.1$ in.

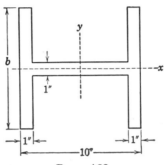

PROB. A32

A5. Product of Inertia. In certain problems involving unsymmetrical cross sections an expression occurs which has the form

$$dP_{xy} = xy\, dA,$$

$$P_{xy} = \int xy\, dA,$$

(A7)

where x and y are the coordinates of the element of area dA. The quantity P_{xy} is called the *product of inertia* of the area A about the x–y axes. Unlike moments of inertia, the product of inertia can be positive or negative.

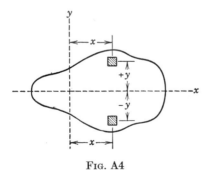

FIG. A4

By reference to Fig. A4 it can be seen for an axis of symmetry, such as the x-axis, that the sum of the terms $x(-y)\, dA$ and $x(+y)\, dA$ due to symmetrically placed elements vanishes. Since the entire area may be considered as composed of pairs of such elements, it follows that the product of inertia vanishes.

A transfer-of-axis theorem exists for products of inertia which is similar to that for moments of inertia. By definition the product of inertia of the area A in Fig. A3 about the x- and y-axes in terms of the coordinates x_o, y_o to the centroidal axes is

$$P_{xy} = \int (x_o + d_y)(y_o + d_x)\, dA,$$

$$= \int x_o y_o\, dA + d_x \int x_o\, dA + d_y \int y_o\, dA + d_x d_y \int dA,$$

$$P_{xy} = \bar{P}_{xy} + d_x d_y A, \tag{A8}$$

where $\bar{P}_{xy}$ is the product of inertia with respect to the centroidal x_o–y_o axes which are parallel to the x–y axes.

A6. Inclined Axes. It is often necessary to calculate the moment of inertia of an area about inclined axes. This consideration leads directly to the important problem of determining the axes about which the moment of inertia is a maximum and a minimum.

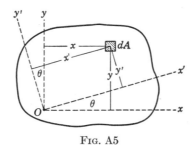

FIG. A5

In Fig. A5 the moments of inertia of the area about the x'- and y'-axes are

$$I_{x'} = \int y'^2\, dA = \int (y \cos\theta - x \sin\theta)^2\, dA,$$

$$I_{y'} = \int x'^2\, dA = \int (y \sin\theta + x \cos\theta)^2\, dA.$$

Expanding and substituting the trigonometric identities,

$$\sin^2\theta = \frac{1 - \cos 2\theta}{2}, \qquad \cos^2\theta = \frac{1 + \cos 2\theta}{2},$$

and the defining relations for I_x, I_y, P_{xy} give

$$I_{x'} = \frac{I_x + I_y}{2} + \frac{I_x - I_y}{2} \cos 2\theta - P_{xy} \sin 2\theta,$$

$$I_{y'} = \frac{I_x + I_y}{2} - \frac{I_x - I_y}{2} \cos 2\theta + P_{xy} \sin 2\theta.$$

(A9)

In a similar manner

$$P_{x'y'} = \int x'y' \, dA = \frac{I_x - I_y}{2} \sin 2\theta + P_{xy} \cos 2\theta.$$

(A9a)

Adding Eqs. (A9) gives $I_{x'} + I_{y'} = I_x + I_y = J_z$, the polar moment of inertia about O, which checks the result of Eq. (A3).

The angle which makes $I_{x'}$ and $I_{y'}$ a maximum or a minimum may be determined by setting the derivative of either $I_{x'}$ or $I_{y'}$ with respect to θ equal to zero. Thus

$$\frac{dI_{x'}}{d\theta} = (I_y - I_x) \sin 2\theta - 2P_{xy} \cos 2\theta = 0.$$

Denoting this critical angle by α gives

$$\tan 2\alpha = \frac{2P_{xy}}{I_y - I_x}.$$

(A10)

Equation (A10) gives two values for 2α which differ by π since $\tan 2\alpha = \tan(2\alpha + \pi)$. Consequently the two solutions for α will differ by $\pi/2$. One value defines the axis of maximum moment of inertia, and the other

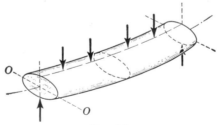

Fig. A6

value defines the axis of minimum moment of inertia. These two rectangular axes are known as the *principal axes of inertia*. Substitution of Eq. (A10) in Eq. (A9a) shows that the product of inertia is zero for principal axes of inertia. A beam of oval cross section loaded transversely, Fig. A6, if free to rotate about its longitudinal axis, will turn until the horizontal axis of its cross section is the minimum axis of inertia $O\text{--}O$.

The relations in Eqs. (A9), (A9a), and (A10) may be represented graphically by a diagram known as Mohr's circle. For given values of I_x, I_y, and P_{xy} the corresponding values of $I_{x'}$, $I_{y'}$, and $P_{x'y'}$ may be determined from the diagram for any desired angle θ. A horizontal axis for the measurement of moments of inertia and a vertical axis for the measurement of products of inertia are first selected, Fig. A7. Next, point A, which has the coordinates (I_x, P_{xy}), and point B, which has the coordinates $(I_y, -P_{xy})$, are located. A circle is drawn with these two points

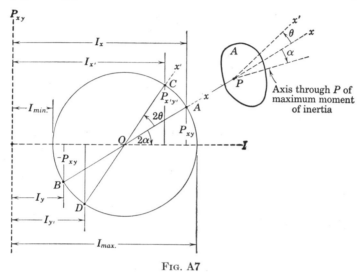

FIG. A7

as the extremities of a diameter. The angle from the radius OA to the horizontal axis is 2α or twice the angle from the x-axis of the area in question to the axis of maximum moment of inertia. Both the angle on the diagram and the angle on the area are measured in the same sense as shown. The coordinates of any point C are $(I_{x'}, P_{x'y'})$, and those of the corresponding point D are $(I_{y'}, -P_{x'y'})$. Also the angle between OA and OC is 2θ or twice the angle from the x-axis to the x'-axis. Again both angles are measured in the same sense as shown. It may be verified from the trigonometry of the circle that Eqs. (A9), (A9a), and (A10) agree with the statements made.

SAMPLE PROBLEMS

A33. Determine the product of inertia for the area under the parabola shown.

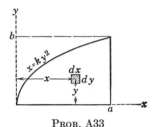

PROB. A33

Solution: The equation of the curve becomes $x = ay^2/b^2$. The product of inertia for the element $dA = dx\,dy$ is $dP_{xy} = xy\,dx\,dy$ and for the entire area is

$$P_{xy} = \int_0^b \int_{ay^2/b^2}^a xy\,dx\,dy = \int_0^b \frac{1}{2}\left(a^2 - \frac{a^2y^4}{b^4}\right)y\,dy = \tfrac{1}{6}\,a^2b^2. \qquad Ans.$$

A34. Locate the principal centroidal axes of inertia with their corresponding maximum and minimum moments of inertia for the angle section.

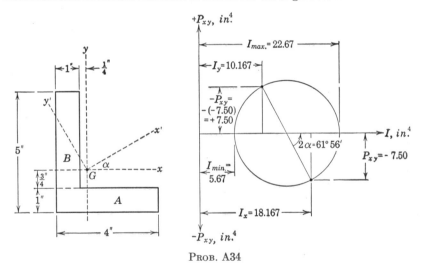

PROB. A34

Solution: The centroid G is easily located as shown. The product of inertia for each rectangle about its own centroidal axes parallel to the x- and y-axes is zero by symmetry. Thus the product of inertia for part A is

$$[P_{xy} = \bar{P}_{xy} + d_x d_y A] \qquad\qquad P_{xy} = 0 + (-\tfrac{5}{4})(+\tfrac{3}{4})(4) = -3.75 \text{ in.}^4$$

Likewise for B,

$$[P_{xy} = \bar{P}_{xy} + d_x d_y A] \qquad\qquad P_{xy} = 0 + (\tfrac{5}{4})(-\tfrac{3}{4})(4) = -3.75 \text{ in.}^4$$

For the complete angle

$$P_{xy} = -3.75 - 3.75 = -7.50 \text{ in.}^4$$

The moments of inertia for part A are

$$[I = \bar{I} + Ad^2] \qquad I_x = \tfrac{1}{12} \times 4 \times 1^3 + (\tfrac{5}{4})^2 \times 4 = 6.583 \text{ in.}^4,$$

$$I_y = \tfrac{1}{12} \times 1 \times 4^3 + (\tfrac{3}{4})^2 \times 4 = 7.583 \text{ in.}^4$$

In similar manner the moments of inertia for part B are $I_x = 11.583 \text{ in.}^4$, $I_y = 2.583 \text{ in.}^4$ Thus for the entire section

$$I_x = 6.583 + 11.583 = 18.167 \text{ in.}^4,$$

$$I_y = 7.583 + 2.583 = 10.167 \text{ in.}^4$$

The inclination of the principal axes of inertia is given by Eq. (A10). Therefore

$$\left[\tan 2\alpha = \frac{2P_{xy}}{I_y - I_x} \right] \qquad \tan 2\alpha = \frac{-2 \times 7.50}{10.167 - 18.167} = 1.875,$$

$$2\alpha = 61° 56', \qquad \alpha = 30° 58'. \qquad Ans.$$

From Eqs. (A9) the principal moments of inertia are

$$I_{\text{max.}} = I_{x'} = \frac{18.167 + 10.167}{2} + \frac{18.167 - 10.167}{2} \times 0.4705 + 7.50 \times 0.8824$$

$$= 22.67 \text{ in.}^4; \qquad\qquad\qquad Ans.$$

$$I_{\text{min.}} = I_{y'} = \frac{18.167 + 10.167}{2} - \frac{18.167 - 10.167}{2} \times 0.4705 - 7.50 \times 0.8824$$

$$= 5.67 \text{ in.}^4 \qquad\qquad\qquad Ans.$$

These results may also be obtained graphically by construction of the Mohr circle as shown to the right of the angle in the figure.

PROBLEMS

A35. Determine the product of inertia P_{xy} of the area of a rectangle about x- and y-axes coinciding with two adjacent sides of lengths a and b. The rectangle lies in the first quadrant.

A36. Obtain the product of inertia for the area of the quarter circle shown with Prob. A5 about the x- and y-axes by direct integration. $Ans.$ $P_{xy} = \dfrac{r^4}{8}$

A37. Solve Prob. A21 for the moment of inertia about a diagonal of the rectangle of sides a and b by the method of this article.

A38. The moments of inertia of an area with respect to the principal axes of inertia x, y through a point P are $I_x = 32.0 \text{ in.}^4$ and $I_y = 12.0 \text{ in.}^4$ With the aid of Mohr's circle determine the moment of inertia $I_{x'}$ and the product of inertia $P_{x'y'}$ for the area about axes x', y' through P and rotated 15 deg. clockwise from the axes x, y. $Ans.$ $I_{x'} = 30.66 \text{ in.}^4$, $P_{x'y'} = -5 \text{ in.}^4$

body about the axis and the weight of the body. The moment of inertia is then calculated from Eq. (A12).

A9. Transfer of Axes. If the moment of inertia of a body is known about a centroidal axis, it may be determined easily about any parallel axis. To prove this statement consider the two parallel axes in Fig. A9, one of which is a centroidal axis through the center of gravity G. The

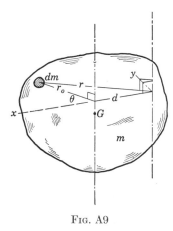

radial distances from the two axes to any element of mass dm are r_o and r, and the separation of the axes is d. Substituting the law of cosines $r^2 = r_o{}^2 + d^2 + 2r_o d \cos \theta$ into the definition for the moment of inertia about the noncentroidal axis gives

$$I = \int r^2 \, dm = \int (r_o{}^2 + d^2 + 2r_o d \cos \theta) \, dm,$$

$$= \int r_o{}^2 \, dm + d^2 \int dm + 2d \int y \, dm.$$

FIG. A9

The first integral is the moment of inertia $\bar{I}$ about the centroidal axis, the second integral is md^2, and the third integral equals zero since the y-coordinate of the center of gravity with respect to an origin at G is zero. Thus the parallel-axis theorem is

$$I = \bar{I} + md^2. \tag{A13}$$

It must be remembered that the transfer cannot be made unless one axis passes through the center of gravity and unless the axes are parallel. When the expressions for the radii of gyration are substituted in Eq. (A13), there results

$$k^2 = \bar{k}^2 + d^2, \tag{A13a}$$

which is the parallel-axis theorem for obtaining the radius of gyration k about an axis a distance d from a parallel centroidal axis for which the radius of gyration is $\bar{k}$.

A10. Product of Inertia. In a few problems of advanced mechanics the integrals

$$I_{xy} = \int xy \, dm, \qquad I_{yz} = \int yz \, dm, \qquad I_{xz} = \int xz \, dm$$

are useful. These integrals are called the products of inertia of the mass m. They may be either positive or negative. In general, a three-dimensional body has three moments of inertia about the three mutually perpendicular coordinate axes and three products of inertia about the three coordinate planes. For an unsymmetrical body of any shape it is found that for a given origin of coordinates there is one orientation of axes for which the products of inertia vanish. These axes are called the *principal axes of inertia.* The corresponding moments of inertia about these axes are known as the *principal moments of inertia* and include the maximum possible value, the minimum possible value, and an intermediate value for any orientation of axes about the given origin.

A11. Moment of Inertia with Respect to a Plane. The moment of inertia of a body with respect to a plane is useful in some problems primarily as an aid to the calculation of the moment of inertia with respect to a line. The moment of inertia with respect to the y–z plane is defined as $\int x^2\,dm$ and that with respect to the x–z plane is $\int y^2\,dm$. Since $x^2 + y^2 = r^2$, where r is the distance from dm to the z-axis, the moment of inertia I_z about the z-axis is

$$I_z = \int r^2\,dm = \int x^2\,dm + \int y^2\,dm.$$

Similar expressions may be written for the two other axes.

A summary of some of the more useful formulas for mass moments of inertia is given in Table B6, Appendix B.

SAMPLE PROBLEMS

A42. Determine the moment of inertia and radius of gyration of a homogeneous right circular cylinder of mass m and radius r about its central axis O–O.

Solution: An element of mass in cylindrical coordinates is $dm = \rho\,dV = \rho t r_o\,dr_o\,d\theta$. The moment of inertia about the axis of the cylinder is

$$I = \int r_o{}^2\,dm = \rho t \int_0^{2\pi}\!\!\int_0^r r_o{}^3\,dr_o\,d\theta = \rho t\,\frac{\pi r^4}{2} = \tfrac{1}{2}\,mr^2. \qquad Ans.$$

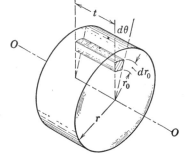

The radius of gyration is

$$k = \sqrt{\frac{I}{m}} = \frac{r}{\sqrt{2}}. \qquad Ans.$$

The result $I = \tfrac{1}{2}mr^2$ applies *only* to a solid homogeneous circular cylinder and cannot be used for any other wheel of circular periphery.

PROB. A42

A43. Determine the moment of inertia and radius of gyration of a homogeneous solid **sphere of mass** m and radius r about a diameter.

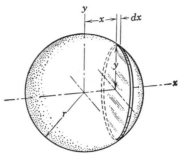

PROB. A43

Solution: A circular slice of radius y and thickness dx is chosen as the volume element. From the results of Prob. A42 the moment of inertia about the x-axis of the elemental cylinder is

$$dI_x = \frac{1}{2}(dm)y^2 = \frac{1}{2}(\pi\rho y^2\,dx)y^2 = \frac{\pi\rho}{2}(r^2 - x^2)^2\,dx,$$

where ρ is the constant mass density of the sphere. The total moment of inertia about the x-axis is

$$I_x = \frac{\pi\rho}{2}\int_{-r}^{r}(r^2 - x^2)^2\,dx = \tfrac{8}{15}\pi\rho r^5 = \tfrac{2}{5}mr^2. \qquad Ans.$$

The radius of gyration is

$$k = \sqrt{\frac{I}{m}} = \sqrt{\frac{2}{5}}\,r. \qquad Ans.$$

A44. Determine the moments of inertia of the homogeneous rectangular parallelepiped of mass m about the centroidal x_o- and z-axes and about the x-axis through one end.

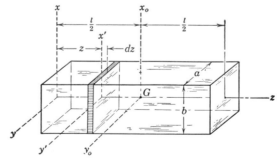

PROB. A44

Solution: A transverse slice of thickness dz is selected as the element of volume. The moment of inertia of this slice of infinitesimal thickness equals the moment of inertia of the area of the section times the mass per unit area $\rho\,dz$. Thus the moment of inertia of the transverse slice about the y'-axis is

$$dI_{y'} = (\rho\,dz)(\tfrac{1}{12}ab^3),$$

and that about the x'-axis is

$$dI_{x'} = (\rho\,dz)(\tfrac{1}{12}a^3b).$$

As long as the element is a plate of differential thickness, the principle of Eq. (A3) may be applied to give

$$dI_z = dI_{x'} + dI_{y'} = (\rho\,dz)\frac{ab}{12}\,(a^2 + b^2).$$

These expressions may now be integrated to obtain the desired results.

The moment of inertia about the z-axis is

$$I_z = \int dI_z = \frac{\rho ab}{12}\,(a^2 + b^2)\int_0^l dz = \tfrac{1}{12}\,m(a^2 + b^2), \qquad\qquad Ans.$$

where m is the mass of the block. By interchanging symbols the moment of inertia about the x_o-axis is

$$I_{x_0} = \tfrac{1}{12}m(a^2 + l^2). \qquad\qquad Ans.$$

The moment of inertia about the x-axis may be found by the parallel-axis theorem, Eq. (A13). Thus

$$I_x = I_{x_0} + m\left(\frac{l}{2}\right)^2 = \tfrac{1}{12}\,m\,(a^2 + 4l^2). \qquad\qquad Ans.$$

This last result may be obtained by expressing the moment of inertia of the elemental slice about the x-axis and integrating the expression over the length of the bar. Again by the parallel-axis theorem

$$dI_x = dI_{x'} + z^2\,dm = (\rho\,dz)(\tfrac{1}{12}a^3b) + z^2\rho ab\,dz,$$

$$= \rho ab\left(\frac{a^2}{12} + z^2\right)dz.$$

Integrating gives the result obtained previously,

$$I_x = \rho ab\int_0^l \left(\frac{a^2}{12} + z^2\right)dz = \frac{\rho abl}{3}\left(l^2 + \frac{a^2}{4}\right) = \tfrac{1}{12}\,m\,(a^2 + 4l^2).$$

The expression for I_x may be simplified for a long prismatical bar or slender rod whose transverse dimensions are small compared with the length. In this case a^2 may be neglected compared with $4l^2$, and the moment of inertia of such a slender bar about an axis through one end normal to the bar becomes $I = \tfrac{1}{3}ml^2$. By the same approximation the moment of inertia about a centroidal axis normal to the bar is $I = \tfrac{1}{12}ml^2$.

PROBLEMS

A45. A bar 10 in. long has a square cross section 1 in. on a side. Determine the per cent error e in using the approximate formula $I = \frac{1}{3}ml^2$ for the moment of inertia about an axis normal to the bar and through the center of one end parallel to an edge. (See Prob. A44.)

$Ans.$ $e = 0.249\%$

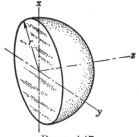

PROB. A47

A46. The moment of inertia of a solid homogeneous cylinder of radius r about an axis parallel to the central axis of the cylinder may be obtained approximately by multiplying the mass of the cylinder by the square of the distance d between the two axes. What per cent error e results if (a) $d = 10r$, (b) $d = 2r$?

A47. From the results of Prob. A43 state without computation the moments of inertia of the solid homogeneous hemisphere of mass m about the x- and z-axes.

A48. Determine the moment of inertia of a circular ring of mass m and inside and outside radii r_1 and r_2, respectively, about its central polar axis.

$Ans.$ $I = \frac{1}{2}m(r_2^2 + r_1^2)$

A49. Calculate the moment of inertia of a homogeneous right circular cone of mass m and base radius r about the cone axis. $Ans.$ $I = \frac{3}{10}mr^2$

A50. Without integrating determine from the results of Probs. A43 and A49 the moments of inertia about the z-axis for (a) the spherical wedge of Prob. 354 (p. 171) and (b) the conical wedge of Prob. 351 (p.171). Each wedge has a mass m.

$Ans.$ (a) $I_z = \frac{2}{5}ma^2$, (b) $I_z = \frac{3}{10}mr^2$

A51. Find the moment of inertia of the slender rod of mass m about the x-axis.

PROB. A51

A52. The moment of inertia of a body with respect to the x–y plane is 0.202 lb. ft. sec.², and that with respect to the y–z plane is 0.440 lb. ft. sec.² The radius of gyration about the y-axis is 1.20 ft. Find the weight W of the body.

A53. Determine the moment of inertia of the elliptical cylinder of mass m about the cylinder axis O–O. $Ans.$ $I = \frac{1}{4}m(a^2 + b^2)$

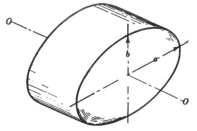

PROB. A53

A54. Determine the moment of inertia about the z-axis of the homogeneous solid paraboloid of revolution of mass m shown with Prob. 338 (p. 169).

A55. Find the moment of inertia of the tetrahedron of mass m about the z-axis.

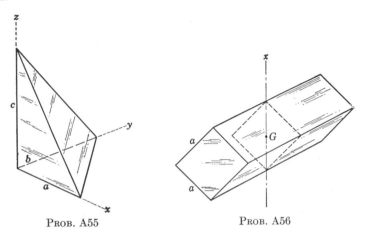

PROB. A55   PROB. A56

A56. The homogeneous bar of square cross section has a mass m. Determine the moment of inertia of the bar about the centroidal x-axis shown which is a diagonal of the square section. *Ans.* $I_x = \frac{1}{12}m(a^2 + l^2)$

A57. Determine the moments of inertia of the homogeneous right circular cylinder of mass m about the x_o-, x-, and y'-axes shown.

Ans. $I_{x_o} = \frac{1}{12}m(3r^2 + l^2)$, $I_x = \frac{1}{12}m(3r^2 + 4l^2)$, $I_{y'} = \frac{3}{2}mr^2$

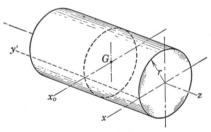

PROB. A57

A58. The density of a sphere of radius r varies uniformly with the radius from ρ_o at the center to twice that value at the surface. Determine the moment of inertia of the sphere about a diameter in terms of the mass m of the sphere.

A59. Determine the moments of inertia of the half spherical shell shown with Prob. 344 (p. 169) with respect to the x- and z-axes. The mass of the shell is m, and its thickness is negligible compared with the radius r.

Ans. $I_x = I_z = \frac{2}{3}mr^2$

A60. Determine the moment of inertia of the conical shell of mass m about the axis of rotation. Wall thickness is negligible.   *Ans.* $I_z = \frac{1}{2}mr^2$

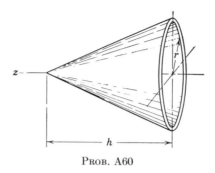

PROB. A60

* **A61.** Determine the moment of inertia about the z-axis of the bell-shaped shell of uniform small thickness described in Prob. 356 (p. 172) if the mass is m.

$$Ans.\quad I_z = \frac{15\pi - 44}{6(\pi - 2)}\,ma^2$$

* **A62.** Determine the moment of inertia about the generating axis of a complete ring of circular section (torus) with the dimensions shown in the sectional view.   *Ans.* $I = m(R^2 + \frac{3}{4}a^2)$

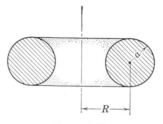

PROB. A62

A12. Composite Bodies. The defining integral, Eq. (A11), involves the square of the distance from the axis to the element and so is always positive. Thus, as in the case of area moments of inertia, the mass moment of inertia of a composite body is the sum of the moments of inertia of the individual parts about the same axis. It is often convenient to consider a composite body as defined by positive volumes and negative volumes. The moment of inertia of a negative element, such as a hole, must be considered a minus quantity.

PROBLEMS

A63. Calculate the moment of inertia about the z-axis of the cylinder with the hemispherical cavity shown with Prob. 346 (p. 170) if the net mass is m.

$$Ans. \quad I_z = \tfrac{7}{10}ma^2$$

A64. Calculate the moment of inertia about the central axis of the aluminum rotor shown in section.

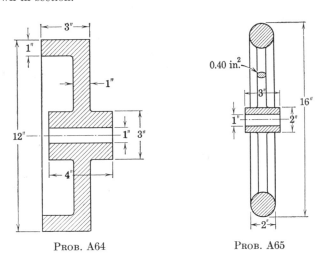

PROB. A64   PROB. A65

A65. Calculate the moment of inertia of the steel handwheel about its axis. There are six spokes, each of which has a uniform cross-sectional area of 0.40 in.²

$$Ans. \quad I = 0.431 \text{ lb. ft. sec.}^2$$

A66. Determine the radius of gyration of the homogeneous rotor, shown in section, about its central axis. $Ans.$ $k = 2.43$ in.

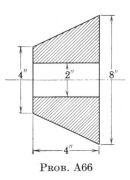

PROB. A66

A67. The slender rod bent into the shape shown in Prob. 366 (p. 175) weighs 0.52 lb./ft. Determine the moment of inertia of the rod about the x-axis.

A68. Determine the moment of inertia of the mallet with respect to the axis O–O. The head is made from hard wood weighing 65 lb./ft.³, and the handle is made from steel weighing 0.283 lb./in.³   *Ans.* $I_O = 0.1896$ lb. ft. sec.²

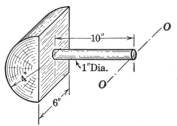

PROB. A68

A69. The part shown weighs 3.22 lb. Determine its moment of inertia about the axis O–O.

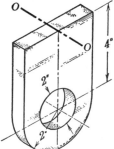

PROB. A69

* **A70.** Determine the moments of inertia of the steel body shown about axes A and B.   *Ans.* $I_A = 0.1446$ lb. ft. sec.², $I_B = 0.302$ lb. ft. sec.²

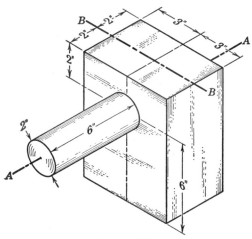

PROB. A70

* **A71.** Determine the radius of gyration of the symmetrical steel link about the axis O–O. *Ans.* $k = 4.36$ in.

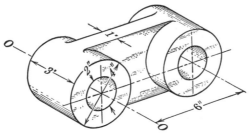

PROB. A71

* **A72.** The desired moment of inertia of the steel rocker about the O–O axis is 0.204 lb. ft. sec.^{2} Determine the necessary thickness t. *Ans.* $t = 3.17$ in.

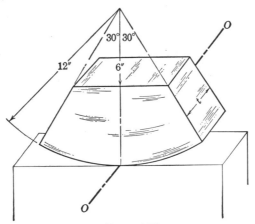

PROB. A72

Appendix B

Useful Tables

TABLE B1. DENSITIES, lb./ft.^{3}

Aluminum	168	Mercury	**847**
Concrete (av.)	150	Oil (av.)	56
Copper	556	Steel	489
Earth (wet, av.)	110	Water (fresh)	62.4
(dry, av.)	80	(salt)	64
Ice	56	Wood (soft, pine)	30
Iron (cast)	450	(hard, oak)	50
Lead	710		

TABLE B2. COEFFICIENTS OF FRICTION

The coefficients in the following table represent typical values only. Actual coefficients for a given situation will depend on the exact nature of the contacting surfaces. A variation of the order of 25 to 100 per cent from these values could be expected in an actual problem, depending on prevailing conditions of cleanliness, roughness, pressure, lubrication, and velocity.

Contacting Surfaces	Coefficient of Static Friction	Coefficient of Kinetic Friction
Metal on metal (dry)	0.2	0.1
Metal on metal (greasy)	0.1	0.05
Rubber or leather on wood or metal (dry)	0.4	0.3
Hardwood on metal (dry)	0.6	0.4
Hardwood on metal (greasy)	0.2	0.1
Hemp on metal (dry)	0.3	0.2
Wire rope on iron pulley (dry)	0.2	0.15
Rubber tires on smooth pavement (dry)	0.9	0.8
Asbestos brake lining on cast iron	0.4	0.3
Metal on ice	...	0.02
Steel on wet grindstone	...	0.7
Cast-iron brake shoes on steel railway tires		
(10 m.p.h.)	...	0.3
(30 m.p.h.)	...	0.2
(60 m.p.h.)	...	0.05

	Coefficient of Rolling Friction, f_r
Pneumatic tires on smooth pavement	0.02
Steel tires on steel rails	0.006

TABLE B3.   USEFUL MATHEMATICAL RELATIONS

A. Series (expression in bracket following series indicates range of convergence)

$$(1 \pm x)^n = 1 \pm nx + \frac{n(n-1)}{2!}x^2 \pm \frac{n(n-1)(n-2)x^3}{3!} + \cdots \qquad [x^2 < 1]$$

$$\sin x = x - \frac{x^3}{3!} + \frac{x^5}{5!} - \frac{x^7}{7!} + \cdots \qquad [x^2 < \infty]$$

$$\cos x = 1 - \frac{x^2}{2!} + \frac{x^4}{4!} - \frac{x^6}{6!} + \cdots \qquad [x^2 < \infty]$$

$$\sinh x = \frac{e^x - e^{-x}}{2} = x + \frac{x^3}{3!} + \frac{x^5}{5!} + \frac{x^7}{7!} + \cdots \qquad [x^2 < \infty]$$

$$\cosh x = \frac{e^x + e^{-x}}{2} = 1 + \frac{x^2}{2!} + \frac{x^4}{4!} + \frac{x^6}{6!} + \cdots \qquad [x^2 < \infty]$$

B. Differentials

$$\frac{dx^n}{dx} = nx^{n-1}, \qquad \frac{d(uv)}{dx} = u\frac{dv}{dx} + v\frac{du}{dx}, \qquad \frac{d\left(\dfrac{u}{v}\right)}{dx} = \frac{v\dfrac{du}{dx} - u\dfrac{dv}{dx}}{v^2}$$

$$\lim_{\Delta x \to 0} \sin \Delta x = \sin dx = \tan dx = dx$$

$$\lim_{\Delta x \to 0} \cos \Delta x = \cos dx = 1$$

$$\frac{d \sin x}{dx} = \cos x, \qquad \frac{d \cos x}{dx} = -\sin x, \qquad \frac{d \tan x}{dx} = \sec^2 x$$

$$\frac{d \sinh x}{dx} = \cosh x, \qquad \frac{d \cosh x}{dx} = \sinh x, \qquad \frac{d \tanh x}{dx} = \operatorname{sech}^2 x$$

C. Integrals

$$\int x^n \, dx = \frac{x^{n+1}}{n+1}$$

$$\int \frac{dx}{x} = \log x$$

$$\int \sqrt{a + bx} \, dx = \frac{2}{3b}\sqrt{(a+bx)^3}$$

$$\int \frac{dx}{\sqrt{a+bx}} = \frac{2\sqrt{a+bx}}{b}$$

$$\int \frac{x \, dx}{a+bx} = \frac{1}{b^2}[a + bx - a\log(a+bx)]$$

$$\int \frac{dx}{a+bx^2} = \frac{1}{\sqrt{ab}}\tan^{-1}\frac{x\sqrt{ab}}{a} \quad \text{or} \quad \frac{1}{\sqrt{-ab}}\tanh^{-1}\frac{x\sqrt{-ab}}{a}$$

$$\int \sqrt{x^2 \pm a^2}\, dx = \tfrac{1}{2}[x\sqrt{x^2 \pm a^2} \pm a^2 \log (x + \sqrt{x^2 \pm a^2}\,)]$$

$$\int \sqrt{a^2 - x^2}\, dx = \tfrac{1}{2}\left(x\sqrt{a^2 - x^2} + a^2 \sin^{-1}\frac{x}{a}\right)$$

$$\int x\sqrt{a^2 - x^2}\, dx = -\tfrac{1}{3}\sqrt{(a^2 - x^2)^3}$$

$$\int x^2\sqrt{a^2 - x^2}\, dx = -\frac{x}{4}\sqrt{(a^2 - x^2)^3} + \frac{a^2}{8}\left(x\sqrt{a^2 - x^2} + a^2 \sin^{-1}\frac{x}{a}\right)$$

$$\int x^3\sqrt{a^2 - x^2}\, dx = -\tfrac{1}{5}(x^2 + \tfrac{2}{3}a^2)\sqrt{(a^2 - x^2)^3}$$

$$\int \frac{dx}{\sqrt{x^2 \pm a^2}} = \log (x + \sqrt{x^2 \pm a^2}\,)$$

$$\int \frac{dx}{\sqrt{a^2 - x^2}} = \sin^{-1}\frac{x}{a}$$

$$\int x\sqrt{x^2 \pm a^2}\, dx = \tfrac{1}{3}\sqrt{(x^2 \pm a^2)^3}$$

$$\int x^2\sqrt{x^2 \pm a^2}\, dx = \frac{x}{4}\sqrt{(x^2 \pm a^2)^3} \mp \frac{a^2}{8}x\sqrt{x^2 \pm a^2} - \frac{a^4}{8}\log (x + \sqrt{x^2 \pm a^2}\,)$$

$$\int \frac{x\, dx}{\sqrt{x^2 - a^2}} = \sqrt{x^2 - a^2}$$

$$\int \frac{x\, dx}{\sqrt{a^2 \pm x^2}} = \pm\sqrt{a^2 \pm x^2}$$

$$\int \sin x\, dx = -\cos x$$

$$\int \cos x\, dx = \sin x$$

$$\int \sec x\, dx = \frac{1}{2}\log \frac{1 + \sin x}{1 - \sin x} \qquad \int x \sin x\, dx = \sin x - x \cos x$$

$$\int \sin^2 x\, dx = \frac{x}{2} - \frac{\sin 2x}{4} \qquad \int x \cos x\, dx = \cos x + x \sin x$$

$$\int \cos^2 x\, dx = \frac{x}{2} + \frac{\sin 2x}{4} \qquad \int \sinh x\, dx = \cosh x$$

$$\int \sin^3 x\, dx = -\frac{\cos x}{3}(2 + \sin^2 x) \qquad \int \cosh x\, dx = \sinh x$$

$$\int \cos^3 x\, dx = \frac{\sin x}{3}(2 + \cos^2 x) \qquad \int e^{ax} \cos px\, dx = \frac{e^{ax}(a \cos px + p \sin px)}{a^2 + p^2}$$

TABLE B4. CENTROIDS

Arc Segment $$\bar{r} = \frac{r \sin \alpha}{\alpha}$$	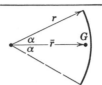
Quarter and Semicircular Arcs $$\bar{y} = \frac{2r}{\pi}$$	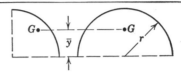
Triangular Area $$\bar{y} = \frac{h}{3}$$	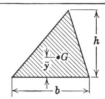
Trapezoidal Area $$\bar{y} = \frac{1}{3}\frac{2a_1 + a_2}{a_1 + a_2} h$$	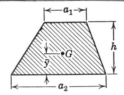
Area of Circular Sector $$\bar{r} = \frac{2}{3}\frac{r \sin \alpha}{\alpha}$$	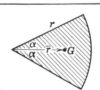
Quarter and Semicircular Areas $$\bar{y} = \frac{4r}{3\pi}$$	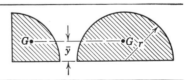
Area of Elliptical Quadrant $$\bar{x} = \frac{4a}{3\pi}$$ $$\bar{y} = \frac{4b}{3\pi}$$	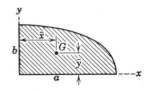

TABLE B4. CENTROIDS—*Continued*

Lateral Area of Cone or Pyramid

$$\bar{y} = \frac{h}{3}$$

Area of Hemisphere, or Hemispherical Shell

$$\bar{r} = \frac{r}{2}$$

Volume of Cone or Pyramid

$$\bar{y} = \frac{h}{4}$$

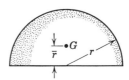

Hemispherical Volume

$$\bar{r} = \frac{3r}{8}$$

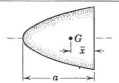

Volume of Paraboloid of Revolution

$$\bar{x} = \frac{a}{3}$$

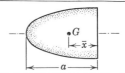

Volume of Half Ellipsoid of Revolution

$$\bar{x} = \frac{3a}{8}$$

TABLE B5. MOMENTS OF INERTIA OF AREAS

Rectangle

$$\bar{I}_x = \frac{bh^3}{12}$$

$$I_x = \frac{bh^3}{3}$$

$$J = \frac{bh}{12}(b^2 + h^2)$$

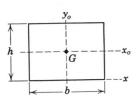

Triangle

$$\bar{I}_x = \frac{bh^3}{36}$$

$$I_x = \frac{bh^3}{12}$$

$$I_{x'} = \frac{bh^3}{4}$$

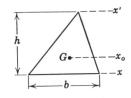

Circle

$$\bar{I}_x = \bar{I}_y = \frac{\pi r^4}{4}$$

$$J = \frac{\pi r^4}{2}$$

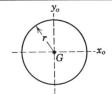

Ellipse

$$\bar{I}_x = \frac{\pi ab^3}{4}$$

$$\bar{I}_y = \frac{\pi a^3 b}{4}$$

$$J = \frac{\pi ab}{4}(a^2 + b^2)$$

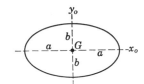

TABLE B6. MOMENTS OF INERTIA OF MASS

(m = mass of homogeneous solid shown)

Right Circular Cylinder

$$I_z = \tfrac{1}{2}mr^2$$

$$I_x = \tfrac{1}{12}m(3r^2 + 4l^2)$$

Sphere

$$I_z = \tfrac{2}{5}mr^2$$

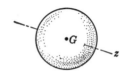

Semicylinder

$$I_z = \tfrac{1}{2}(\tfrac{1}{2} \times 2mr^2)$$

$$= \tfrac{1}{2}mr^2$$

Hemisphere

$$I_x = I_z = \tfrac{1}{2}(\tfrac{2}{5} \times 2mr^2)$$

$$= \tfrac{2}{5}mr^2$$

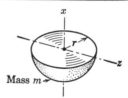

Rectangular Parallelepiped

$$I_z = \tfrac{1}{12}m(a^2 + b^2)$$

$$I_x = \tfrac{1}{12}m(4l^2 + a^2)$$

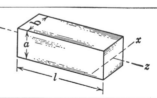

Uniform Slender Rod

$$I_x = \tfrac{1}{3}ml^2$$

$$\bar{I}_x = \tfrac{1}{12}ml^2$$

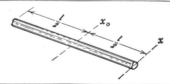

Right Circular Cone

$$I_z = \tfrac{3}{10}mr^2$$

TABLE B6.   MOMENTS OF INERTIA OF MASS—*Continued*

(m = mass of homogeneous solid shown)

Elliptical Cylinder

$$I_z = \tfrac{1}{4}m(a^2 + b^2)$$

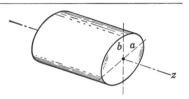

Hemispherical Shell

$$I_x = I_z = \tfrac{2}{3}mr^2$$

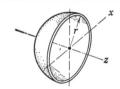

Torus (complete)

$$I_z = m(R^2 + \tfrac{3}{4}a^2)$$

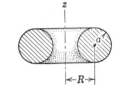

INDEX